To the Ends of the Earth

Ireland's Place in Bird Migration

ANTHONY McGEEHAN, from Belfast, has been watching and photographing birds since childhood. Following a 'hands-on' career in conservation his energies are still directed at instilling interest and concern for Ireland's birds. He does this through writing, leading wildlife tours on Inishbofin, County Galway, maintaining a steady flow of bird and natural history information on Facebook (**f** anthonymcgeehanphotography) and via contributions on Medium.com. His previous books (with Julian Wyllie) include *Birds Through Irish Eyes* and *Birds of the Homeplace*, the latter hailed as Ireland's 'bird book of the year' in Birdwatch Ireland's *Wings* Magazine.

The writings of three giants intoxicated me in my youth. Years later, they all contributed to this book, which I am thrilled to dedicate to them: Alan L. Durand, J.T.R. Sharrock and D.I.M. Wallace.

To the Ends of the Earth

Ireland's Place in Bird Migration

ANTHONY McGEEHAN

The Collins Press

First published in 2018 by

The Collins Press
West Link Park
Doughcloyne
Wilton
Cork
T12 N5EF
Ireland

© Anthony McGeehan 2018

Photographs © Anthony McGeehan unless credited otherwise.
Maps and all illustrations (except those on pp. 22 and 192) © Michael O'Clery 2018
Illustrations on pp. 22 and 192 © David Quinn 2018

Anthony McGeehan has asserted his moral right to be identified as the author of this work in accordance with the Irish Copyright and Related Rights Act 2000.

All rights reserved. The material in this publication is protected by copyright law. Except as may be permitted by law, no part of the material may be reproduced (including by storage in a retrieval system) or transmitted in any form or by any means, adapted, rented or lent without the written permission of the copyright owners. Applications for permissions should be addressed to the publisher.

A CIP record for this book is available from the British Library.

Hardback ISBN: 978-1-84889-352-8

Design and typesetting by Studio 10 Design
Typeset in Goudy and Trade Gothic
Printed in Poland by Białostockie Zakłady Graficzne SA

Every reasonable effort has been made to trace all copyright holders. Any omissions are unintentional and regretted. The publisher will be happy to hear from any copyright holders not acknowledged and undertakes to rectify any errors or omissions in future editions.

Photographs:
p. i: Great Shearwater; pp. ii: Arctic Tern chick PHOTOGRAPH SINDRI SKULASON; pp.iv–v: Ring-Billed Gull.

CONTENTS

Among sediments laid down in the bed of a tropical lagoon 147 million years ago, Bavarian quarrymen chanced upon the fossilised imprint of a reptile. Named Archaeopteryx – 'ancient wing' – the creature looks like a bird. About the size of a crow, it had feathered wings and a tail resembling a Magpie. Unlike modern birds, the tail was bony, the bill was lined with teeth and the wings were equipped with claws. Although Archaeopteryx could take to the skies, it was probably ungainly and remained so until its descendants saved weight by dispensing with the bony tail and developing a keeled sternum (breast bone) to support wing-powering muscles for sustained, agile flight. When that happened, birds came of age.

INTRODUCTION

What defines a bird? Most people would say 'flight and feathers' and leave it at that. The coupling is impressive. Feathers are nature's Swiss Army knives: multipurpose equipment that facilitates flying, waterproofing the wearer, wooing a mate – and hugging the destiny of the species by brooding eggs. However, beneath a svelte exterior lies a sophisticated box of tricks. A respiratory system that takes in oxygen during both inhalation and exhalation powers avian bodies like fuel-injected engines. Hollow, air-filled bones aid flight, and life in the fast lane is sustained by a large forebrain that acts as a computer, enabling birds to control the complicated 3D world of flying.

It is now widely accepted that birds evolved from dinosaurs. Species that we recognise today have been around for approximately five million years. Most dinosaurs could not get airborne but evolution produced small prototype birds whose powers of flight probably spared them from an apocalyptic event – the impact of a 10km-wide asteroid slamming into Earth – that wiped out all other dinosaurs. Since then, birds have conquered the new world that emerged from the ashes. It is no surprise that their ability to travel is second to none.

In a way, when it comes to migration, there is no need for hyperbole. Although we can divide Ireland's birds into broad categories based upon the regularity with which they occur – resident, summer visitors, winter visitors and the many 'transit passengers' that pass through – migration is not set in stone. Like evolution, the behaviour is shaped by the never-ending, but always-changing pressures of the environment and competition. Although it seems crazy, birds migrate because, one way or another, it suits them. In the

For many songbirds, the seasons represent traffic lights. Vanishing food resources and winter chill impel millions to fly south, all the way to the tropics. Thrushes, like this Fieldfare, that attempt to beat the winter by switching to a combination of berries and earthworms, are caught out when prolonged cold envelops the north-western reaches of Europe. Sooner or later they trek west to Ireland, where the oceanic climate provides a mild haven.

Within weeks of fledging, these young Swallows will be chasing insects under African skies where they will rub shoulders with other members of the swallow tribe that never leave the continent. Why is this? Migration occurs where birds benefit from leaving breeding areas for a period, rather than staying there year-round. Lack of food is a main consideration. Plant growth stops for part of the year, and insect or other prey dies off or becomes inaccessible, such as under snow. Also, in high latitudes, day length shortens to such an extent that many diurnal birds would have insufficient time to find enough food, even if food was available. So it is obvious why many birds move south in autumn. But why come back in spring? In theory, they could remain in areas where they spent the winter, especially if conditions there – as in the tropics – were similar year-round. By coming north they exploit seasonal abundance of food at high latitudes and have the added benefit of longer daylight within which to find sufficient nourishment to rear young. So, if they stayed in low latitudes, breeding success would be reduced. Hence, for Swallows and other migrants, autumn migration means survival; spring migration maximises breeding chances. And, over the course of one Irish summer, as many as three broods can be raised.

contest to produce a new generation, jostling for advantage often leads to range expansion. New pastures that are seasonal generate home-and-away movements – but also a sense of loyalty. For this reason, Swallows fly back from Africa to Irish barns, whereas lookalike African species stay put or travel comparatively short distances. Maybe birds know the motto: 'if it ain't broke, don't fix it'? Prompting a fundamental change in our understanding, Swallow migration is a feat of detachment in reverse because 'our' Swallows are really African birds that come here to breed. Equally bizarre, Arctic Tern has a doppelgänger – Antarctic Tern – that occurs on most of the Southern Ocean's sub-Antarctic islands and does not undertake spectacular migrations and, except for populations that nest on archipelagos close to the Antarctic Peninsula, remains close to the nesting islands all year.

The touchstone that activates birds' impulse to migrate is not, in most cases, provided by following elders who know the way. Offspring are born to fulfil preordained plans that must seem as natural to them as a human baby's instinct to cry. You could say that, although birds do not believe in the force of nature, there is some evidence to suggest that the force of nature believes in them because at an age not exceeding six or eight weeks, most young birds perform the first migratory journey of their life alone, yet with the same unerring certainty as their parents.

The question of where summer visitors went in autumn puzzled us for centuries. You did not have to be a scholar to understand that, when insects became scarce, the insectivorous birds of summer must leave or perish. A myth has grown up that cultivated mankind believed tales of Swallows and House Martins hibernating inside bushes or in nooks and crannies. Gilbert White, an eighteenth-century English parson who wrote *The Natural History of Selborne*, had to take at face value reports from parishioners, as well as the tenor of belief held by contemporary science, that summer migrants spent the winter in 'hibernacula' (safe places for hibernating). He never disproved the myth, which dogged him all his life, despite demanding evidence from correspondents and even hiring men to scour dense vegetation for dormant birds. A century later, in 1895, Heinrich Gätke, at the end of 50 years studying migration on the island of Heligoland in the North Sea, had amassed sufficient reports of White Storks and other European birds in Africa during the winter to speculate that, even for songbirds, the familiar companions of flower-laden summer months, journey's end was beyond the Sahara: 'the expanse of the Mediterranean is also passed over, and the scene shifts to the boundless sandy desert, trembling beneath the fierce rays of the African sun.'

The mystery deepened when wild-caught birds kept as pets exhibited odd activity in spring and autumn. The phenomenon was remarked upon from as long ago as the 1700s. They became restless, especially at night, when they were prone to damage themselves by banging against the roof of cages. Irrespective of what they were fed, they also put on weight. The two changes – migratory restlessness and weight gain – were not just simultaneous in one individual but occurred at the same time among all members in a captive population. More curious yet, the behaviour occurred irrespective of where the birds were housed. Many were kept indoors with no view of the outside world or changing seasons. Scientists, in their perplexity to account for these remarkable events, which, they acknowledged, coincided with migration seasons, sought refuge in 'instinctive action'. In other words, by virtue of some unconscious power or signal, the birds embarked on the right course of action to attain a chosen goal.

When, in May, warm southerly breezes blow up along the Irish coast, Arctic Terns arrive to breed. To avoid predators, lonely islets such as this 'glassillaun' – the small 'green island' at the centre of the photograph below – provide a safe breeding haven. The species is the long-distance champion of bird migration. It nests as far north as Inuit peoples live, while in (our) winter it patrols the shores of Antarctica. It sees more hours of daylight and of sunlight than any other creature on Earth. Two or three eggs are laid on bare ground. No nest is made; the clutch is designed to blend against a patch of terra firma. Incubation, mainly by the female, takes a little over three weeks. Although each egg is laid on a different day, growing chicks call to each other from inside the egg. Cheeping serves to synchronise hatching, because all emerge within 24 hours. To chip out of its shell, the chick is born with a disposable calcium 'egg tooth'.

To begin with, the baby stays where it hatched but once imprinted on its parents, it hides and then runs to receive fish when a calling adult arrives. Flight feathers are grown first; the youngster has to become airborne as quickly as possible. Young can fly at around 21–24 days. Some fliers still retain un-moulted down plumage. Parents and offspring remain in contact – youngsters initially 'copy mum' to hone their fishing skills – but only for a fortnight or less. Juveniles set off for the southern hemisphere completely alone; their maiden flight to the ends of the Earth falls under genetic control. Most of the new generation stay south until their second birthday after which they revisit breeding colonies and attempt to find a mate. Experienced breeders tend to be aged four and older – some live long enough to have an annual tryst with the same breeding partner for a decade or longer.

Further investigations, especially in the new millennium, have expanded our knowledge of what birds do. This book attempts to follow the plot, which is complicated and engrossing. The theories, practice, resulting awareness and understanding only take you so far. Watching the subjects – such as hemisphere-crossing Arctic Terns assembling over a lonely islet and preparing to lay a clutch of speckled eggs on bare rock – elevates awe to a level as yet beyond the reach of words.

TATTIE-HOAKER BIRDS

Greylag, Pink-footed, White-fronted
Geese, manifold
Fly south from tundra climes
Honking, hissing, splashing down
On wetland leys.
Riffling stubble for barleycorn ears
Planing the green, green sward
Then parading, on bare earth fields
To feast on a potato hoard
Tattie-hoaker birds.
Through winter's twilight
Cradled by Ireland's clement hold
Renewed, rebuilt, they repair
To Arctic fold.

Dennis Hawke

PHOTOGRAPH: EINAR GUDMANNS

PART ONE
TIME TO FLY

Spotted Flycatcher

1. The day imagination caught fire
Footsteps that inspired awe

. . . .

Blue, blue windows behind the stars, yellow moon on the rise.
Big birds flying across the sky, throwing shadows on our eyes.
Leave us helpless, helpless, helpless.

NEIL YOUNG

The great chart seemed to hold the classroom in its gaze. It dominated the wall in front of my ancient desk. Graduated colours spooled out along two scales. Brown hues differentiated height above sea level whereas increasingly saturated shades of blue drew the mind deep into the ocean. Ireland blinked like a green kernel in a Technicolor world. I knew what Technicolor meant because the term accompanied Walt Disney cartoon titles, even though colour television sets were yet to reach my housing estate near Belfast. Lodged like a film title at the foot of the map were the words 'Mercator Projection'. That, I assumed, was another trademark of the motion-picture industry.

To us, maps are visual. Eyesight conveys pictorial information for processing in the brain. Quite how birds find their way around the planet is a different matter. An inbuilt satnav response underpins their feats of navigation. We understand the concept but are denied their sensory experience of corkscrewing into a night sky and knowing where to go. Thanks to the power of flight, birds are envoys from afar. Ireland sits with its back to the Old World and its face to the New World, a global position that bestows a cosmopolitan extravaganza of visitors.

Although birds had always fascinated me, it was the classroom map that launched my marvelling at migration. That thunderbolt hit home when a neighbour gave me a copy of *The Second BBC Naturalist* (1960), which smelled of wet newspapers, the whiff of ageing printed words. The dust jacket was missing; the well-thumbed cover exuded the gravitas of a book of prayer. The sucker punch was Ken Williamson's article entitled 'Bird Visitors from America'. One paragraph began: 'How do they do it?' Those five words magnetised me to a topic to which my imagination is still attached, and left me with the exaltation of having received a revelation.

Williamson's perception upgraded my outlook from local to global. He continued: 'the Atlantic is more than 3,000 miles wide and for a long time ornithologists steadfastly refused to believe that most vagrant songbirds from

Books can be instrumental in unpacking dreams. Kenneth Williamson was an ornithological visionary. In 1960 he expounded his belief that when American birds are found in Europe during migration seasons, they got here under their own steam. His convictions spurred a broadening of minds and ushered in an age of discovery. Among the living proof was this Rose-breasted Grosbeak, guzzling blackberries on Cape Clear Island, County Cork, after flying across the Atlantic.

North America could get across this wide stretch of sea unaided. Alleged wisdom said that such of these American species as were not escaped cage-birds must have had assisted passage, travelling most of the way on ships.' Williamson challenged the doubters. Rather than being able to marshal contemporary knowledge to demolish the cynics – such as the ability of some long-haul migrants to lay down enough fat to power a continuous flight lasting 100 hours – he became Sherlock Holmes. Why did not equal numbers of European birds reach North America, given that boat traffic was two-way? And why did vagrants arrive only at migration seasons? He rejoiced at being alive in a post-Second World War era of high-powered birdwatching in which more and more people were intelligently interested in how, when and why birds perform 'those staggering journeys which we call migrations'.

Unlike lemmings, birds do not set off on fated journeys spurred by excessive breeding. For them, migration is a planned means to an end. Arbitrary impulses do not enter into the equation. They fly to survive. As with an aircraft, a flight to distant lands burns fuel that will need to be replenished either at a designated stopover or at the final destination. The goal is to return to base and produce heirs. We can relate to that concept: there is home and then there is the road. Few would argue with the principle but the realisation that birds as small as Swallows might be travelling across entire climatic zones required a paradigm shift in our awareness. Because, over the days before they head south, Swallows gather to roost in reed beds, it is easy to excuse the myths that arose, which claimed they went into winter torpor at the bottom of ponds. More incredible was the seasonal hatching of Barnacle Geese from the underside of logs floating on the sea, as allegedly vouchsafed in Ireland.

This rumour was started by Giraldus Cambrensis, a Welsh medieval cleric, during a visit in 1185. In *Topographica Hibernica*, Giraldus claimed, 'there are in this place [Ireland] many birds … like marsh geese but somewhat smaller. They are produced from fir timber tossed along the sea and are at first like gum. Afterwards they hang down by their beaks as if they were seaweed attached to the timber … in the process of time they become clothed with feathers and fall into the water or fly freely away … hence bishops and religious men in some parts of Ireland do not scruple to dine off these birds at the time of fasting, because they are not flesh.' It seems that finding loopholes has been a long tradition in Ireland. Alongside such ill-informed explanations, real enlightenment existed. John Ray, a precocious English naturalist who observed nature with a sceptical eye, showed considerable foresight in 1691 when, in *The Wisdom of God*, he wrote: 'the migration of birds from an hotter to a colder country, or a colder to an hotter, according to the seasons of the year, I know not how to give an account of, it is so strange and admirable. What moves them to shift their quarters?'

Although the annual return of a Swallow is enough to gladden the heart, the fact that the same individual will endeavour to revisit the same locality is doubly endearing. How did migration arise? The behaviour must have developed because it supported the species and became incorporated in a survival routine. Probably, sophisticated globetrotting grew from basic needs, such as finding food. Although not all birds migrate, even sedentary species are capable of exploring pastures new. Crossbills, because of annual variation in the ripening distribution of conifer cones, from which they extract seed, are impelled to roam. Thus periodic, irregular irruptions occur. The advantages of this tactic are obvious: hungry birds can search for plenty. It is plausible to speculate that in some such way did the habit of wholesale migration evolve, natural selection

Crossbills are inextricably linked with conifers – the bill's crossed mandibles are designed to extract seed from closed cones. However, across conifer forest, seed crops fluctuate. Hence the birds wander. In most years, they remain within the forest, concentrating where cones are plentiful. In some years, when high population levels coincide with poor cone crops, flocks leave the forest and head west across Europe – including crossing the North Sea and Irish Sea in search of suitable habitat that may provide food. If the birds had remained within their traditional range, they would probably have starved. By moving out, some will survive and subsequently return. Food-driven emigration is similar to regular migration: birds move to avoid food shortage. For Crossbills, an irregular food supply generates ad-hoc movements that, although impressive, are not true migration.

favouring those whose wanderlust proved most successful for the next breeding population.

Food-driven nomadism is one thing but the twice-annual global exchange of millions of birds from temperate regions to the tropics is, by comparison, a giant leap. What selective steps might have been involved in their evolution? One of the challenges is determining when birds first made these journeys. The big news is that fossil evidence shows that some species were capable of migratory flights at least 100 million years ago.[1] Although the fossil record is scant and difficult to decipher, most species that we recognise today were around five million years ago. Since then, global climate has changed many times, as has the polarity of Earth's magnetic field. Over the last two million years there have been 22 glacial–interglacial cycles, epochs that represented the coolest time in the history of all living things. Global fluctuations in temperature, precipitation and vegetation generally increase with latitude. Does this mean that bird families rooted in the tropics during ice ages expanded polewards when the climate warmed and founded new migratory counterparts, some of which, due to seasonality, became long-distance migrants? Interpretations are difficult but permanent residency in the frozen latitudes that encompassed Ireland would have been impossible. However, some groups have been around long enough for their genes to tell us how their ancestors coped with the ebb and flow of climate change. DNA-based evolutionary histories of pipits and wagtails (and other families) suggest multiple switches between residency and migration.[2] It seems that over millennia or longer time scales, the breeding, migratory and wintering distribution of any species that chooses to divide its year between two climate zones has had to be flexible.

It is therefore likely that aspects of migratory behaviour emerged in ancestors that lived in the tropics but which were drawn to higher latitudes by the bounty of food available there during summer. Ice ages disrupted continuity. In their wake, new migratory pathways become established as species sought to reoccupy ancestral ranges. Recovering the genetic history of recolonisation often reveals mechanisms of change. Evolution does not stand still and if range expansions take different directions then, over time, changes may arise within the birds themselves. In any phase of recolonisation after ice ages, physical boundaries within continents, such as mountain ranges or deserts, also serve to split formerly contiguous breeding ranges.

Swainson's Thrush is a small North American species that breeds from west of the Rocky Mountains to Alaska and across Canada and into the eastern United States. All of the population are long-distance migrants. Swainson's Thrushes breeding west of the Rockies travel south along the Pacific coast to

In North America, thrushes look like their European equivalents in plumage only. Otherwise, they chime more closely with Nightingales – in size, voice and long-distance migration. Swainson's Thrush winters in the tropics but, like other New World migrants that embark on epic flights, a few individuals miscue in autumn and cross the North Atlantic. This individual was found in the Shetland Islands.

PHOTOGRAPH: ROBBIE BROOKES

Central America; the remainder migrate along an eastern route to Panama and South America. Curiously, those that breed in Alaska – north of birds breeding in California – fly thousands of kilometres east before turning south to winter in South America. Hence the respective 'arms' of the population are segregated by breeding range and choice of wintering location. In other words, a migratory watershed has developed and a tribe has divided. Why do the Alaskan birds not migrate as the crow flies instead of tracking east? The explanation is that their circuitous route is an artefact of recolonisation that occurred at the end of the last glaciation, around 12,000 years ago. Research into the molecular genetic make-up of the Alaskan Swainson's Thrushes shows them to be eastern stock, not western.[3] For that reason they follow their parents' historical footsteps, which began in south-east North America and reached the Pacific coast of Alaska. Thus post-glacial migration strategies have driven Swainson's Thrushes apart. And not just in their travels. A further indicator that never the twain shall meet is a difference in appearance and choice of breeding habitat: west-coast birds are russet-backed (other populations are olive-backed) and prefer to nest in deciduous scrub, not young conifers. Therefore, given time, migration can facilitate divergence – the first step on the road to the evolution of new species.

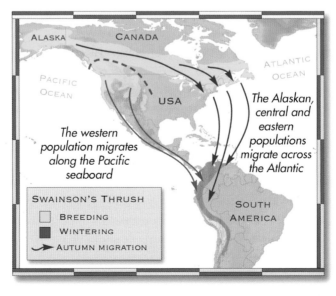

2. Types of migration
Nurture, then departure

*Birds are capable of wonderful parental affection and self-sacrifice.
The mother Linnet who would not leave her chicks in a gorse fire,
and covered them until she was burnt to death.*

STEPHANA VERE BENSON

The most important thing that a bird does in its life is to raise young.
Reproduction is all. It has to be. Otherwise the species would soon be
extinct. At the heart of the matter is a breeding site. For offspring, all
journeys begin there. Youngsters map the world from their home place and even
if the bird never returns there, it is unlikely to forget where it started. As yet,
nobody knows what bearings are taken for imprinting. Migratory salmon are
said to recognise the chemical trace of the waters in which they hatch. For birds,
every star in the sky shines into their eyes, the air they breathe contains a unique
isotope signature and the differential pull of Earth's magnetic field indicates
latitude. Are these the cues they use? Juvenile dispersal represents first gear in
migration. What follows, depending on the genetic make-up of the species, may
entail a maiden flight across as much as two hemispheres. Migration, like an
Irish funeral, requires a fair degree of stamina. The mental processes that control
this behaviour are beyond our ken. We struggle with the puzzle. Splendidly, like
good magicians, the performers do the seemingly impossible while keeping their
secrets under wraps.

It is impractical to shoehorn all types of migration under one banner. It is
not an activity wherein birds go north or south in line with the seasons, for
they go in all directions at all times of the year. Moreover, migratory habits
may change during the course of their lives. Youngsters face the toughest
challenge and it is no surprise that this age class suffers the highest annual
rate of mortality. Although not designed to be expendable per se, they serve
a useful purpose as their explorations might turn up trumps for the species as a
whole. For this reason, colonising movements generally contain a vanguard of
immature birds, not old hands. Certain species enshrine 'go west, young man'
principles. The results of ringing reveal that during their first winter at sea,
young Gannets are more migratory and travel further south than older members
of the population. For species incapable of breeding until they are two years of
age, such as Arctic Terns, teens spend a gap year in equatorial regions or even in

Gannets produce a single egg. When the bare-skinned chick hatches, it looks reptilian but quickly becomes cute by growing fluffy white down that lasts until real feathers – brown and star-spangled – emerge in late summer (right). When good-to-go, the juvenile jumps from a cliff without prior flight practice. Safe on the sea, it swims off on the first leg of its migration. It is too heavy to fly and lives off fat deposits for the first week or so. Once airborne, it heads south – most young spend their first winter in tropical seas off the coast of West Africa. It returns to home waters in its second or third year and starts to visit breeding colonies – not just the colony from which it hatched. As it undergoes a series of moults, brown 'teenage' plumage is shed and replaced with white, adult-like kit (facing page, upper two insets). During its third or fourth year it circulates among colony-attending adults. If it lands at an occupied space it will draw the ire of an adult. Because Gannets nest colonially the new recruit will – if it is a male – have to compete for a foothold (facing page, lower inset). After establishing its own spot, the newcomer advertises to prospective females with a ritualised display. When breeding partnerships are cemented they usually last a lifetime. Once part of 'adult society' the bird spends its days in the cold grey waters of the North Atlantic and no longer visits the warmer seas of its youth.

the opposite hemisphere from the breeding grounds. By way of loading the dice to potentially acquire new territory, sporadic mutations may arise randomly and come to persist in populations if they prove to be profitable, thus establishing a bridgehead leading to colonisation or the foundation of a new winter home (as happened with the Blackcap – see Chapter 25).

Even within the same species some populations are more migratory than others. Many northern and central European Blackbirds travel south-west to escape the onset of winter and the overall percentage of migrating birds increases from south to north and from west to east.[1] Norwegian and Swedish Blackbirds mostly come to Britain and Ireland,[2] only a small proportion going south of the English Channel to winter quarters in France and the Iberian Peninsula. Although some Danish Blackbirds come to Britain and Ireland, most head south and stay within Western Europe. German and Swiss Blackbirds go south-west

to France and Iberia. In winter, Blackbirds occur throughout the Middle East, so Eastern European populations probably migrate due south for the winter. In terms of age and sex profiles, a study showed that youngsters formed a significant proportion of those migrating and that, among adults, a higher proportion of females occurred than males, implying that old males preferred to remain closer to established breeding territories lest they forfeit them in spring.[3]

The Blackbird is the bard of spring in suburbia. Its song is cheery yet wistful. The fanfare launches an annual cycle designed to produce a new generation. Adults busy themselves with courtship rituals, territorial battles and the hatching of young who, as in any household, complicate matters considerably. When the chicks hatch they are naked, blind and helpless. If a predator finds the brood all will be lost. Parents, at the slightest suggestion of a threat, go into high dudgeon. Worms and other high-protein food are ferried incessantly to accelerate development and enable half-grown young to flutter away from the nest, separate and hide. Feather growth is rapid but reflects survival priorities. On the one hand, wing and tail feathers need to be robust and long-lasting. Flight is a vital requirement and wing and tail feathers grown in the nest will have to last at least a year. Their quality cannot be compromised. Body plumage, on the other hand, consists of many small feathers that are grown quickly. Their function is to clothe the juvenile in order that it can stay insulated and leave the nest. This plumage is low-grade. Compared to adult plumage, each feather has fewer barbs and the tip is loose with no interlocking structure to hold the end together. Although structurally inferior, the first-generation cloak is good camouflage. The dappled speckling of juvenile plumage helps the parvenu blend among shadowy undergrowth.

Blackbirds, whether male or female, are born speckled. In effect, speckled plumage is the youngster's baby clothes and the mottled feathers are weak and not meant to last. During summer, juveniles moult and replace the plumage on the head and body. Because the process begins on the body, head plumage is the last to be upgraded. For a few weeks in late summer it is possible to see the transition. Young females will emerge looking predominantly brown – like their mother – whereas young males blacken up. Of the three youngsters in the photograph, two are males (facing page).

When they wander away from their parents' territory and become independent, all young Blackbirds undergo a change in appearance. Irrespective of whether they hatched early in spring or were the last to fledge from a second brood in summer, they moult their 'milk teeth' body plumage during August. Not only do they now look like an adult but they start to think like one too. Depending on the land of their birth, they may be predestined to migrate a considerable distance. However, before that, they disperse. In this way they become familiar with a sizeable area of breeding habitat. The following season, provided they return, they can expect to find somewhere suitable to rear a family of their own. Indeed, an analysis of British nestlings recovered in subsequent breeding seasons showed that 72 per cent returned to within 5 miles of their birthplace.[4]

No matter if the hallmark of a species is wholesale migration, involving a twice-yearly shift in the centre of gravity of the entire population, juvenile dispersal is a precursor. It is tempting to regard the activity as random prospecting, which, through a combination of accident and sagacity, stumbles across potential future breeding habitat. Just because dispersal is generally a solitary activity undertaken by a novice, its importance should not be underestimated. Dispersal and migration are closely related. Migrants are known to have remarkable powers of orientation and navigation and are born with senses that tell them where to go on an itinerary encompassing home and away. Nature disposes that none is destined to be a lost soul.

Until a youngster is old enough to breed, personal survival is the goal. Solo, a migrant can fend for itself. Acquiring a mate and breeding territory sufficient to raise a family is much more onerous. For a long-distance migrant returning

Some species scarcely move any distance in the course of a lifetime. House Sparrow is one. Does this make the bird any less extraordinary than a far-ranging migratory bird? Nothing could be further from the truth. House Sparrows conquered the Old World by themselves and, once introduced to North America from 1850 onwards, they slowly and steadily colonised that continent to its furthest reaches. The bird's rate of spread across the USA was put around 30km per year. Instead of dispatching envoys to search for pastures new, the entire corps expands like bacteria – the species is a closet colonist that thinks like a tortoise, not a hare. House Sparrow does not come any more humdrum than this drab demoiselle, her plumage threadbare after a year picking crumbs from the pavements of Lyon, in France. Gentle spring rain dislodges yellow flowers from the city's trees and the plainest of street maidens is suddenly centre-stage amid a froth of saffron blossoms.

like a prodigal son to the land of its youth, different cognitive decisions have to be made, including remembering locations not seen for a year or more. Learning the natal area is, therefore, critical. Some evidence suggests that the direction of post-fledging exploration differs between the young of long-haul migrants and species that perform shorter flights or are mainly resident. By analysing recoveries of birds ringed within the previous 100 days as nestlings in Britain, Baker[5] compared dispersal movements made by two trans-Saharan migrants (Wheatear and Redstart) and compared them with similar shifts for Robins that, in Britain, travel less. The two migrants explored a larger area to the north and orientated their exploration along a north–south axis parallel to their standard migration direction. The British Robins showed no particular preference for any direction. Does this indicate another purpose in post-fledging exploration? Might globe-trotting migrants map out a navigational target that helps them find their way back to the natal area in spring? If so, the strategy is remarkably prescient.

3. The source of Ireland's visiting Blackbirds
Home thoughts from abroad

Its twinkling Travels it pursues
Above the Haunts of men

Emily Dickinson

Everywhere Blackbirds make themselves at home in gardens. They leapfrog over the lawn with the body language of a chess piece making a decisive move. Leaf mould is their happy hunting ground. This hunter's head stretches and crooks like a neighing horse before lunging. Precisely how they find worms remained a mystery until a study in 1997 revealed that quarry is located primarily by listening.[1] Is there yet more to Blackbirds than we realise? As early as January, their behaviour starts to synchronise with the calendar – goodbye winter, the days are getting longer. By scattering dry porridge oats in my backyard I tap into a network of dozens of winter visitors. Where do they come from? Although some are distinctive and can be recognised on repeat visits, most form an anonymous rank and file. Irrespective of age, their plumage is exquisite. Adults sport a full coat of unworn feathers grown in the wake of the previous year's breeding season. Males are in sleek new charcoal slacks, like a boy starting secondary school. Young males, on the other hand, retain the brown, kelp-coloured wings and tail that they grew in the nest. The contrast of brown wings against an ebony body sets young males apart. All females, irrespective of age, are as brown as turf stacks and distinguishing mothers from daughters is not as straightforward as telling the age of males.

Over the course of several winters I formed the impression that late February was a time of exodus or at least a period when there was a high turnover of individuals. Where were they going and why? Was the perceived emigration reflected in the composition of ages or sexes? Was there any way I could find out? If some were caught and ringed then I stood a chance. My hunch was that a fair proportion hailed from Scandinavia and that some might even be Finnish. Imagine that! I had a basis for my conviction. Most Blackbirds born in Britain show unspectacular seasonal movements, although a proportion of Scottish birds commute to Ireland. However, breeding populations from Norway to the Russian border show a strong westerly component in their direction of travel. They winter from Britain and Ireland south to Spain, with some reaching as far north-west as Iceland or south-west to Morocco.

Thanks to ringing data accumulated from dozens of recoveries (derived from a staggering grand total of half a million ringed in Britain and Ireland from 1955 to 1974), changes in the distribution of overseas records have helped to demonstrate a spread into Finland. After gaining a toehold along the country's south-west coast in the early part of the twentieth century, Blackbirds had started to breed throughout the southern third of Finland by 1950. The colonists came across the Gulf of Bothnia from Sweden. Once the original pioneers broke out from their bridgehead, the subsequent spread was accomplished by

Main photograph: Blackbirds, female (top left) and male (top right). In Ireland during winter, Blackbirds from overseas probably outnumber 'native' Blackbirds. Many come from Scotland and northern Britain – but the majority may be from Scandinavia and further east. When a feeding station is maintained throughout the winter – by sprinkling dry porridge daily, as here[5] – it becomes clear that, even though food is available, most Blackbirds leave suburbia at the end of February. Where do they go?

In the main photograph, it is possible to tell the age of the male. It is a young bird, hatched the previous spring. Because the wings are brown, not black, they belong to a one-year-old. All young Blackbirds retain the (brown) wings and tail grown in the nest. Unlike the juvenile body plumage (see pp. 16–17), the wings and tail are not replaced and are intended to last until just after the bird's first birthday. Hence, the contrast between the 'old' brown wings and 'new' black body plumage establishes age. On an adult male (inset for comparison), all the plumage is uniform black, including the wings and tail.

Finnish-bred birds. Mining the data revealed a prevalence of males: confirmation that, as a general rule in all range expansions, young males are usually responsible for breaking new ground.

Between 1931 and 1974 the proportions of Blackbirds ringed in winter in Britain and Ireland and recovered in Fenno-Scandia in the breeding season charted the rise of the new Finnish population. Between 1931 and 1957 all 'home country' recoveries had come from Norway and Sweden. This started to change in the early 1960s and by the 1970s Finland contributed an equal measure of Blackbirds ringed in Britain or Ireland during winter.[2] Around the same time, mist-nets were introduced that facilitated trapping in suburban gardens and orchards. There, in addition to Swedish and Norwegian winter visitors, Finnish Blackbirds were among the captures in Ireland.

Watching Kerry Leonard extract the first Blackbird from the mist-net that he erected in my garden in February 2010 reinforced my respect for the disentangling abilities of bird-ringers. I would not know where to start. Blackbirds do not suffer the indignity quietly. Depending on the angle of strike, a snagged bird may keep fluttering and bury itself deeper into a spider's web of gossamer mesh. Safe in Kerry's hands the victim calmed, allowing vital statistics to be compiled and a shiny ring fitted. This was the first of three captures, all female. One was an adult; the others were first-winters. It felt strange to behold one of 'my' Blackbirds in the hand. All looked cross at having their privacy violated and made me feel as though I had been part of a conspiracy against them. Perhaps this was why they never came back? Nonetheless, their ring numbers entered the British Trust for Ornithology database where they sit like an investment of lottery numbers.

A calm morning had been picked for the visit. Everything was silent so the sudden puff of Kerry's breath was almost startling. He blew against the breast plumage of the adult female to expose the underlying skin. Like a patient anaesthetised on a slab, the bird's anatomy was revealed (see p. 22). The abdomen, breast muscles and neck looked like a tiny plucked chicken. At the point where the horizontal collarbone fused across the chest, I could make out the wishbone or furcula, an endearing Latin moniker meaning 'little fork'. Among the pellucid musculature Kerry pointed out the location of fat deposits, swollen patches the colour of earwax. Ringers classify the amount of fat on a scale between zero and eight. Fat is laid down just beneath the skin in three epicentres: in the hollow at the wishbone (the furcular depression), at the breast and at the abdomen. Fat is fuel. A resident bird with no intention of leaving home or flying far has no need to lay down a significant supply. That diagnosis applied to the adult female. In terms of accumulated fat, she was as lean as a marathon runner.

Like a human endurance athlete, birds prepare themselves for long flights. Fat is fuel and it is laid down mainly across the chest. Nearly fully loaded, the right-hand Blackbird has enough fat to power a sustained flight lasting 24 hours or more. Although migrants eat to prepare themselves, they do not eat any more than their peers. Instead, hormonal signals link the brain and body and trigger a greater digestive ability, capable of converting a higher proportion of food to fat.
ILLUSTRATION: DAVID QUINN

A migrant preparing to migrate is a different kettle of fish. Depending on how far the flier needs to go to get back home – and how long it plans to be on the wing – an adequate amount is vital. A maximum score is achieved when fat girdles the entire body like a corset. Adding fat adds weight. Indeed, depending on the urgency of a migrant's schedule, the sooner the weight is accumulated the better. Migrants on a mission increase their food intake rapidly and store the energy. The process is called hyperphagia and subcutaneous fat is rocket fuel. Birds caught for ringing give an insight. If fat score and weight equate to a full battery, their motives are clear.

Nightingales migrate from Europe to spend the winter in the rainforests of West Africa, a trek they complete, if possible, in one or two giant leaps. A migrant caught at Portland Bill Bird Observatory on the south coast of England on the evening of 27 August 1968 weighed 22.8g. It remained in the area for a fortnight during which time it was trapped again. During the first week its weight remained stable but over the course of its last six days it shot up from 25g to 35g: an increase of over 50 per cent.[3]

I hoped that similar measurements might suggest plans for foreign travel on the part of the two remaining Blackbirds, which were young females. Kerry repeated his examinations. The first patient had more fat than the adult; its furcular depression was padded yellow. However, the quantity was insignificant. The prognosis was a healthy teenager, possibly Irish and with no overseas aspirations. Close but no cigar. Even I could see that the final candidate was different. Its abdomen was layered like a toasted cheese sandwich, matched by a bloated furcular depression. The two pockets resembled ballast tanks. The analogy made sense when I remembered that symmetry in loading is also paramount for flight. For its fat score, Kerry gave the second female just under half marks. I asked the crucial question: was that a sign that it was about to migrate? Possibly. Migration strategies differ between species and even within species tactical decisions are the whims of the individual. If the second female was about to set off for Helsinki she could get there by a series of short hops and replenish her supply of body fat at stopovers en route.

I took a last look at the restless maiden before she took off like an Olympic sprinter from Kerry's palm. I imagined her crossing the Norwegian Mountains and seeing the untamed rivers and numberless trees of the Scandinavian taiga. Emily Dickinson's line – 'hope is the thing with feathers' – came into my head. Migratory birds are not, however, kamikazes. Airborne, they may enter the kingdom of time and sky but not without preparing for departure. Although migration is innate, other factors control the moment when a bird decides to take its chances and go. Are there periods when migration is out of the question? Moulting plumage would appear to constitute an obvious handicap, although some species that habitually roam the planet, such as Sooty Shearwaters, have a business-as-usual attitude and track long distances with long wings that are a mixture of old and new feathers. Most adult songbirds undergo a complete moult either prior to autumn departure, at stopover sites en route, or upon reaching winter quarters. One interruption that cannot be ignored is the extra weight that comes with the onset of breeding condition. During courtship the internal sex organs – called gonads – expand (gonads are reproductive glands that produce sex cells – egg cells in a female and sperm in a male). Although flight abilities are not compromised, the bird is operating at close to its baggage limit. For a male Starling, testes' weights increase from 8mg in January to 500mg in March and peak at 1,000mg in April.[4] Egg-producing females are, of course, even more encumbered.

4. Triggers of migratory behaviour
The light switch

Sleep, minstrel, sleep; the winter wind's awake,
And yellow April's buried deep and cold.
The wood is black, and songful things forsake
The haunted forest when the year is old.

WILLA CATHER

Nearly all plant and animal activities are related, in one way or another, to the influence of the sun. As winter turns to spring, daylight changes and the gradual increase in sunlight allows plants to photosynthesise and produce glucose, energy that powers growth. In Ireland, at the beginning of March, we have about eleven hours of daylight but by the end of May we have about sixteen. By then, Swallows that have spent the winter in South Africa will have returned and the Cuckoo can be heard. Could it be that movements of birds and the emergence of new vegetation are a shared response to changes in a light-time switch or 'photoperiod'? Is this the trigger that releases an impulse in birds and urges them to fly such great distances every year? Incontestably, they need some kind of stimulus allied to an internal chronometer that tells them when to go and when to return.

Nowadays the cairn of knowledge about much of the natural world has reached dizzy proportions. Past discoveries, once they fit into place, are amalgamated into a narrative whose milestones tend to be forgotten. Galileo's championing of heliocentrism – suggesting that Earth rotated around the sun and not vice versa – led to him being investigated by a religious inquisition. He was found 'vehemently suspect of heresy'[1] and forced to recant. Professor William Rowan almost met a similar fate. Born in Switzerland, he divided most of his life between England and Canada. He had a lifetime interest in bird migration and field biology[2] and in 1921 became the sole member of a newly established Department of

As winter turns into spring, daylight lengthens – a change that acts as a trigger in the natural world, particularly for plant growth and bird activity.

Zoology at the University of Alberta. At that time, leading theories suggested that food supply, temperature or barometric pressure were the cues that birds used to calibrate the seasonal changes in their biology.

Rowan saw things differently. He pointed out that many migratory species depart in July before their food has attained its annual peak and that supply varies in abundance and regularity from one year to the next, a dubious basis for a phenomenon – bird migration – that is outstandingly regular. Similarly, vagaries of climate applied to temperature and barometric pressure. While both followed broadly similar patterns that chimed with the seasons, neither was consistent. Although Alberta's climate contained four marked seasons ranging from mild summers to snowy winters, some years had a hard frost in June or August and occasionally the region's anticipated winter chill did not bite until January, a full two months later than normal. To boot, switches from high to low pressure did not instigate migration during birds' sedentary periods of summer and winter.

Rowan postulated that changing day length was the chief mechanism that initiated migration and breeding. Furthermore, he reasoned that if variation in daylight affected migratory instinct, it must do so through the seasonal growing and shrinking of the gonads. His views – and his wish to investigate the hypothesis as part of his research – were shot down by the university president, Henry Marshall Tory. This was an era when studies were conducted in laboratories on subjects such as invertebrates, fish and amphibians. Living birds and fieldwork were not in vogue. Unable to investigate matters in academia, Rowan decided to work on the project on his own time at home.

Although not the first to consider the importance of photoperiod, he was the first to test its role directly on animals. He devised a trial involving wild-caught Slate-coloured Juncos, a common wintering finch that migrated north

Slate-coloured Junco is a North American finch. In autumn, northern populations move south. During the Canadian winter of 1928/29, the species was used in a pioneering experiment. By detaining wild-caught migrants in autumn and exposing them to artificial light levels simulating the arrival of spring, William Rowan brought the birds into breeding condition at Christmas – demonstrating that the change in day length stimulates hormones affecting not just sexual activity but also migration timing.

through Alberta each spring. At autumn migration time he caught a quantity of southbound migrants. He housed them in two purpose-built aviaries. Half served as an un-manipulated control group to observe and use for comparison with the experimental group. One aviary was fitted with electric lights that were left on past darkness. By leaving the lights on, Rowan hoped to simulate the increasing length of days that the birds would experience in spring. As the nights got longer and the temperature dropped, the experimental group received electric light well into the night for three months. He increased the duration of light by five minutes each day to replicate the gradual onset of spring. Except for the artificial light, the birds lived in winter conditions. Over the course of the trials (November 1928 to January 1929) the weather was severe and remained well below zero for days on end, a fact that delighted Rowan because it put his theory to a stern test. Every two weeks he recorded behavioural observations and measured the size of gonads. Despite the intense cold, the increasing light caused an increase in gonad size in the experimental birds. By the end of the study the experimental birds courted and sang as if it were spring. 'No control [bird] was ever heard to sing during the winter months. The experimentals, on the other hand, were in full song at Christmas even at zero.' The birds' sweet trills must have been music for his soul.

During this and subsequent investigations Rowan proved that by subjecting birds to increasing or decreasing amounts of artificial light, the cyclical development of their gonads was dependent upon seasonal fluctuations in day length. Searching for the secret of migration, he found a universal truth and proposed that a gonad hormone might be the switch that sets off an inherent migratory impulse.

Reaction to the discovery was hardly ecstatic. The scientific community, instead of lauding the revelation, pointed out a fatal weakness. Many migrants winter on or near the equator where the days remain approximately the same length throughout the year and where temperature varies little between months. What factor in such a stable environment might indicate to wintering migrants that it was time for them to head north? And what about trans-equatorial migrants, such as Willow Warblers from Ireland's latitude, arriving in the southern hemisphere at a time when the days were getting longer but leaving when the days were getting shorter? Various arguments have sought to explain how birds might bend their detection of photoperiod and use it to mark the calendar. Might they align their internal rhythms once a year on the breeding grounds, thereby making an annual adjustment? Rowan suspected as much. 'If one supposes that in these species [trans-equatorial migrants] the annual rhythm has become stabilised and is not susceptible to interruption by

Willow Warblers spend the winter in tropical regions where day length is relatively constant – yet they time their departure for Europe to coincide with the arrival of spring in the northern hemisphere.

exposure to adverse light conditions for a whole winter, then sojourn in the south would have no effect.'

By way of corroboration, he noted astutely that 'deciduous trees, taken from the northern hemisphere to the tropics, retain the habit of shedding their leaves during the northern autumn – but only for a few years. Thereafter the periodicity ceases. The leaves are cast at any time of the year.' As botanists know, not all plants are switched on to flowering by long periods of light. Some need very short days. Red Goosefoot is an annual herb of bare, damp ground whose seeds are loved by many birds, including ducks. If exposed to light for a mere eight hours, it grows from a seedling and flowers within three weeks. However, if bathed in light for twenty hours a day, it will grow up to two metres and yet not flower.[3] Botanists classify Red Goosefoot as a 'short-day' plant. Other plants are 'long-day' and require many hours of light over a series of days to produce flowers. Just to make things more difficult, some plants get switched on *because* of the change from long to short days, or vice versa.

For birds the timing of seasonal breeding is inextricably linked to predictable changes in photoperiod. Rowan discovered the short answer; the full explanation is more complicated. Although a long-day photoperiod certainly sets migration in motion, the effect varies between species. Responses are tailored to fit migration strategies and are under genetic control. Migratory birds do not so much possess a light switch as a switch-cum-timer. In some species, such as high-latitude Arctic breeders, long summer days result in a short rapid burst of breeding activity. Research shows that the stimulating effect of a long-day photoperiod on the gonads is short-lived and that, in little over a month, the organs become unresponsive to long days and quickly start to regress.[4] Is this why Arctic Terns seem to be in a hurry to leave as soon as summer days shorten, even deserting clutches about to hatch?

Mid-latitude species that experience shorter maximal day length and enjoy longer breeding periods are the corollary. Where does that leave tropical species that live in a world with little variation in season or day length? Their resources may be less tightly linked to photoperiod. Food availability or cues that herald ideal breeding conditions, such as rainfall, may be the chief influencing factors.[5] In summary, for northern-hemisphere species, we can adopt the view that day length provides the environmental stimulus that arouses the migratory impulse and that reproductive hormones act as a green light for the physiological preparations needed to embark on the journey ahead. But the 'starting-pistol' urge to migrate is different, and is correlated with temperature, wind and time of day. In the spring migratory period, restlessness occurs mainly on balmy nights and is inhibited during daylight or if the weather is cold and windy. In experiments conducted in early spring in Germany with captive European Robins which, unlike their Irish and British counterparts, are strongly migratory, researchers found that restlessness was at once shown when room temperature rose from 5 °C to 20 °C.[6] In autumn, on the other hand, migratory restlessness is stimulated by a sudden fall in temperature.

5. The physiology of migration
Operation Transformation

The discovery, in 2009, that Bar-tailed Godwits fly from one side of Earth to the other, some 10,400km in a single, non-stop 175-hour flight, left ornithologists awestruck.

BIRKHEAD, WIMPENNY & MONTGOMERIE

At the end of the nesting season adult birds look to their own needs. On the breeding grounds, the name of the game was reproductive success. Now the primary goals are to moult, move to winter quarters and garner enough sustenance over the next eight months for a quick and timely return to natal areas the following year. With the exception of juvenile geese, swans and cranes, who typically remain with a parent until around the time of their first birthday, youngsters have independence thrust upon them.

As a group of species, shorebirds cover greater distances than any other family of birds. Little Stint is one of the smallest: a titch with a body length less than that of a House Sparrow. Key wintering grounds are in central and southern Africa and the main migration route from breeding haunts in Siberia lies across the eastern Mediterranean. Handfuls of youngsters pass through Ireland in autumn. This juvenile was on the shores of the Black Sea in September. It fledged in July, leaving enough time for it to fatten up during the Arctic summer before heading south. Independently of its parents and peers, it sets off on its first migration single-handed – all the way to a distant continent and wintering haunts that it has never seen before. How does it know where to go? And how does it find the way?

Like human adolescents, boundaries are about to be tested. Little wonder, therefore, that mortality is greatest in the first year of life. Many recruits will perish on migration. Those that die in the attempt leave a bittersweet legacy of a strengthened gene pool. Most offspring migrate solo and are guided by instinct. Adults, on the other hand, call upon experience and memory. Irrespective of age, all birds intent on movement need to prime themselves. Preparations are psychological and physiological. The gonads, or internal sexual organs, shrink. They atrophy and lie dormant for perhaps six or eight months. Not only is energy-sapping courtship abandoned, weight is also reduced because the gonads virtually disappear.

Like astronauts preparing a spacecraft, finding room for fuel is paramount. Everything is pared back. A long-distance migrant, intent on flying continuously for two days or more, has no need to eat while en route. The digestive system is, consequently, a millstone when the bird resides in the air. Maintaining large guts is also costly because digestive organs are some of the most metabolically active tissues. Hence carrying the extra mass imposes both a weight and energy burden. Before they embark on long-haul flights of more than 24 hours' duration, shorebirds such as Knots and Bar-tailed Godwits travelling from the Arctic to Ireland fatten and then reduce their digestive organs just before departure.[1] In a nutshell, guts don't fly. The same principle applies to certain songbirds. Migrant European Blackcaps trapped at an oasis in the Sahara had reduced digestive organs that increased in size when they were temporarily held in captivity and provided with food.[2] Possessing astonishing transformative abilities is one thing but just how quickly can a bird resume 'normal service' and rebuild the complex web of gut size and digestive enzymes? The answer appears to be around two or three days. Moreover, to begin with, digestive efficiency is compromised. For this reason many species opt to migrate in a series of hops with layovers at 'stopover' sites where energy reserves are rebuilt in a steady-as-you-go fashion. In truth, long-haul aviators are obliged to cut their cloth to cross inhospitable terrain or track bountiful food resources thousands of kilometres apart.

Nor should it be assumed that a bird's successful arrival amounts to breathless exhaustion, evoking a marathon runner staggering over a finishing line. It has taken decades for ornithologists to accept avian feats of endurance that seem superhuman. One of the first biologists to speak up on the birds' behalf was Wells W. Cooke, employed by the Bureau of Biological Survey in the United States. In the late 1800s and into the last century, Cooke analysed data relating to migration patterns around the Gulf of Mexico. By comparing the location of arrivals and departures he concluded that most migration was trans-gulf and over water, rather than overland and around the Gulf's long coastline. He went

Bar-tailed Godwits that breed in Alaska and Siberia spend the winter in New Zealand and Australia. Over 30 have now been tracked from Alaska to New Zealand. Data for one female showed a direct flight from Alaska to New Zealand of 11,700km, lasting nine and a half days (and nights). That equates to 228 hours of continuous flight with no rest or food. The bird averaged 56km/h at a steady height of around 3 or 4km. After wintering in New Zealand, it took a different route back to Alaska – wind conditions suited a different route with respect to seasons. It flew 10,300km non-stop to the estuary of the Yellow Sea on the China/North Korea border. That flight took seven days. Next, it refuelled for about a month and flew another 6,500km to Alaska. In total, around 70,000 Bar-tailed Godwits follow this strategy. How do they do it? They set off at more than double their normal weight. About 55 per cent is fat. To carry the fat, the birds shrink body tissue that is not concerned with flight, including the gut, which, at take-off, resembles a thin piece of string. All other tissues are converted to flight muscle and fat. Hence, in preparation for departure, the fat tissue, flight muscle and the heart and lungs are expanded, while other body organs are shrunk. Therefore, the birds are not like aeroplanes – they do not simply land, refuel and take off again. Instead, fattening involves a lot of internal reconstruction to give maximum fuel with minimum other tissue. Ironically, once the bird lands, it cannot feed immediately because it must first reconstruct the gut in order to start to process food again.

PHOTOGRAPHS: ARIE OUWERKERK

As recently as the turn of the millennium, most information about where birds go came from rings or colour bands fitted to the legs. Based on a series of sightings, this Black-tailed Godwit, ringed on its breeding grounds in Iceland, passed through France and, in three consecutive years, staged in springtime on Belfast Lough (where the photograph was taken). Although these insights seem impressive, they are peanuts when set against the data gleaned from modern recording devices – such as sunlight-sensing geo-locators that weigh as little as a paperclip. For example, might the Black-tailed Godwit have wintered in Africa and what other sites did it rely upon in the course of a year? Nowadays, technology is answering these more important questions.

further and suggested that, unless they encountered turbulent weather upon arrival along the Gulf's opposite shore, the migrants did not pause but travelled on, unseen and over the heads of observers who doubted the existence of the migration route. He commented, 'it would thus seem that the popular idea that birds find the ocean flight excessively wearisome and that after labouring with tired pinions across the seemingly endless wastes, they sink exhausted on reaching terra firma, is not in accordance with the facts'.[3] Cooke published his data in 1904 and stoked a hornet's nest of disbelief that was only finally quelled by radar studies after the Second World War.[4]

Many of Ireland's summer visitors, along with millions of European kin, spend the winter south of the equator. To get there they must cross or circumvent the Sahara, an inhospitable barrier with a mean north–south width of 1,500km (900 miles). Until the 1960s the widely held belief was that migration was concentrated at each end. In 1961, Reginald Moreau, an English academic who had spent many years in Africa, spelled out the nature of the challenge in a classic paper that illuminated the true manner of desert crossings.[5] He wrote, 'the birds of most of Europe west of Russia are faced with the necessity of crossing the Sahara and also crossing [or detouring around] the Mediterranean. Because of the size of the desert and because sea and desert follow each other with no little interval, the combination would seem to make this journey exacting physiologically and potentially the most arduous to be performed regularly by a mass of land birds anywhere in the world.'

Moreau's study was a masterpiece of deduction. He demonstrated that species that were common in autumn on the northern coast of the Mediterranean were very scarce along the opposite coast in North Africa. Moreover, the same range of birds were not recorded in any significant numbers again until south of the Sahara. Into the bargain, given the scale of numbers decanted from Europe in autumn and travelling beyond the Sahara into the tropics – estimated at '250,000 per mile of longitude, which over a two-month period gives an average daily passage rate of about 4,000 birds per mile' – the paltry amounts encountered at desert oases meant that the vast majority did not halt. Taking the facts in conjunction, Moreau proposed that most migrants crossed both the Mediterranean and the Sahara in a single flight. His hypothesis, which took 30 years to complete, was constructed by scrutinising haphazard bird observations scattered over a vast region of Africa north of the equator and the Mediterranean basin. Crucially, he also studied weather, notably published data dealing with the recorded wind speeds in the lower and upper air over the Sahara. These began to show an effect on the speeds of migrants following various courses across the desert in both spring and autumn. Many accounts were graphic and dwelled in catastrophe:

> southerly winds … are often associated with what is known in Egypt as *Khamsin* conditions, extremely hot, dry and dusty winds, which constitute a special hazard to migrants. They blow with devastating violence, typically for periods of two or three days, and at their worst cause sand-storms … so turbulent is the wind, many birds are forced to land, and on the ground itself they have little hope of escape, being either buffeted to death or buried in sand. Yet safety would lie only a very short distance upwards, for the scurry of sand, which is appalling even to human beings, does not extend more than about 100 feet above the ground.[6]

Back in Britain, evidence from radar observations for small night-migrants, assumed to be mainly warblers and flycatchers, indicated that the birds flew at no more than 40km/h (25 mph). Moreau's study showed that, like a yachtsman setting sail, the speed of departing migrants was boosted if they set off in a tailwind. Calm conditions at take-off meant that side winds did not displace them en route nor head winds impede progress. Moreau did the maths and determined that a direct north–south crossing of the Sahara would, in still air, require a non-stop flight lasting 36 hours. This calculation did not, however, take into account the changeable nature of regional weather. Moreau examined prevailing winds in different sectors of the Sahara, taking altitude and seasons into account. By thinking like a bird he cracked the code. He discovered that, by selecting seasonally available tailwinds, some of which blew best at altitudes up to 3,000 m (10,000 ft), there was good reason to suppose that 'the main directions may be south-west in autumn and north-east in spring, involving somewhat diagonal crossings of the desert, rather than directly north and south.'

Rising from the sands of the Sahara, the Ennedi Plateau conjures a scene from *Raiders of the Lost Ark*. Labyrinthine rock walls conceal ribbon lakes and pockets of vegetation. Camel trains come here for water but, to the outside world, this could be Mars. The area played an important part in confirming that birds migrated from Europe and crossed both the Mediterranean and Sahara in a single flight.
PHOTOGRAPHER: G. NIETHAMMER. COURTESY OF ZFMK ARCHIVES, BONN

To embark on a long-distance single hop, Moreau knew that a migrant needed fuel for the journey in the form of fat. At the time there was little information about the extent to which European migrants accumulated fat. So he turned to data from the US used to calculate flights across the Gulf of Mexico.[7] Citing American studies, he concluded, 'if the birds that cross the Mediterranean and the Sahara put on as much pre-migratory fat as those which cross the Gulf of Mexico, they should be able to keep in the air for 30 hours and perhaps for 60.' In 1959 an important piece of the puzzle was provided by a German ringer, Franz Kollmansperger[8] who trapped and weighed migrants at Ennedi, a cliffed plateau in north-east Chad bordering the southern edge of the desert. Assailed by sand on all sides, Ennedi was replete with cool valleys and lush pockets of wetland.

By Moreau's reckoning, this was one of the first places where birds would touch down if they had flown 2,000km (1,200 miles) over the Mediterranean and Sahara. Compared to the normal weight of several of the same species

As part of an expedition in the autumn of 1959, Franz Kollmansperger compared the weights of European migrants – such as Redstarts, Tree Pipits and various flycatchers – trapped at Ennedi with weights for the same species before they left southern Germany. He discovered that many had used so much body fat that the only conclusion was they had been flying constantly and had not halted before reaching Ennedi – and had probably been airborne since leaving Europe.

Redstart

Tree Pipit

Pied Flycatcher

weighed in Germany by Kollmansperger during the breeding season (that is, before deposition of any migratory fat) those at Ennedi had lost weight in varying degrees. At one extreme, Spotted Flycatchers, Redstarts and Tree Pipits were up to 40 per cent under weight, whereas Swallows and Wheatears – which were either able to feed en route or had used stopovers – were only 10 per cent down. For the severely underweight migrants, Moreau concluded, 'on the face of it, not only had all the migratory fat been consumed but other tissue besides.'

When Popeye was in need of extra strength, he opened a tin of spinach and instantly sprouted bulging biceps. One could argue that migratory birds undergo a similar transformation. In comparison to non-migrants, individuals gearing up for a major flight need first to become eating machines and then flying machines. Migrants acquire necessary fat on two different timescales: seasonal fattening prior to migration and daily fattening in response to short-term food shortages. Whereas daily fattening is a pragmatic response to environmental conditions, migratory fattening is regulated by a genetically predetermined set of controls.[9] It seems extraordinary, but species earmarked to travel to distant lands inherit the fattening programme they will need for future journeys. Left to its own devices, how could a young songbird or shorebird honed by evolution to fly from its Arctic birthplace directly to the southern hemisphere, know how to prepare itself?

It is tempting to simplify fattening and other changes in metabolic activity as no more taxing than a mammal laying down fat prior to hibernation or a jet plane filling fuel tanks before heading off over a curve of the Earth. For birds, the process is more complicated. For one thing, the distances that migrants travel and the behavioural and physiological strategies they use to reach their destinations are diverse. Before setting off on momentous journeys, migrants indulge in gluttonous eating (hyperphagia). However, certain closely related species show marked differences in ability to absorb and assimilate fats. Blackpoll Warblers breed in northern latitudes across North America and spend the winter in northern South America, which they reach by performing a colossal single flight lasting in excess of 48 hours over the western North Atlantic. Myrtle Warblers, a close cousin that shares its breeding range with Blackpoll Warbler, is a shorter-range migrant that winters in the southern United States and Mexico. Both are similar-sized insectivorous species and weigh around 13g. Yet, based on the same daily food intake before migration, Blackpoll Warblers metabolise food differently. When trapped at migration time and compared with Myrtle Warblers, Blackpolls had greater body mass and accumulated more than double the quantity of fat; some tipped the scales at 36g, almost three times their normal body weight.[10] By being able to put on such extensive fat reserves,

At the end of the breeding season, Sedge Warbler (left) and Reed Warbler migrate from Ireland to sub-Saharan Africa. To prepare for the journey, both gorge on aphids found on the stems of reeds and other marshland vegetation, including osiers (a species of willow). Stored fat is the birds' fuel, and for each species, the fattening process comes under genetic control. Because they use staging areas en route between Ireland and Africa, Reed Warblers put on less weight. Sedge Warblers however, particularly adults, double their weight and, in so doing, are capable of completing the journey in one go. Energy can only be stored in three biological tissues: fat, carbohydrate and protein. A gram of fat contains as much as seven or eight times as much energy as a gram of carbohydrate or protein. Hence, the reason that migrants store fat is obvious. Fat can also be stored in the body with very little water. Protein, on the other hand, has a high water content (around 75 per cent). Research suggests that migrants can metabolise proteins stored in muscle tissue to meet their hydration requirements without needing to drink.

Blackpoll Warblers have the wherewithal for a bespoke migration strategy.

Before attributing a unique label to the Blackpoll Warbler's fattening strategy, it is worth remembering that research into bird migration can have a narrow focus. The discovery of novel information can blind us to similar abilities among species in our own back yard. Across Ireland, Sedge Warblers are widespread in damp thickets. Reed Warblers, on the other hand, require stands of tall reeds growing in water. Reed Warblers interweave their nest around the base of growing stems. Because reed growth is rapid, the nest is elevated and concealed over water. In late summer, irrespective of nesting proclivities, both species utilise reed beds to fatten up on aphids before departing for African wetlands where they spend the winter. During the breeding season each weighs a mean of 11.6g. When fattening for migration, Sedge Warblers reach 19–21g, whereas Reed Warblers seldom exceed 15g. Migrants trapped in early autumn at Rye Meads in Hertfordshire were typically a little above the summer weight average and remained in the site's extensive reed beds until both species attained a 'migration-ready' weight and then left.

The acquisition of large fat reserves suggested a difference in the distance of planned flights – those envisaged by Sedge Warbler being potentially greater, a conclusion supported by analysis of subsequent ringing recoveries: 'it is interesting to note that although more than twice as many Sedge Warblers as Reed Warblers have been ringed in Britain, there are many more foreign recoveries of Reed; mostly from western Portugal and north-west Spain. In other words, Sedge Warblers [at least adults that put on more weight than juveniles] make a longer flight, direct to Africa [and therefore are not encountered at ringing locations en route].'[11] Based on the researchers' figures, if the lean weight of a Sedge Warbler is 11.7g, an individual weighing 21g will have 9.3g of fat. Assuming weight loss to be at the rate of 0.7 per cent of departure weight per hour, a Sedge Warbler will be capable of a sustained flight lasting 60 hours which, at 40km/h (25 mph), would enable it to fly 2,500km (1,500 miles).

For any migrant, the ability to fly continuously for hours or days on end also entails in-flight modifications in the very structures and bodily processes that sustain flight – from decreasing body mass to mechanisms for coping with water stress and reduced oxygen supply available at altitude. The fat, in which the energy is stored, when oxidised during migratory flight, does not produce water as a by-product. Herein lies a problem. Although a bird's drinking needs are met mostly from its food and by limiting water content in waste products,[12] some water is still required to power muscles. It has long been known that migrants that use up their fat stores completely will metabolise muscle tissue (protein) in order to prolong flight. Why? Because muscle tissue, when metabolised, produces water. The skeletal muscles of the legs and subcutaneous tissue girdling the chest can become an important source of energy when fat reserves drop below a threshold.[13] The sad truth of this can be felt by pressing a finger against the chest cavity of a spent and recently expired migrant and feeling a sharp-edged sternum devoid of muscle. However, if water stress is a concern, migrants routinely switch between stores of fat and protein. If water is in short supply, as

Strangford Lough: beholding great flocks of Brent Geese is a privilege that we take for granted in Ireland. On nesting grounds in the Arctic the birds disperse over vast areas. When they arrive in early June, snow still carpets the ground. As soon as it melts, breeding commences – even though plant growth is yet to begin and there is almost nothing to eat. For this reason, females accumulate sufficient body reserves on the wintering grounds and spring staging areas to produce a clutch of eggs and to last through a four-week incubation period during which the sitting bird almost never leaves the nest. In other words, the birds migrate carrying more fat than they need to complete a migratory flight. Bart Ebbinge, a Dutch Biologist who monitored Brent Geese over consecutive years on the wintering grounds, discovered that only those geese that had attained 'breeding weight' prior to arriving on the nesting areas, returned from the Arctic with young.

perhaps in long flights at high temperatures over ocean or desert, use of a higher proportion of energy stored as muscle may be advantageous.[14] Furthermore, at the beginning of a migratory flight, a significant portion of the bird's mass is made up of fat (in some cases more than 50 per cent) or muscle. As this energy supply is used up and diminished, mass declines, affecting optimal altitude for flight. All else being equal, as mass declines, some migrants gradually move to a higher altitude where drag is less – especially for small songbirds – and less energy is required for flight per unit of time.[15]

Physiological attributes make birds uniquely equipped to tackle long-haul flights. While some individuals of certain species are capable of migrating non-

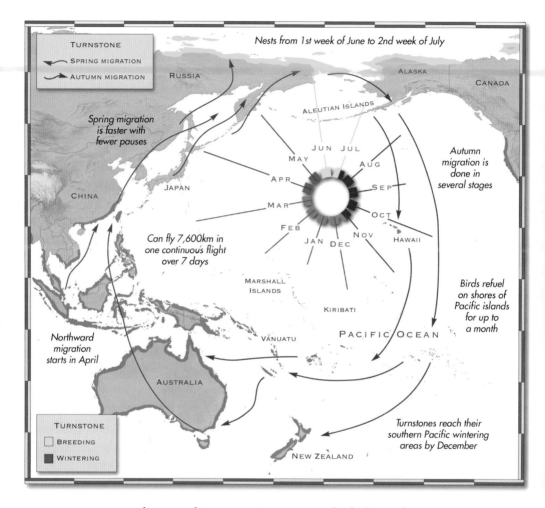

Within the figure:

TURNSTONE
SPRING MIGRATION
AUTUMN MIGRATION

Nests from 1st week of June to 2nd week of July

RUSSIA   ALASKA
                                         CANADA
            ALEUTIAN ISLANDS

Spring migration
is faster with
fewer pauses

JUN   JUL
MAY   AUG   Autumn
APR   migration is
JAPAN   SEP   done in
MAR   several stages
CHINA
              OCT
FEB   NOV
JAN DEC   HAWAII

Can fly 7,600km in
one continuous flight
over 7 days

MARSHALL
ISLANDS
                         Birds refuel
              KIRIBATI   on shores of
                         Pacific islands
                         for up to
              PACIFIC OCEAN   a month
VANUATU

Northward
migration
starts in April

AUSTRALIA

TURNSTONE
BREEDING
WINTERING

Turnstones reach their
southern Pacific wintering
areas by December

NEW ZEALAND

stop over a vast distance, this pattern is not a general rule. Instead, most migrants make one or a series of stops along a route connecting breeding and wintering areas. Moreover, depending on requirements for winter survival, the notion of a winter home is fallacious. This is because many species are essentially 'on tour' during the non-breeding season with a roving abode that may span an entire geographic region. Cuckoos and other European songbirds that winter in the African tropics track seasonal rains that maximise verdant conditions and, therefore, food availability. Hence, to maintain a route's viability, all destinations must integrate. Stopover sites are every bit as important as end points. Pauses are needed to replenish fat reserves or because a species is essentially a nocturnal migrant and prefers to halt by day (or vice versa). Breaks may be temporary and last less than a day or may be planned to last for weeks. Geese that winter in Ireland use Iceland as a stepping stone to Greenland. In spring and autumn, Barnacle Geese and White-fronted Geese spend several weeks in Iceland, feeding and waiting for favourable tailwinds before continuing on to breeding quarters in Greenland. Brent Geese do likewise, although they nest in Arctic Canada. Across arid regions, wetlands are of crucial importance. Many European migrants heading for Africa rely on a network of natural habitats strung out like pearls in a necklace among inhospitable terrain spanning thousands of kilometres. Deltas, lakes and seasonal floodplain wetlands are vital oases. Many of these are threatened with destruction for dams or water abstraction. Historically, the increased desertification of the northern half of Africa must have already tested the migration capabilities of many European species that face an annual return trip over – or around – the Sahara.

Spectacular facts excite the imagination. It is no surprise that we are awed at discoveries of giant leaps in migration. A few decades ago, research calculated the fuel (fat) carried by shorebirds travelling non-stop over 'ecological barriers', such as oceans, and then estimated the 'range' that this much fat would allow. The maximum distances in these computer models were around 4,000km. In the new millennium, the tracking of individual birds with satellite transmitters and geo-locators has extended our appreciation of the non-stop capacity of many species. Examples include Turnstones making 7,600km non-stop flights in six days from Australia to Taiwan[16] and Bar-tailed Godwits flying 10,400km in spring from New Zealand to China (an interim feeding area en route to Alaska) in just under a week and then embarking on an even greater eight-day odyssey in autumn by flying from Alaska to New Zealand, a distance of around 12,000km.[17]

These Turnstones, photographed in Ireland in May, are probably a breeding pair. Although the nearest breeding grounds are in Scandinavia, ringing returns suggest that they are probably bound for Greenland or Canada. Each has moulted body plumage and acquired a whiter head and a brighter chestnut back. The male (at rear) is more brightly coloured; female plumage, although still spectacular, is designed to blend with tundra vegetation. Females do most of the incubation; males patrol the nest area and look for danger.

6. Assessing the weather
Gone with the wind

. . . .

At last one little spider took time enough to stop and talk to Wilbur before making its balloon. 'We're leaving here on the warm updraft. This is our moment for setting forth. We are aeronauts and we are going out into the world to make webs for ourselves.' 'But where?' asked Wilbur. 'Wherever the wind takes us. High, low. Near, far. East, west. North, south. We take to the breeze, we go as we please.'

E.B. WHITE

By flying in the direction of air movement an individual can increase its groundspeed – the sum of its own speed plus that of the following wind. Simply stated, wind is both an ally and a foe. Tailwinds are a godsend; headwinds are at best an inconvenience, at worst a fatal final straw. Side-winds and calm bring mixed blessings. Migrants compute this meteorological mix and endeavour to use it to their advantage. Birds migrating through central Europe and the Mediterranean have to cope with winds that range from half to roughly the same as their own airspeed. To complicate matters further, wind strength and direction are highly variable with respect to season and altitude. This applies to migrants entering the Middle East en route to the Nile Valley, a choke point for European species travelling to countries such as Ethiopia. The range of tailwinds within a night increases – but only at certain altitudes. Analysis of the impact of wind on theoretical predictions of flying times through the Mediterranean demonstrated that a bird migrating selectively during nights with favourable wind conditions would speed up its flight by approximately one third compared to an individual disregarding the wind situation.[1]

Taking wind into account, a bird can almost double its flight speed and save half of the energy needed for a leg of its migratory journey. Less time is required for refuelling and fat reserves are less depleted. Accordingly, for birds flying long distances in a single hop, the choice of favourable winds should be more important than adjusting departure to fat accumulation rates. Given that migrants are, to a certain extent, in a race against their own hormones, some may have to sit out ideal weather until they reach (or regain) an optimum departure weight. Prima facie evidence supports the view that there is a benefit to birds that select favourable winds during migration. On the other hand, acquiring the necessary information – that is, an accurate weather forecast – must be difficult.

During winter, flocks of Lapwings feed over inland fields across Europe as far west as Ireland. When snow or cold weather makes conditions impossible, mass flights occur. In search of mild ground, movements to the west and south-west are frequent enough for the Spanish to call migrants '*avefria*' – the bird of the cold. Evacuations tend to be short-lived. At the first opportunity the refugees return. Herein lies a mystery. How do the birds gauge a thaw back in the areas they came from?

Across Europe, winds are rarely stable over a long time period. The ability to make short-term forecasts covering the immediate outlook for the next one or two days of a prospective flight would certainly be advantageous.

Bird movements in response to weather are commonplace. Responding to frozen or snow-covered ground across Britain, flights of thrushes and Lapwings evacuate to mild Ireland. Fleeing cold weather and potential starvation is one thing; possessing meteorological clairvoyance is a different matter. Field studies on patterns of migration intensity do not tend to support a forecasting savvy. Waves of migration are often observed immediately after the end of a spell of bad weather, even though conditions for migrations are less than ideal, while lower intensities of movement have occurred on subsequent days when conditions were optimum.[2] Nonetheless, like a barometer that reads 'change', birds react to events. Whether they respond, automaton-like, to stimuli or have learned to react to weather patterns conducive to migration, is still a mystery.

In Ireland, especially on the country's inhabited western islands, a few surnames cover a host of people. Sharing a name tag with a stranger does not, however, make you a blood relative. Similarly, among some bird species, having a name in common belies differences as stark as chalk versus cheese. All of

Wheatears are restless. Analogous to the stern of a deer or rabbit, a white rump flashes when the bird flies. Photographed in brand-new plumage in autumn, this airborne migrant (right) is en route to ancestral winter quarters on Africa's sub-Saharan plains. No matter where it was born, the same set of feathers will be kept until it completes a round trip back to its breeding site – that could be in the Arctic. In their rush to migrate huge distances, Wheatears push themselves to the limit. Rather than sacrifice valuable time moulting, almost the entire feathered costume is retained for a year and even courtship colours are acquired by abrading the fringes of body plumage – transforming shades of brown into black and grey. Closer inspection of the breeding-plumage male's (left) attire reveals wings that are threadbare and faded (bleached by sunlight) and, among grey upper-parts, traces of unburnished brown remain. As much as half of the outer filament flakes off some body feathers, leaving a stub of a different colour.

the world's Wheatears (full title, Northern Wheatear *Oenanthe oenanthe*) spend the winter in Africa south of the Sahara from the Atlantic coast of Senegal to Somalia on the shores of the Indian Ocean. About the size of a Robin, Wheatears occupy grassland and open ground where the vegetation is short or sparse. They live on insects. In early spring the world population decamps to the northern hemisphere, including Ireland. The breeding distribution is circumpolar except for an (as yet) uncolonised gap spanning around 2,000km (1,200 miles) in the centre of northern Canada.

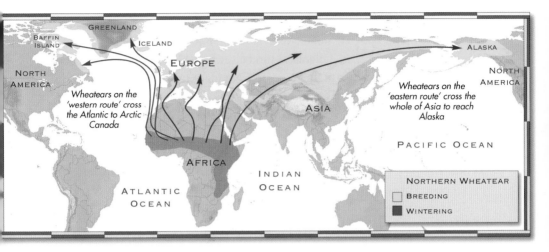

Depending on where they call home, Wheatears travelling out of Africa trek across Asia to reach Alaska or, going in the opposite direction, embark upon a flight straddling the North Atlantic to Iceland, Greenland or north-east Canada. Despite the enormous distance from the horn of Africa to the coast of Alaska (12,000km or almost 7,500 miles) the birds' route is overland. Likewise, in Europe, with the exception of relatively short hops over parts of the Baltic, North Sea and Irish Sea, Wheatears heading north to breed in Scandinavia, Britain or Ireland are spared the challenge of crossing the ocean. Those that do are slightly different. They are larger and have longer wings better suited to cope with, for some, a non-stop flight of 3,400km (nearly 2,500 miles) from Ireland to Baffin Island lasting four days.[3]

Although a partial misnomer, north-western populations are subtitled Greenland Wheatear O. o. leucorhoa. In taxonomic terms, they are regarded not as a species but as a subspecies: a distinguishable variation on a theme (see subspecies explanatory panel included in Chapter 27, p. 187). Because spring arrives late at high latitudes, Greenland Wheatears migrating through Ireland do not appear until the middle of April, by which time local Wheatears, present since the second half of March, are already incubating clutches. Across other parts of Western Europe, both groups occur together on migration. How might the birds' intention for the next leg of contrasting onward journeys manifest itself, particularly selection of departure weather?

The twin islands that make up Heligoland sit in the south-east corner of the North Sea 46km (29 miles) off the German coast. During spring migration, Wheatears bound for northern Europe, as well as Greenland Wheatears preparing to depart north-west, arrive simultaneously. All began northward journeys in western Africa and headed up through the Mediterranean and into

Europe, interspersing (in most cases) a single night flight with daytime pauses to feed and top up body fat sufficient to give them a two-day cushion of fuel.[4] Overlapping, time-wise, at Heligoland (and elsewhere along the southern coast of the North Sea), members of the respective populations switch their migration orientation. To determine if either group was more discriminatory in choosing advantageous departure weather, migrants were trapped, offered food and held in cages during the day.

One hour before sunset the cages were exposed to the natural sky. When the sky was completely dark the birds were released and their departure direction was measured by compass.[5] Almost all the European Wheatears quickly departed north or north-east, irrespective of weather conditions, including setting off in deteriorating conditions of cloud and a lack of tailwind. The Greenland Wheatears, on the other hand, adjusted a north-west departure to avail of tailwinds and clear skies. They stayed put during unfavourable weather. Taking everything into account, including differential fuel loads that chimed with the length of impending flights, it seemed that, for the European Wheatears in the final furlong of arriving back in Scandinavia, weather considerations mattered less. However, for aeronauts primed to fly to the New World, wind assistance was worth waiting for.

Are we close to understanding the decision-making processes that migrants use when they assess wind? We have got some things modestly right. Wind can outstrip a bird's flight speed; therefore an individual's ability to gauge conditions at departure time is key. For migrating songbirds, bedrock stimuli that favour departure include a gentle wind, clear sky, rising barometric pressure and high visibility. Ironically, for many species, initial wind direction does not seem to be of overriding importance. Because wind speed and direction can vary dramatically with altitude, it would be advantageous to acquire information about the height at which beneficial airflow is available. Given that wind conditions on the ground may differ from those aloft, how might a budding traveller determine the existence of a favourable wind at a cruising altitude?

Robins are short-distance, nocturnal migrants. Large numbers arrive in Ireland throughout the autumn, most of which come from northern England and Scotland, although others originate from Scandinavia. Upon arrival at a stopover site they instinctively become territorial, even though many are in transit. The establishment of a territory – proclaimed by singing – is a temporary expedient to facilitate refuelling. This pattern is repeated across Europe where, because the species is not present year-round, the occurrence of transients is obvious. Onward flights are not particularly onerous. Individuals that have failed to procure a suitable daytime feeding site may opt to depart at dusk if, by

Anyone who has watched flocks of Starlings wheeling and twisting over a potential roost, seemingly waiting for just one bird to make its mind up and turn the entire corps to bed, would concede that every bird is a free spirit. Although Robins (silhouetted) also dream of being warm, most face the additional challenge of a lengthy nocturnal migration from breeding areas to winter quarters. Dusk departures amount to crunch time but before committing to an overnight flight, individuals assess flying conditions aloft – by making short sorties to cruising altitude – as well as judging conditions at ground level.

flying under good weather conditions, they can 'make hay' and get closer to journey's end. In this endeavour, departure in good weather outweighs refuelling. By trapping migrant Robins on a daily basis during three autumn seasons in Switzerland, researchers were able to determine nightly emigration rates and correlate departures with weather.[6] The results were startling: 'our analyses showed that the daily emigration probabilities of Robins from the stopover site were strongly influenced by the prevailing rain and wind conditions aloft but not by the local ground wind conditions.'

Robins and many other small songbirds fly at altitudes up to 1,000 m, where wind conditions are often better in maximising flight range than those on the ground.[7] At the Swiss ringing site, nocturnal emigration peaked when conditions were calm or featured a gentle breeze and no precipitation. Avoiding flying in rain is important for several reasons. Visibility is impaired, potentially compromising navigation by obscuring celestial references (the moon and the stars) and drag is increased when raindrops buffet the wings. Fewer Robins departed on nights with a moderate wind and no rain, and on rainy nights with weak wind. Almost none left when wind and rain combined. The results showed that, overall, it paid to wait for evenings when there was little or no wind, conditions that correlated at both ground level and altitude. By departing in low wind speeds and gaining height, the bird could assess conditions aloft without much risk of being displaced by a strong headwind. Following a dusk ascent, it could select optimum wind by shifting altitude (alternatively, it could break off or shorten a flight in headwinds). Nonetheless, the bulk of emigration occurred when conditions aloft were more favourable than indicated by the weather at ground level. Crucially, results suggested that Robins were able to predict ideal conditions aloft: 'departure was almost independent of wind conditions on the ground and it seems that wind speed aloft is predicted by other means.'

What cues might be tapped? One possibility was the general weather situation. On nights with the largest departure rates, high pressure prevailed.

The air in high pressure is comparatively stable with relatively light winds, ensuring that a migrant could be confident of no adverse weather ahead and a possible tailwind boost, depending on the direction of travel. A smaller number of nights that witnessed good emigration consisted of slow-moving weather fronts or a stationary low-pressure centre. In both, no wind prevailed. Presumably, the virtual absence of wind served as a kind of 'Plan B' tipping point in a decision to depart. Do Robins have a trick that enables them to sense weather? They might be able to anticipate wind speed aloft by changes in air pressure, as evidenced by research on homing pigeons, the domesticated progeny of wild Rock Doves.[8] It is certainly true that most songbird migration occurs during high-pressure conditions.

Frigatebirds attacking Red-footed Booby near equator in Atlantic, November 2013. PHOTOGRAPH: TOM McGEEHAN

Frigatebirds, unlike other seabirds, never rest on water. They are remarkably specialised fliers and new research suggests that, buoyed by a pillow of wind, they are nature's finest flying machines. A 2.5m wingspan only partly explains their aerial skills. The trick lies in combining a lightweight body with broad wings that span 40 per cent more wing area than those of any other bird of comparable size. They move between beauty and buccaneer from moment to moment. Hanging motionless high in tropical skies, they swoop low to catch flying fish and ambush smaller seabirds and force them to drop dinner.

Researchers fitted solar-powered transmitters to Great Frigatebirds at a colony in the Indian Ocean off the coast of Mozambique and discovered that, after breeding, the birds migrated and remained airborne for months at a time.[9] They may not even have slept – as the transmitters recorded that they were motionless for only about two to twelve minutes at a time. They certainly made the best use of insomnia. Their travels were powered by air around the doldrums – the huge windless basin in the middle of the Indian Ocean. Along its margins, trade winds blow toward the equator and enable the birds to circulate on a conveyor belt of wind. The air is warm and rising. By spiralling aloft, the frigatebirds reach heights of 1.6km (5,250 feet) without flapping. Once at cruising altitude, between 30m (100 feet) and 1.98km (6,500 feet), they were recorded gliding continuously for up to 185 days (26 weeks) and covering 54,700km (34,000 miles) – considerably more than the circumference of Earth. On fewer than a handful of occasions, loners have been encountered in Ireland and Scotland. The most recent – one in poor health in July 2013 on the Scottish island of Islay, facing north Antrim – came from a colony on an islet beside Ascension Island, just south of the equator and midway between South America and Africa.

7. Atmospheric motion – its influence on migration
Weather station Ireland

So let the water sizzle
Upon the gleaming slates,
There will be sunshine after
When the rain abates
And rain returning duly
When the sun abates.

LOUIS MACNEICE

When, in 1479, Christopher Columbus visited his brother-in-law in Madeira, he noted that the island lay in a zone of steady north-east winds.[1] Ultimately, these became known as 'trade' winds, a Middle English term meaning 'track', denoting the route taken by Portuguese mariners to reach the African coast. Columbus put his observation to good use when, departing from Palos on the south-west coast of Spain on 3 August 1492, he plotted a southerly course to tap the trades and fill his sails. The winds were steady and in 36 days carried him west to San Salvador. But how would he ever get home? Fortune sprang from an error. In the mistaken assumption that a route to Spain lay north-east, he headed so far north that he inadvertently entered the belt of prevailing westerlies. Although the winds blew favourably along his direction of travel, he was twice beset by winter storms near the Azores before reaching the Portuguese coast. In effect, his home leg was along the track followed by Atlantic weather fronts: Ireland's default wind circulation.

We live in a wet and windy corner of the world. Our weather never stays the same for long and, in just a few hours, a sky buttered with cloud turns to wet confetti, followed by fortissimo sunshine. This instability stems from the fact that Ireland falls under the influence of air masses generated by four continents and one ocean. Like elements in an intercontinental Venn diagram, the birds that reach us share the same bailiwick. Wind and weather determine migration outcomes. When summer ends, before the dark days of winter draw in, birds from the coolest latitudes of the northern hemisphere head south. When, six months later, seasons switch, the mass movement goes into reverse. Such a simple overview, when expanded to take account of routes, strategies and avian navigation systems, swells into a multitude of complex considerations. Most departures are controlled by weather, as are delays, diversions and

Fair weather day

Mares' tails

Mackerel sky

Cirrus layers

Like scenes in a play that we have seen many times before, signs of rain are writ large in the sky over Ireland. When benign tumble-dryer accumulations of puffy white cumulus (above) are accompanied by ribboned whips of 'mares' tails' or the rippling rows of a 'mackerel sky', they are an omen. Both patterns denote high-level winds associated with an advancing weather front. Although mares' tails have the texture of rice paper, they equate to white horses on the crest of powerful atmospheric waves. The old rhymes 'mackerel sky, not twenty-four hours dry' and 'mares' tails and mackerel scales make lofty ships to carry low sails' enshrine the onset of rain — about six or more hours later. Before that, cirrus masses (bottom), the sky lowers and the horizon disappears. Soon brightness shrinks and a sill of grey nimbus (rain cloud, facing page) looks solid enough to walk along. A drenching is imminent.

Rain over ocean

destination mix-ups. Despite the risks, some species prepare for truly momentous journeys entailing flights passing through more than one climate zone. To succeed, they need to integrate with weather patterns and seek a course along which the winds can be expected to blow in the direction of travel. Until the invention of powered engines, sailing ships sought a similar collaboration with the elements. Upon leaving the coast of Virginia in 1838, an American naval expedition bound for the Southern Ocean found its progress was dictated by wind: 'the direction of the prevailing winds required them to sail a zigzag course to Brazil, heading east and south toward Africa, before sailing west and south across the equator to Rio de Janeiro.'[2]

Our inquisitive nature is stimulated by the will to understand. Weather plays a huge part in facilitating migration and, consequently, birds' travels. To grasp how the system works, some familiarity is required with the processes that grind our planet and keep it to an orderly and predictable pattern. We could skip the detail and travel light by reducing an understanding of weather and bird movements to the kind of clichés trotted out in the media, such as reports of waifs blown off course and hopelessly lost. In fact, weather is the wellspring, not the wrecking ball, of migration. Modern technology gives us a bird's-eye view of a local story in a global play. In Ireland, at some point each day, we are transfixed to a forecast of our national obsession. Fortune smiles on us in the shape of a free national meteorological service, whose presenters on television and radio have the knack of dramatising a technical topic without fudging the science.

Since the 1960s weather satellites have provided increasingly accurate meteorological information. Nowadays, more than 120 circle the globe, transmitting data and images. The European Meteosat satellite, stationed at

37,000km over the equator at the Greenwich Median (0 degrees longitude) takes a picture containing Ireland every fifteen minutes. From space, Earth resembles a defrosting blue marble. Land-mass colours correlate with climatic zones. Verdant green indicates tropical forest; khaki signifies desert and corrugations of brown and white pinpoint snow-capped mountain ranges. Great swirls resembling cinnamon-raisin Danish pastries prick out constant storms raging in the roaring forties. Zooming in closer to home, a typical view of Ireland reveals cloud lying west of us in the Atlantic. The belt has an elongated north–south axis, wider than our island. And it is, as usual, coming our way. However, in the satellite snapshot, Ireland sits under clear skies. This is when forecasters say the words, 'let's run the satellite sequence.'

We know the story. The only questions that concern us are the timing: how long before the rain arrives and when will it stop? Pragmatism is understandable but analysing the sequence is fascinating. Undeniably, our regular airflow hails from the North Atlantic. Masses of cloud push over us, interspersing sunny skies with not one, but several types of cloud, not all of which produce rain. High wispy cirrus consists of ice crystals that do not fall as precipitation but whose streaky mares' tails are an indication of wind that we do not experience at ground level. Another portent is rippled rows of fleecy white cloud interspersed with blue gaps – like the back of a mackerel. Gradually it thickens into a veil of cirrus that is subsumed by lowering grey cloud containing rain and wind. For several hours we are under a dull wet blanket. When steady rain gives way to scattered showers and gilded slivers of sky open up to the west, the worst is over. In a nutshell, a weather front has passed.

Choice of the word 'front' was deliberate. At our latitude, circling Earth at around 50 degrees north, there is an interfacing boundary between warm tropical air coming up from the south and cold polar air plunging down from the north. Where these air masses meet, turbulence is created and 'depressions' develop. While this transition zone moves within the temperate mid-latitudes, it is semi-permanent. Around the time of the First World War, Norwegian meteorologists were beginning to understand the genesis of depressions. Central to their hypothesis was the clash of air masses stretching across the Atlantic. The meteorologists were impressed by a likeness to two great powers of equivalent strength facing each other along a dividing line of trenches running continuously from the North Sea to the Swiss Alps. They took the connotation of a military front and transposed it.

The analogy also mirrors disturbances that occur periodically along the front. When warm and humid 'southern' air makes an incursion into colder 'northern' territory, the skirmish follows predictable rules of engagement. In the swirl of

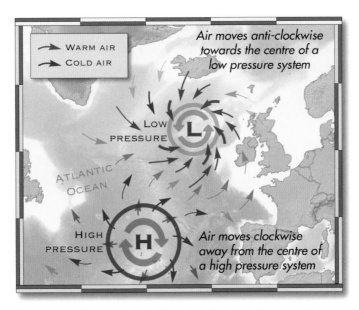

WARM AIR
COLD AIR

Air moves anti-clockwise towards the centre of a low pressure system

LOW
PRESSURE

L

ATLANTIC
OCEAN

HIGH
PRESSURE

H

Air moves clockwise away from the centre of a high pressure system

Weather map diagram: to show differential wind circulation around low and high pressure.

contact, warm air is pushed upwards and eastwards and is undercut by cold air streaming in from the west. Around the epicentre, the wind circulation is anticlockwise. The scene is represented on weather maps as a series of wobbly concentric circles, like a lopsided knot in wood. The lines on each circle (known as isobars) connect points of equal air pressure but the contours reflect something else: ever-lowering pressure towards the centre, hence the weather-speak term 'low'. When a low approaches close to Ireland we get strong winds. Just like contours on a map that, as they coalesce, denote a steep gradient, tight isobars signify dramatic changes in pressure. The upshot is an increase in the strength of the wind. Generally speaking, the closer a depression comes, the heavier the rain and the greater the likelihood of gales. The strongest winds may be on the southern side ahead of the low but sometimes the north-west airflow that follows in the wake may pack the biggest punch. Progress can be followed on satellite images. Akin to an anticlockwise spiralling Catherine wheel, the coil travels north-east at around 50km/h (30 miles per hour) across the Atlantic. Even though the centre usually stays out at sea, frontal cloud envelops Ireland as the giant trundles towards Norway where most depressions fizzle out.

Before weather satellites were invented, meteorologists devised graphics to tab a depression's battle lines. Trailing south from the centre, two curved lines carry pennants. Invariably leading the way is the warm front with half-moon symbols, followed by the cold front's shark's teeth. Between the two lies a triangular zone, known as the warm sector. Precipitation is almost constant here because moisture is trapped between the competing forces of warm and cold air. Like a rainmaking production line, cloud and drizzle are at their worst until the cold front arrives. Now things pep up. The cold front has momentum behind it. Rain might increase temporarily but when it stops the air is sharp and clear in a freshening wind.

As a foil to low pressure, high pressure takes the form of anticyclones. Arguably, anticyclones exist because there are no depressions in their vicinity. For this reason, weather forecasters regard anticyclones as stable features that endure until they 'break down' following onslaughts from depressions. Around the region of the Azores high pressure is semi-permanent. The air is slack and slowly descending. Put another way, the air is subsiding. Pressure is, therefore, increasing towards the Earth's surface and is termed 'high' because the air is being compressed. For birds that seek to exploit the characteristics of highs and lows, there are important lessons to be learned. Lows, for all their volatile wind energy and precipitation, can provide the fastest tailwinds. Highs, stable with more sedate airflows, would seem to be a better bet for a migrant. Either way, one consideration is paramount. Whereas air circulates anticlockwise in a low, it travels in the opposite direction in a high. For a bird, awareness of that fact could be the difference between life and death.

8. Giant-leap travellers
Water, water everywhere

May, the month of increased heat
Prompts green wildness to peep and meet
Above the ground and towering in bloom
Perfuming the air, scenting the room

Tony McGeehan

Among older inhabitants in Ireland the popular view is that spring begins on St Bridget's Day, 1 February, when longer, milder days signal the end of winter. Buds bursting on plant life signal the season's true arrival. Insects quickly follow and, hot on their heels, migrant birds arrive from the south. During April a green wave can be observed on successive satellite images moving northwards across Europe at an average of roughly 160km (100 miles) per day. By May, cyclonic activity in the Atlantic ought to be at its weakest. Depressions amount to small affairs and, over Ireland, anticyclones gain the upper hand. Meteorologists declare that high pressure prevails. Blue skies, little wind and an absence of precipitation evoke outside broadcasts of the *Antiques Roadshow*. Our summer visitors, having arrived on warm zephyrs – fictionalised by Flann O'Brien as 'the wind from the south … a fine shining silver' – are in clover. Lucky them. For our winter visitors, May is a month to return to breeding grounds in the Arctic, the land of the midnight sun. To get there and back necessitates long-haul flights over water. Moreover, as Ireland warms under the control of anticyclones, areas of low pressure are displaced to higher latitudes, particularly Iceland, and may lie in the path of northbound migrants.

Arctic Tern's right to the title of the world's greatest migrant is incontestable. Most of the population breeds well north of Ireland and passes our latitude in May, en route to halcyon Arctic shores where little time is lost laying two camouflaged eggs on stony ground. The birds know absolutely everything about global oceanic weather because they follow time-honoured routes to the

In a life spent travelling Earth from top to bottom, it is hard to know where Arctic Tern's heart calls home. Lightweight, stiletto-tailed and sickle-winged, its shape is modelled to fit the wind.

roaring forties and on to Antarctica. The species gives shape to those facts. It is built like a shuttlecock. Long, impossibly slim wings seem to claw air currents rather than cruise them. The poppets match and then exceed the distances flown by Ireland's Manx Shearwaters that spend winter in the Atlantic east of South America. By fitting geo-locators to tern backs, the providential nature of migration from separate colonies in Greenland and northern Iceland has been revealed.[1] These tiny 1.4g devices operate by recording light levels to detect sunrise and sunset and thereby determine location. Although birds from the same breeding site took separate southbound routes – following the African or South American coast – all returned along a similar trajectory and crossed the Atlantic in tropical seas by flying from east to west, deriving maximum benefit from trade winds. Because some flew east across the Indian Ocean to Australia and New Zealand (as did an Arctic Tern ringed on County Down's Copeland Islands) before turning south into the Southern Ocean, distances in excess of 90,000km (54,000 miles) per annum were recorded.

As a child I felt sorry for Arctic Tern. I read about its epic journey and envisioned blizzards and fierce winter storms. I knew that no bird has wings of clay and that, like Blackbirds that can only hop forward, waifs at sea have no choice but to complete the transglobal odyssey for which they are born. However, so long as a migrant can live within its means, it can go anywhere. That notion spun a metaphor and allowed me to paint emotions upon the species. Only later did I appreciate that the name *Sterna paradisaea* – 'tern of paradise' – commemorates a life spent flying from pole to pole in perpetual summer. Moreover, the penalty of miscuing and being swept off course is not starvation or death. Arctic Terns could, theoretically, find small fish anywhere

Arctic Tern (*Sterna paradisaea*)

There were only four foreign recoveries, but all merit publication in full. The recovery in Australia is much the most distant for any species to result from British ringing and would command a very high place in any world list of the most spectacular recoveries.

| CKj1037 | nestling | 28.6.66 | Valley: 53°17′N. 4°34′W (Anglesey) Wales |
| | found dead | 31.12.66 | Bega: 36°40′S. 149°55′E. (New South Wales) Australia |

In 1967, wonder and incredulity greeted the news that a young Arctic Tern, ringed as a chick in Wales on 28 June 1966, reached a beach in New South Wales, Australia, six months later. It now appears that such flights form part and parcel of Arctic Tern's globetrotting reach. Not only have others reached Australian waters but this part of the Southern Ocean is regularly traversed by European migrants heading even further east – towards New Zealand – before they turn south to the edge of Antarctica.

SOURCE: BRITISH BIRDS (NOVEMBER 1967) 60:452

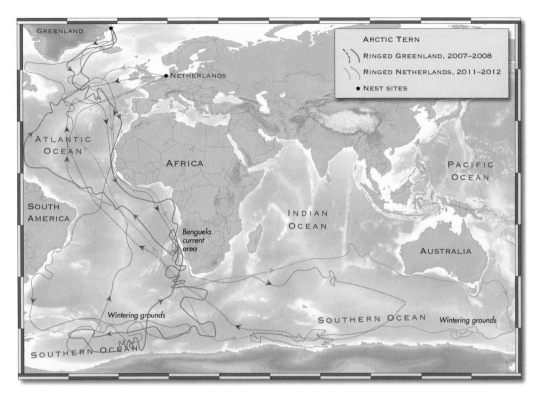

In July 2007, Carsten Egevang attached lightweight trackers to 50 Arctic Terns when they left nesting sites in Greenland. The following summer, ten devices were still attached to returning birds. On average, each device recorded a round trip of almost 71,000km (44,000 miles). Four years later, Ruben Fijn and Jan van der Winden tagged five Arctic Terns from the Netherlands. These averaged an even greater distance – 90,000km (56,000 miles). Although the species' 'winter' quarters (in truth, the birds migrate from northern summer to southern summer) was known to be the seas around Antarctica, it came as a shock to discover that some Dutch birds travelled beyond Australia before heading to the frozen continent. For both groups, the southbound cross-hemisphere trip took three to four months. With thoughts focused on breeding, travelling home took less – about 40 days.

and settle on the sea if the going gets tough. Rather than heaping admiration on a globetrotting tern, maybe Purple Sandpiper, a Jude the Obscure of rocky coasts, is more deserving?

Between tides, Purple Sandpipers live lace-curtain lives gleaning minute molluscs and arthropods among seaweed in splash zones. Their garret is frequently hidden from view. Grey garb and a quiet, almost voiceless, demeanour bolster the anonymity of their presence. Even in breeding plumage, the species prefers a middlebrow look, unlike other Arctic-nesting shorebirds whose courtship finery can be admired before they head north. Save for a handful of pairs in Scotland, the closest breeding grounds to Ireland are located in Norway and Iceland. That, however, is not where our winter visitors go.

Human curiosity is hard to kill. Technology is revolutionising migration insights and writing brand-new chapters. Bird ringing, conducted on a large scale for more than half a century, tabbed, at best, a handful of locations visited during the course of a bird's life. Colour-ringing targeted on a species group and better-quality optics, enabling code markings to be read in the field, added extra sightings but they did not explode the seed pod of knowledge. The enormous difference between ringing statistics versus information retrieved from modern electronic devices – termed, collectively, 'data loggers' – is that the bald fact of a trapping location tells you just that, whereas a downloaded file of activity tells you almost everything else.

Concise information about, among other things, stopovers, choice of routes and travel responses to weather, foster new understanding and brush away conjecture and sentimentality. Through colour-ringing it was known that Purple Sandpipers wintering in eastern Britain migrated to Norway where they bred. However, biometrics of the population wintering in northern Scotland, whose movements might have been similar, showed intriguing differences.[2] On the one hand, they were slightly longer-billed. This might reflect feeding habits. On the other hand, they were longer-winged. The difference in wing length hinted at an ability to tackle longer-haul flights than a hop across the North Sea. Sightings in Iceland of colour-ringed migrants from Scotland pointed to unknown breeding grounds elsewhere. Around the same time, attention focused on Purple Sandpipers in western Ireland. Their measurements matched those shown by the Scottish population.

Because Purple Sandpipers are faithful to wintering sites, a plan was hatched to capture a sample there, rather than search wilderness for a colour-ringed needle in a haystack. From 2009 to 2013, fifty devices were fitted to birds in Scotland and western Ireland. Vitally, several were re-trapped, allowing their logs to be read. The hidden door finally opened. The birds were flying to Baffin Island and Devon Island in Arctic Canada to breed.

In many ways the disclosure of nesting whereabouts was only the tip of an iceberg. Details of travel itineraries were revelatory. Spring departures from Ireland and Scotland took place mainly in late May. On average, Irish Purple Sandpipers left significantly later (median date 29 May) than Scottish counterparts. The difference pertained to where they staged on the way north. Whereas most Scottish birds halted in Iceland, the majority from Ireland (and one from Scotland) went straight to Greenland. Given the necessity to arrive promptly in Canada in June, minds were fastened to the calendar. Hence

It takes the low angle of winter sunshine to reveal Purple Sandpiper's eponymous name. Combined with a coy lifestyle spent close to the splash zone, it is little wonder that the denizen of wet rocks is hard to locate. The bird seems to revel in the commotion of oncoming surging waves, leaping clear at the last moment or running, swimming or fluttering to safety. At high tide, groups adjourn and catnap on boulders above swell height. Because many haunts are on sea-washed islets off the coast, most of Ireland's winter population are more familiar to seals than people.

stopovers in Greenland were shorter than in Iceland and lasted less than a week. Most were back on breeding quarters during early June, although a vanguard of keen males arrived in late May. Interrogating the statistics showed that each leg of the journey was between 1,100 and 1,500km (680 and 930 miles) and was accomplished in under a day. The migration via Iceland and Greenland required changes in direction, whereas the flight to Baffin or Devon Island via Greenland was direct. Depending on the route taken and including sojourns along the way, the overall time from Ireland or Scotland amounted to between six and 30 days.

Autumn journeys were far from the reverse of spring flights. In common with all birds, adults need to moult and renew plumage, an obligation that many species schedule for the end of the breeding season. Purple Sandpipers nest among mossy tundra, habitat that ensures a rich supply of insect food for chicks. As soon as offspring fledge, parents return to the coast to moult and resume feeding on marine invertebrates. When cold weather and the first snow in September put an end to feeding among tundra, juveniles join the moulting adults. Before the season changes, other Arctic-nesting shorebirds depart south and opt to migrate first and moult at stopovers or postpone the process until arrival on winter quarters. But not Purple Sandpipers. Along unfrozen shorelines, quarry is available up until sea ice forecloses intertidal zones. So they stay put in high latitudes. The moulting grounds of the tracked birds were on southern Baffin Island, northern Labrador and south-west Greenland. Migration from the Canadian sites took place in late October and early November. Birds in Greenland, where the coast remained ice-free for longer, stayed until December before migrating back to Ireland and Scotland. Return passage from the western hemisphere avoided Iceland and was a direct flight lasting about two and a half days. The distance covered per day was calculated to be in the region of 1,400km (870 miles), a staggering achievement.

Crossing the North Atlantic during winter from north-east Canada or Greenland to Ireland or Scotland entails long nights and very short days. In our mind's eye, weather across such an enormous swathe of ocean is likely to be unsettled or worse. Conversely, it is easier to imagine more benign conditions during the birds' spring commute. Perhaps, given the proclivity of migrants to time departure to coincide with tailwinds, Purple Sandpipers northbound in May adopt meteorological wait-and-see tactics? It is tempting to conceive a scenario in which travelling birds are virtually levitated and helped along by an invisible carpet of warm air. Although tailwinds are desirable, often essential, they are not exclusive to anticyclones. A shift against a prepared expectation is needed. Birds get that point. In low-pressure systems (depressions) air flow is anticlockwise. Depending on direction of travel, that may be ideal.

In a sense, the tracking results showed that, although the Purple Sandpipers selected advantageous wind, they were also able to take the rough with the smooth. Migrating over such great distances and not being able – or prepared – to settle on the sea, the likelihood was that not everything would be plain sailing. A marked difference in travel speed between the two migration seasons is explained by the more vigorous nature of winter depressions. Analogous to the semi-permanent cell of high pressure in the vicinity of the Azores, an area of low pressure is found between Iceland and Greenland. As winter sets in and cold grips land masses north of the temperate zone, the ocean remains relatively warm. The contrast between land and sea is responsible for the location of the Icelandic low, which dominates the wind circulation. In summer the low weakens and is often divided into two cells, one located over Iceland and the other further west, over the Davis Strait between southern Greenland and northern Labrador.

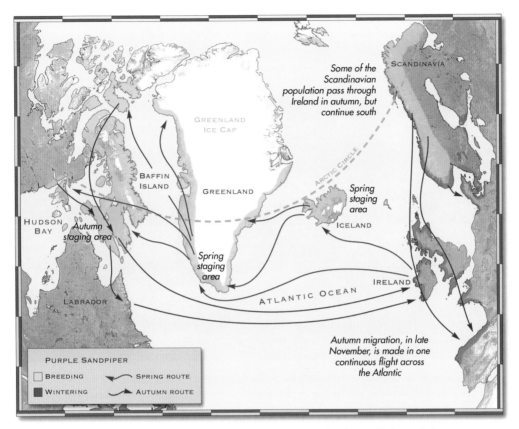

Tracking results have shown Purple Sandpiper to be a transatlantic migrant. Underneath demure looks lurks an avian Amelia Earhart.

For a savvy migrant, the higher wind velocity generated in winter has a silver lining. By flying into the slipstream of depressions, speed is increased. Given that air circulation is anticlockwise around the centre of a low, wind on the south-west flank will boost a migrant heading east. Winter logs of nine birds recorded 'sleigh-ride' flights buoyed by predominantly north-west winds over part or all of the Labrador Sea, middle and east Atlantic. Caprice affected others. One individual encountered a south-east gale in the Labrador Sea and broke off its migration in Greenland where it remained for three weeks before departing for the west of Ireland. Not only did it appear to backtrack to Greenland, demonstrating memory of Greenland's position, but it was able to recast its route when beset by contrary winds approximately 200km (120 miles) south-south-east of Greenland.

Spring departures from Scotland had favourable winds but several Irish birds were assailed by headwinds that impeded progress but did not curtail migration. However, in flights to either Iceland or Greenland, most birds circumnavigated

In preparation for courtship and breeding, Purple Sandpipers moult plumage across the head and shoulders. A costume that was low-key against wintry seas becomes drabber still – although perfect camouflage among the tawny-grey mossy plains where the species breeds. This photograph was taken in Iceland, an important breeding destination – home to Ireland's wintering population? No: Iceland's breeding population is largely resident. Nonetheless, Irish and Scottish Purple Sandpipers travel to Iceland en route to breeding haunts even further afield.

the northern flanks of depressions, thereby benefiting from the anticlockwise wind flow. Whatever thoughts cascade through their head, the birds know that, to maximise tailwind, they should follow a more northerly route via Iceland in spring and a more southerly route in early winter. Both options are geared around seasonal shifts in Atlantic low-pressure systems and the anticlockwise spin of their wind.

For a student of migration wanting to summarise the tracking results, three points would probably suffice. Firstly, tailwinds are selected, particularly at the outset; second, once under way, migrants attempt to forge ahead in all weathers; third, light airs make light work. Physical condition determines the decision to depart. A prerequisite is the accumulation of sufficient fat to fuel the journey. Flights on an 'empty stomach' are out of the question, even if weather is ideal. It seems that path-finding is directed by weather nous, overwritten by individual fuelling needs. Flight plans are, therefore, adapted to circumstances. No bird is an autopilot.

If Purple Sandpipers could read history books, the species would asterisk the events of October 1960 as a dark episode in the annals of migration. During that month, migrants bound for Europe had no inkling that persistent east winds held sway over the bulk of the North Atlantic. Instead of helpful tailwinds, fliers faced energy-sapping cross winds. Observations were made from Atlantic weather-ship *India* stationed 450km (280 miles) south of Iceland and 880km (530 miles) west of the Faeroe Islands.[3] Toiling against a 40km/h (25 mph) north-east blast, a Purple Sandpiper pitched down at *India* on 19 October and was joined by eight others over the course of the next day, by which time the wind was blowing hard from the east.

Little did the birds know that a *deus ex machina* twist lay in store. On board *India*, Ivor McLean kept a supply of mealworms for any tired migrants that settled on the ship. All the Purple Sandpipers readily took the emergency rations. One quickly set up a territory centred on the food and kept its companions away. Quick-thinking McLean distributed more mealworms at discrete distances to ensure chances for all. Even so, one weakened and died two days later. It weighed 47g, a low weight compared with another individual that struck the ship and died, which weighed 63g. Two years before, at weather ship *Juliett* stationed 1,350km (880 miles) south of Iceland and 700km (420 miles) west of Kerry, McLean noted that the weights of migrant Purple Sandpipers there fell between 42g and 56g; a far cry from birds measured in Iceland that ranged from 74 to 95g.[4]

Two conclusions emerge. The first is that migrants can be cowed by sustained adverse wind and succumb to a watery grave if they run out of fuel. The second is a discrepancy in migration timing. As shown by the 2009–2013 tracking study, nowadays autumn flights take place not in October, but in November or December. In terms of providing food for Purple Sandpipers, Arctic shorelines are remaining habitable for longer. Might this mean that if Earth's climate continues to ameliorate, populations breeding in Arctic Canada may not have to travel any further than southern Greenland to survive the winter?

Global warming may be a reality but before using it as an argument that explains a perceived change in the migration timing of Purple Sandpipers, it is useful to refer to nineteenth-century data compiled from birds that struck lighthouses around the Irish coast.[5] From 1881 to 1898 Richard Barrington organised Ireland's lighthouse men and keepers of lightships into a nationwide observer corps. His endeavour was supported by the Irish Lights Board. Irrefutable facts arose through forwarding, for the purposes of confirming identification, a leg and wing of any bird that collided with lanterns ('killed striking'). During the survey, 30,000 separate observations were tabulated and corroborated by over 2,000 specimens. Among them were eight Purple Sandpipers. Two were killed striking in May, six in autumn. Then, as now, timing is everything. The autumn dates spanned from 29 October to 8 December. Most were in November. Although Barrington acknowledged that 'the Purple Sandpiper strikes more frequently in November than in any other month,' he speculated that 'the advance guard probably arrives in September', an assertion that contradicted the specimen evidence. Perhaps, after all, Purple Sandpiper migration has always been that of a tail-end Charlie, sticking it out 'up north' until dithering migrants see the writing on the wall? If so, it pays to remember that our only fixed idea should be to avoid one.

9. Tracking through hurricanes
Triumph and tragedy

And some upon day's shores are cast,
And some in darkness lost
In waves beyond the world, where float
Somewhere the islands of the blest.

KATHLEEN RAINE

Irish estuaries resonate to the unintended pathos of Curlew calls throughout the year. Most disappear during spring. Their breeding grounds are unknown and could be anywhere from northern Scotland to Scandinavia or northern Russia. Nowadays, hardly any find succour among Ireland's much-altered bogland. Curlews wintering in Scotland have been tracked to nesting areas in Finland[1] and sightings of tagged birds in England traced their origin to northern Russia.[2] Big brother Curlew has a jockey-sized relative that dresses to kill. Whimbrels are not just smaller than Curlews, they also sound different and whistle at town-crier pitch. High against a blue firmament, migrating flocks resemble swarms of arrowheads and create a rousing chorus that makes you feel civilised, as though you were at an open-air opera, not a rock concert.

To catch the sight and sound of groups winking out to dots on their way north to breed in Iceland, you need to check the calendar. May is their time. Winging their way from winter quarters in Africa, many overfly Ireland in spring. They are restless to get home. During inclement weather grounded flocks roost up

In Ireland, May is the time to see – and hear – Whimbrels. Bound for Iceland, they are focused on breeding and keen to push north. They mostly alight on outlying parts of the coast, although larger numbers track over midland lakes in flocks formed like those of wildfowl. The voice is a series of around seven clear, penetrating staccato whistles.

Back in Iceland, breeding partners reunite and attempt to raise just one brood. Nearly three quarters of the European population – over half a million birds – nest in Iceland. As soon as the young are independent, adults leave and fly back to Africa. The autumn flight south is at sea and generally much further west of Ireland. Most departures are in late July and early August. Tracking results have revealed that, in order to complete a direct flight to Africa, some birds fly continuously for up to five days. A breeding pair's total time in Iceland is a mere three months – maybe the species regards winter quarters as its real 'home'?

A Whimbrel is more compact than a Curlew with a bill that seems similarly scaled-down in length. The striped head markings, although diagnostic, are not obvious at distance. European populations have a white rump – North American Whimbrels are dark-rumped – but, as this photograph shows, the white rump can be partly concealed by the set of the wings in flight.

Gales at sea occasionally drive migrants onto the west coast. On 18 May 2014 heavy rain and bad visibility caused hundreds of Whimbrels to sit out a storm on Connacht's islands. This group was on Clare Island, County Mayo.

discreetly rather than feed, as though seeking privacy in public. At the end of a successful breeding season the population reaches a peak and, once more, bags are packed for coastal wetlands beyond the curve of Europe (although some spend the winter on the Iberian coast). If aspects of migration are veiled in mystery, then the fact that Whimbrels are AWOL in Ireland in autumn is a conundrum. So what is their route south?

Two studies published in 2016 sought to provide the answer. Out of a total of 6,077 Whimbrels ringed from 1921 to 2014 in Iceland, 35 were recovered abroad and a further four ringed overseas reached Iceland.[3] Because recoveries came exclusively from Britain and the adjacent European coast in spring, the pattern strongly suggested that the autumnal route was over the sea. This inference was confirmed by the hard currency of tracking results.[4] Modern technology provides insights on a par with unravelling secret scriptures. Of ten Whimbrels fitted with geo-locators on their Icelandic breeding grounds in June 2012, seven were resighted in June 2013. Researchers managed to catch four and retrieve their tags. All had flown south on trajectories hugging invisible meridians of longitude that connected points of departure in Iceland with points of arrival on the bulge of West Africa. Little wonder that so few pass our way in autumn: the closest track was over 1,000km (600 miles) west of Ireland.

Because they were adults, all four left as soon as the breeding season was over. Whimbrels opt to get under way quickly and postpone moulting frayed plumage until they reach journey's end. They departed during the first week of August. Each flew solo and non-stop. One made landfall along the coast of Western Sahara (a distance of 3,900km (2,400 miles)); the three others went further (5,500km (3,400 miles)) and finally halted at tropical wetlands in Guinea-Bissau. The trio were continuously airborne for an eyebrow-raising five days but a bigger revelation was the speed they achieved. At between 64km/h (40 mph) and 86km/h (54 mph), these are the highest recorded speeds for a land bird on a long-distance flight over an ocean. Although tailwinds boosted progress over parts of the journey, especially when the birds entered the north-east trade winds off north-west Africa, the data also documented battles with progress-sapping headwinds. On the return leg in spring, two chose to repeat the autumn route (in a similar time) but others chose a different track and used Ireland for stopovers lasting several days. By choosing a dog-leg route in spring, distance was added. Why go the long way around? The explanation is probably based on innate knowledge of seasonal wind patterns accrued by the Whimbrel nation over millennia. Luckily, the worst that the weather can throw at them in the eastern North Atlantic is rattling rain and clawing crosswinds. They do not have to worry about being swept up by a hurricane. Canada's Whimbrels do.

Affixing a small spy-in-the-cab device to a migrant bird is a brief encounter that leaves a lasting impression. Most species are placid and radiate a sense of vulnerability invaded. Whimbrels look much smaller in the hand than they do in life. Their long legs count for nothing and get in the way, a pair of unwanted chopsticks. Big dark eyes exert a baleful gaze on a face made comical by a Pinocchio bill. The combination is endearing. In the same way, an awkward schnozzle confers a kind look on a human visage. You cannot help wondering what sights the bird will see. A good motto for Whimbrels could be: 'we are what we fly.' Populations that breed across Canada's tundra embark on Jules Verne odysseys that make their Old World counterparts look humdrum. During autumn, the coastal waters of North America spawn hurricanes, chiefly

In North America, Whimbrels nest across the 'barren grounds' of northern Canada and Alaska. In autumn, the population swings east through north-east Canada before heading south over the ocean to South America. To prepare for the journey, migrants stage across wilderness extending from Labrador to Newfoundland and feed on berries and snails. The photograph, taken in late August near the south-east tip of Newfoundland, shows typical habitat. A multitude of berries, produced by various species of heath, were underfoot almost everywhere. High overhead, flocks of calling Whimbrels headed south.

Over vast areas, succulent black berries of Crowberry were as numerous as blades of grass. At bottom: Bunchberry.

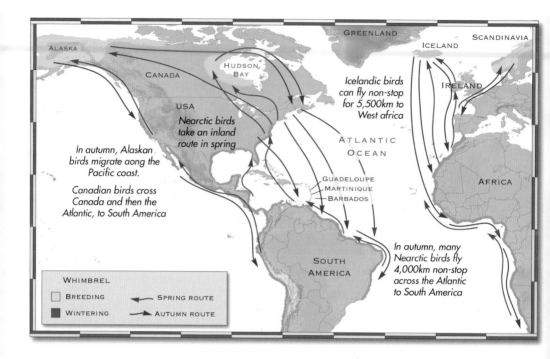

where warm tropical seas interface with colder currents east of Florida and the West Indies. For Whimbrels, weather worries and migration routes collide because they fly out to sea from the coast of north-east North America, aiming to make landfall in South America between Guyana and Brazil. Tracking results show that most do not stop when they sight land. Several individuals headed straight for estuaries on the north-east coast of Brazil in the states of Para and Maranhão; some even went directly to a particular mudflat where they had had spent a previous winter.[5] What happens if, en route, they encounter a hurricane?

I asked Bryan D. Watts. Along with Fletcher M. Smith, Bryan works at the Centre for Conservation Biology at Virginia Commonwealth University. By visiting remote breeding grounds west of Hudson Bay, the researchers trapped Whimbrels in August 2009 and fitted them with transmitters that clocked up migratory flights over the western North Atlantic for four seasons. Bryan explained:

> We have documented several interactions with large storms but have yet to complete a definitive assessment. I suspect that the birds go with the flow. If they enter the storm and follow the tailwinds they would eventually be slingshot out. More skirt around storms than fly into them but six tracked birds have survived maelstrom weather, including one in August 2011 that

Autumn is hurricane season and recent tracking results show that North America's Whimbrels – one of the strongest fliers among shorebirds – are able to confront severe weather of this magnitude. Named 'Hope', an adult female took 27 hours averaging just 14km/h (9 miles per hour) to fly non-stop through a storm to get to its centre. Then she flew at an average of almost 190km/h (118 mph) for 1.5 hours out of the storm, using its power to slingshot herself towards land.[6] In August 2015, 'Upinraaq' (the Inuit name for summer), a female that bred in Alaska, encountered Hurricane Erika around 1,600km (1,000 miles) east of the West Indies. Up to this point, Upinraaq had been flying for more than three days and 4,345km (2,700 miles). Nonetheless, she flew through the epicentre of Erika and continued on to the coast of Suriname.

PHOTOGRAPH: ALEX LEES

made it through Hurricane Irene, a monster that caused extensive damage along the eastern seaboard of the United States. In 2008, another was tracked into Hurricane Hanna and landed in the Bahamas. In 2005, one ran into Tropical Storm Gert over the Gulf of Mexico and was blasted by gale-force headwinds for 27 hours, during which it averaged only 9 mph (14km/h). However, once through the turbulence, flight speed increased to more than 90 mph (145km/h) as the bird was pushed by tailwinds and made it back to Cape Cod, Massachusetts. Whimbrels departing from the North American coast follow two routes, one of which takes them very far out to sea and directly from south-east Canada to Brazil. These birds appear to travel over waters that have relatively low surface temperatures. By doing this they avoid areas with the highest potential to form or sustain storms. Part of this route is adjacent to the Lesser Antilles, the outermost islands of the West Indies. It seems that the birds utilise these islands as a port in a storm. One of the most surprising things shown by the data is that, if any of the tracked adult Whimbrels encounter a storm, they steer toward safety,

Back where it belongs. Photographed on 6 October 2013 in north-east Brazil (at Ajuruteua, near Bragança, state of Pará) wearing the data logger fitted to its leg in the Arctic, this unassuming shorebird had probably encountered more hurricanes at first hand than most armoured-car storm chasers. Nowadays, data loggers have become small enough to attach to birds as small as warblers.
PHOTOGRAPH: ANDY JOHNSON

take a break and then reorientate and pick up their migratory track. They seem to know exactly where they are and what options are available when an emergency occurs.

Although the birds have a savvy sense when it comes to avoiding bad weather, their detours are deadly. Islands that should be sanctuaries are, instead, killing fields. Huge numbers of North American shorebirds pass over the eastern Caribbean in late summer and early autumn on their way to wintering grounds in north-east Brazil. When they encounter storms, all of them use islands such as Guadeloupe, Martinique and Barbados as refuges. Their arrival is not just anticipated, it is planned. Local gunmen have created wetlands – 'shooting swamps' – which the tired migrants crave. Here, for recreation, thousands are killed. Several of the birds tagged by Bryan D. Watts and Fletcher D. Smith emitted dying signals on Guadeloupe. It is no accident that the last Eskimo Curlew known to science – a species that once migrated in teeming masses from the same subarctic regions where dwindling numbers of Whimbrels breed – was shot on Barbados in 1963.[6] It is bad enough to think of the premeditated callousness of luring stressed migrants to their execution without cosmeticising the slaughter as sport.

10. A hurricane called Daisy
The fate of migrants at sea

While playing deck-tennis, eastbound and 1,100km [680 miles] out from New York in RMS Queen Mary, I collided with a Magnolia Warbler, one of several migrant songbirds which were about the ship.

ALAN L. DURAND

Contrary to what one might expect, birds do not fly faster when it comes to setting off on migration. Indeed, there is a tendency to credit them with much faster speeds than they are normally able to achieve. Tables of speed records in books create a false impression of alacrity. Most go about their daily lives accomplishing short journeys at modest speeds. Songbirds tip along at between 30 and 45km/h (19–28 mph). This is air speed, i.e. the velocity they generate themselves. It is important to draw a distinction between air speed and 'ground speed' (the rate at which a bird is travelling, relative to the ground) because the strength and direction of the wind can make an enormous difference. In a nutshell, the speed of the wind is *superimposed* on the speed of the bird. If a tailwind of 30km/h is added to the bird's air speed of, say, 40km/h, the resultant ground speed becomes 70km/h. A headwind, on the other hand, is deducted. A 40km/h air speed in a 30km/h headwind means that the bird's speed relative to the ground is reduced to a mere 10km/h. Therefore, although progress can still be made against the wind, a migrant eager to depart would be wise to await the advent of tailwinds because its flight time will be less, even though the distance travelled is unchanged.

For us, a terrestrial mammal, the concept is relatively easy to grasp. Moving on a bicycle, wind can blow from behind or in front. Because we are still in contact with the ground we are able to detect the wind's impact on our progress. Only a swimmer experiences being swept along by an invisible current. Unless you use a point on a shoreline or bank as a reference, you are oblivious to how far you are being transported by external forces. A bird in the air on a dark, windy night has no physical contact with the ground. It is part of the air mass in which it is travelling. Like a swimmer, the only exertion that it senses is that produced by its own physical output, which is neither more nor less than if it was flying through still air. Luckily, it has a plan. That plan is to stick to a heading. If weather conditions go awry and it is displaced en route, it still knows where it wants to finish up.

There is little doubt that birds prefer to set off in optimum conditions. Clear skies, little wind and no precipitation act as a springboard. Because migrants have prepared themselves physiologically for what lies ahead, they are like sprinters on starting blocks. In ornithological parlance, the German word *zugunruhe* is commonly used as a rubric denoting migratory restlessness. But do migrants, before they depart, have a capacity to assess weather – in short, a 'meteorology of the mind'?

Migration by flight is not unique to birds. Many insects undertake seasonal long-distance movement. Historically, biologists considered that migrant butterflies and moths threw caution to the wind and embarked on ambitious journeys on the premise that, through persistence, luck or sheer weight of numbers, enough would reach destinations desired for feeding, reproduction or overwintering. Because insect cruising speed is significantly less than that of a bird – around 15km/h (9 mph) – migrants are at the mercy of wind currents. Birds are more powerful. They can, if needs be, carry on through thick and thin. By comparison, insects are a one-trick pony. However, there is a trade-off between birds' ability to control direction and insects' speed of travel. Given a favourable wind, migrating insects can match and occasionally exceed songbird migration speeds.

Migrant insects that utilise tailwinds need to be careful. Unlike birds, they are at the mercy of the elements. Yet they are able to gauge optimum flying conditions and remain grounded until favourable winds blow. The Silver-Y Moth is highly migratory – named after the y-shaped squiggle on its wings – and travels in spring from North Africa to Europe and southern Britain. This individual was on Inishbofin, County Galway, in April. Migrants, pushed well beyond their intended destination, have reached Iceland and Greenland. The Painted Lady Butterfly (inset) also migrates from North Africa to Europe. Migrants are common in Ireland, mainly in late summer. Because the species cannot survive the winter in Europe as an adult, it was assumed that migrants died after they bred. In fact, the insects make a return migration in autumn – seeking out tailwinds at a higher altitude than those that brought them north in the spring.

Because airborne insects have almost no control over the direction in which they are carried, everything rests on choosing a correct wind bearing. Recent research has shown that insect migration is much more sophisticated than formerly believed. In radar studies that tracked annual invasions of Silver Y Moths from Europe into Britain, researchers discovered that the insects were able to determine optimal conditions for migration and stayed put when wind patterns were not ideal.[1] Over a seven-year period, the data showed that the moths made use of wind in a precise manner, calculating the direction in which air was moving and maximising their flight speed accordingly. The mechanism underpinning this intelligence is not yet understood.

Irrespective of insects' skill in sensing the direction and strength of airflows, their flights equate to opportunistic wind-assisted spurts rather than – as for many birds – undertakings that require fuel levels to be prefigured and weather conditions factored for travel times lasting more than just the coming night. Furthermore, insect migration routes either avoid sea crossings or, except for strong fliers such as dragonflies, keep them to a minimum. Unlike many songbirds and shorebirds, migratory butterflies and moths do not forsake land and fly far out to sea, crossing an alien environment and entrusting personal survival to ley lines transmitted through their genes.

Migrant birds flying south from Europe towards Africa or the Orient are, for the most part, flying with land beneath their wings. In contrast, overland pathways linking North America to South America are constricted to a narrow waist at Central America. Although migrants departing the North American continent have the option of following coastlines all the way to the tropics, that is a long way around. Instead, many prefer to shorten their journey and fly over water. The saving in distance is considerable. Travelling from Nova Scotia via the Outer Antilles to South America, an Atlantic route is almost 50 per cent shorter than a route through Florida. Furthermore, if all goes well, the passage ought to be blessed with tailwinds and next-to-no predators. Physiologically, because they have stored sufficient fat to burn as fuel, the flight range is within the birds' capabilities. The major danger, therefore, is adverse winds, which would prolong flight time beyond the limit of physical endurance or blow migrants off course. Unlike European songbirds heading south towards Africa, North American counterparts do not have the safety net of landfall if they are overwhelmed and drifted by strong west winds.

Huge numbers of migratory birds breeding in the northern part of North America follow a relatively similar route in autumn: they move across eastern North America and funnel towards the Atlantic seaboard. Here they turn southwards and move en masse along the coast towards their wintering grounds.

Departing waves are initiated in settled weather, when anticyclones hold sway, or are triggered by the passage of a cold front whose north-west tailwinds usher the birds on and towards the coast. Radar observations from stations stretching from eastern Canada to Bermuda and the Caribbean reveal large numbers of migrants moving over the sea.[2] With few exceptions, the birds cross shorelines with no detectable deviation and move on a broad front, overflying all points along the coast, rather than concentrating at headlands or promontories.

What can go wrong? Irrespective of whether the migrants have chosen to cross the western North Atlantic in one long maritime loop from Nova Scotia and the north-east states of the USA, or if they are travelling south along a coastal 'flyway', the expectation is that they will eventually encounter broken cloud, probably the remains of the very weather system that created the tailwinds assisting their migration. Once through the cloudy wake of the depression, whose centre ought to be well out to sea and heading north-east, improved flying conditions can be anticipated – but not always. Although most migrants can penetrate and fly through frontal cloud and light wind without being displaced, some cold fronts behave differently. Should the front's trailing cloud mass align itself north-east/south-west with the Gulf Stream – that serves as a flash-point caused by the meeting of cool green northern water with warm blue tropical water – the result is not clearing skies but thickening cloud and reinvigorated atmospheric activity.[3]

Over parts of the Gulf Stream, the sea temperature contrast can be as great as 10 °C within 20km (12 miles). Along what was a uniform boundary between a cold air mass on one side and warm one on the other, a distortion develops. Referred to as a 'frontal wave', the feature is, in effect, a baby depression. Picking up energy, it matures into a 'wave depression' and tracks north-east and out to sea. Remembering that wind rotation in depressions in the northern hemisphere is anticlockwise (and clockwise in the southern hemisphere – see p. 53), this means that migrants encountering the front are liable to be disorientated by bad visibility and strengthening winds blowing from a south-west direction. Such winds drift the birds – and also any migrant butterflies and moths that happen to be in the vicinity – eastwards towards the open ocean. Where do the migrants finish up? If the wave depression moves rapidly across the Atlantic without 'filling up' and slowing down, it may entrain birds all the way to Europe. Depending on its track, the nearest landfall for its airborne cargo may be Iceland, Ireland or Britain. Analysis of New World land birds in Britain and Ireland between 1967 and 1976 showed that 70 per cent arrived in association with such airflows.[4] Those that made it were believed to have travelled within warm sectors (between warm and cold fronts) that crossed the North Atlantic within one to three days.

Of course, the passage of a tropical storm or full-blown hurricane across the path of migrants wreaks havoc. For small songbirds, the least powerful fliers, the mortality rate must be considerable. However, such maelstroms, because they are relatively slow-moving, are unlikely to carry displaced birds far; certainly not all the way across the Atlantic. Engulfed in a vortex of wind, migrants most likely fly in a spiral trajectory, looping around the eye of the storm until they succumb to exhaustion and perish. Ironically, landfall of a hurricane normally spells the beginning of its end, because it relies upon high sea temperatures for its vigour. Nonetheless, their tracks vary and a few, instead of turning north into the USA or along the Atlantic seaboard, curve well out to sea.

On 2 October 1962, a tropical storm originating in the West Indies developed into Hurricane Daisy and moved slowly north-west between Bermuda and the Carolina Outer Banks, continuing offshore up the American east coast. Gradually spending its force, the hurricane turned north-east. By 7 October, it was off Cape Cod, Massachusetts, and brushed past Nova Scotia to hit Newfoundland, where it did considerable damage before spilling east and blowing itself out in the ocean west of the Faeroes a day or two later. Daisy's north-east track generated a wake of prolonged strong winds from between west and north-west far out into the Atlantic. The event coincided with – and indeed contributed to – peak land-bird migration down the eastern seaboard of America. In terms of place and timing, the weather conditions also overlaid transatlantic shipping lanes.

For many years, when American birds were sighted anywhere in Europe their provenance was attributed to 'ship assistance'. The assumption was that a New World waif, lost at sea, settled on a vessel and was transported to a European shore. Although some crossings can be attributed to ship assistance, most are unaided. Between April 1961 and September 1965, Alan Durand travelled regularly on ocean liners plying between England and New York. Notwithstanding professional duties aboard ship, in between times he recorded all the species that he saw, whether passing at sea or alighting. As luck would have it, he was present and witnessed the convulsion caused by the passage of Hurricane Daisy: 'the highlight of five years of voyaging across the North Atlantic'.[5]

His journalism is gripping, a case of human hindsight analysing where avian foresight went wrong.[6] He departed from New York on the RMS *Mauretania* on the afternoon of 7 October, destination Southampton. At the time of sailing, Daisy was centred roughly 80km (50 miles) off the coast of Maine, approximately 450km (280 miles) north-east of the *Mauretania*. Towards evening, the vessel cleared the coast and headed for the open sea in a freshening west-north-west wind. Durand starts his account straight from the shoulder; he has no misconception about the drama and scale of the unfolding events.

BLACK-AND-WHITE WARBLER

ALAN DURAND

HOODED WARBLER

BIRDS SEEN ON THE
RMS MAURETANIA
OCTOBER 1962

BLACKPOLL WARBLER   MOURNING DOVE   COMMON YELLOWTHROAT

ARTWORK BY MICHAEL O'CLERY. PAINTING OF *MAURETANIA* BY DENTON SHOESMITH (1890–1939). REPRODUCED BY PERMISSION.

Migrating Monarch Butterflies and Pipevine Swallowtails accompanied us well out to sea in the following winds, and visibility was very clear that evening, the sun sinking into a fiery, apocalyptic sky. An American Robin was about the ship until dusk, and at about 17.30 hours I noticed a curious small bundle attached to a wire hawser leading down from the aft funnel to the deck. On closer examination, this proved to be a Yellow-shafted Flicker, well fluffed up and apparently roosting in some discomfort. Shortly afterwards, an Osprey appeared, circling the ship for some time before settling on the very top of the mainmast.

Overnight, the west-north-west wind strengthened and became a near gale, blowing at over 40km/h (25 mph). Since the *Mauretania* was steaming at just a little under the same speed, birds could land in conditions of a following wind, because airflow was reduced over the decks, enabling them to settle. Most would have had no chance of doing so if the ship had been cutting into a strong wind. Durand had a restless night, his mind racing with thoughts of potentially discovering a treasure trove at dawn. He was not to be disappointed.

Monday, 8th October, will live long in my memory. Up early in the hope of seeing migrants, I found the ship echoing with bird calls, and parts of the open deck space almost inundated with small songbirds. The weather was curious. The sky was heavy and overcast, and a very big sea was running, but there was clear visibility and one could walk the decks in nothing more than light airs. Conditions [of a following wind] were ideal for birds staying with the ship, and at noon we were we were about 400 miles [650km] east of New York. The most remarkable sight was ten woodpeckers dividing their time between the forward and after masts, sallying forth in little parties, occasionally to land on the ship's boats, on the open deck, or on the edge of a funnel. These were all Yellow-shafted Flickers, although later in the day they were joined by a Yellow-bellied Sapsucker and a Hairy Woodpecker.

Hopping about the covered promenade deck were House Wrens and Winter Wrens, several Golden-crowned Kinglets and one or two Ruby-crowned Kinglets, and several warblers, including Blackpoll Warblers, Yellowthroats, Magnolia Warblers and a fine male Mourning Warbler. [All] were easily outnumbered by White-throated Sparrows. I conservatively estimated them at more than 20, though they seemed to be everywhere. At one time I was holding a Golden-crowned Kinglet in one hand and a Winter Wren in the other, and I was continually looking to see if any birds were ringed. The first-class sun-deck facing the after end of the ship, together with the games deck and the open-air swimming pool, provided something of a magnet, as food and water were being put out by stewards. In this area were Myrtle Warblers, Slate-coloured Juncos and six or seven species of sparrows. A charming sight in the afternoon was presented by five Cedar Waxwings, which moved up between the railings around the swimming pool. [Other birds] were to be found around the cabin-class games deck. These included at least two Catbirds, a Hermit Thrush, a Blue Jay and one Rusty Blackbird. I observed a Mourning Dove pop up out of one of the ship's boats, just aft of the rear funnel. At dusk we were well over 500 miles [800km] out from New York.

Over the next four days, before the *Mauretania* docked at Cobh, County Cork, the wind remained north-west or west. Few newcomers arrived – the most notable being a Merlin that settled on rigging when more than 1,000 miles out and then tore past a funnel in pursuit of prey. It left later the same afternoon. As the voyage continued, birds started to leave. These were the insectivorous species, such as warblers. In particular, by the time the ship approached the halfway mark (2,400km/1,500 miles out), 'the last of the fairly numerous [ten] Blackpoll Warblers had disappeared'. Several birds died. But not, in most cases, from exhaustion or starvation: 'the biggest single cause of mortality was the hosing down of the decks at night. After midnight, sailors wash down all the open and promenade decks with powerful jets up to four feet above the deck floor, and many small birds roosting in stacked-up deck chairs, and other odd corners, were washed out and drowned.'

In terms of seeking shelter on the *Mauretania* when the elements turned against them, you could say that the benighted migrants, having made an un-planned entrance, were wise enough to save themselves by making a planned exit.

Not surprisingly, the provision of fruit and other unspecified food meant that some species either survived when they might otherwise have succumbed, or they simply delayed departure because the sustenance enabled them to replenish lost body fat. On the whole, seedeaters (such as White-throated Sparrows and Slate-coloured Juncos) and fruit-eaters (such as Baltimore Oriole) were those best able to tap the food provided. None of the migrants that came on board the *Mauretania* had done so on business or pleasure. All had arrived through the accident of a great storm. And one at least jumped ship in Ireland:

At dusk on 12th October, a few hours before we passed the Fastnet Light at the approaches to the south Irish coast, there were at least nine birds still alive in a free-flying state on board, including the last Yellow-shafted

Flicker, a Baltimore Oriole, one Slate-coloured Junco, three White-throated Sparrows, two Song Sparrows and a Field Sparrow. At dawn the following morning we dropped anchor just inside Cobh, and at 08.00 hours the Yellow-shafted Flicker, after circling the ship two or three times, flew strongly away on to the eastern headland at the entrance to the harbour, beyond Roche's Point.

Between 1961 and 1965 Alan Durand made up to twelve transatlantic round trips per year. His published information is not just fascinating; it is also a reliable guide to the birds he encountered. Did the range of species that he saw mirror arrival patterns in Europe, assuming that the same selection of migrants would, more than likely, make up the bulk of birds swept by strong winds and deposited on our side of the Atlantic? Perhaps surprisingly, for one species in particular, the answer is no. The New World land bird most frequently recorded in Europe is Red-eyed Vireo, an insectivorous songbird with habits not dissimilar to a Blackcap. Britain and Ireland receive the lion's share of annual occurrences, which occasionally exceed ten. Not only did Alan Durand not see the species on the *Mauretania*, he failed to record it on any voyage.

Red-eyed Vireos are abundant in deciduous and mixed forest throughout eastern North America. While results from annual surveys conducted from 1966 to 2014 showed a small increase in north-eastern parts of their breeding

At 0800h on 13 October 1962, just inside Cobh Harbour, County Cork, a Yellow-shafted Flicker (since renamed Northern Flicker) that had come aboard the RMS *Mauretania* left the ship. Presumably, the sight – or perhaps the smell – of land prompted it to depart. Across North America, the species breeds from southern Canada eastwards through the Great Lakes and north-east USA. The population is migratory and winters from southern USA to Central America and the West Indies. Although not predisposed to migrate in a huge hop or to use a mainly at-sea route south, migrants are encountered along the coast. So it was no surprise that Alan Durand documented six records involving at least twenty birds on his transatlantic crossings. Since the bird that flew ashore in County Cork, the only other individual seen alive in the wild in Europe was in Denmark on 18 May 1972 near the harbour of Ålborg.[10]

PAINTING BY D.I.M. WALLACE

range,[7] the species has been ubiquitous from the time it was first recognised by nineteenth-century ornithologists: 'this is by all odds our most common vireo of the woodlands.'[8]

It is good to be baffled. No definitive line of argument explains why Red-eyed Vireos are very rare on boats at sea, not just the vessels in which Alan Durand sailed. The species is a long-distance migrant, wintering in the Amazon basin. Whilst some of the population travel south around the Gulf of Mexico, thought to be those with less stored fat,[9] most are believed to fly from eastern North America direct to South America.[10] Could it be that migration span is matched by an equivalent power of endurance? Although other hypotheses might explain the anomaly – behavioural reticence to land on boats or ascending higher to tap stronger winds than other songbird migrants – there may be some merit in attributing superior flying prowess because, among the handfuls of New World visitors that arrive in the Old World, only Red-eyed Vireos penetrate the European continent. More than a dozen have made it as far east as, *mirabile dictu*, Poland. What's more, their arrivals are contemporaneous with arrivals in Ireland and Britain. This suggests that, even when they see the west coast of Ireland, Britain or France, they are still not running on empty.

Although we now know that some New World songbirds intentionally embark on long-haul oceanic flights, there is still reluctance to accept that shorter-range migrants, because they do not lay down as much pre-migratory fat, would survive a major drift and reach Europe. In particular, the arrival at migration seasons of various American sparrows (not 'true' sparrows but the equivalent to Old World buntings) and other seed-eating birds, is still deemed best explained by 'ship assistance'. Because the species involved are not classed as 'elite' migrants, they are pooh-poohed and treated as though they made it only by hitching a ride on a ship and – somehow – feeding on scraps. And so, even today, ornithological understanding is still doomed to creak forwards. Yet, as Alan Durand's journalism demonstrated, some New World migrants dally longer than others and may even remain until coast appears. In any scenario, the ability of a bird to fly the Atlantic is, first and foremost, down to endurance. Although species whose genes have honed them to be true Olympians are most likely to survive displacement and 'routinely' occur on our side of the Atlantic, others that occasionally find themselves drifted off course and faced with a choice of flying or dying are no less capable of completing the journey. Standing the argument on its head, European songbirds – such as Redwings and Fieldfares – have successfully flown from Europe to America when impelled to do so by severe weather.

11. The role of instinct
Learning on the job

A small bird came toward the skiff from the north. He was a warbler flying very low over the water. The old man could see that he was very tired. The bird made the stern of the boat and rested there. Then he flew around the old man's head and rested on the line where he was more comfortable. 'How old are you?' the old man asked the bird. 'Is this your first trip?'

ERNEST HEMINGWAY

In terms of selection for short or long life expectancy, size generally matters. Parent birds of large species such as geese, swans and cranes, capable of defending their offspring, lavish attention on their bloodline for almost a year. In contrast, small songbirds have independence thrust upon them within weeks. Evolution sets the bar high because their efforts at personal survival are solo. In the first year of life mortality is catastrophic. Losses are offset by large clutches, double broods, rapid growth rates and an ability to reproduce in the following spring, before the bird is even one year old. A study of longevity in North American Purple Finches yielded 1,746 recoveries from 21,715 ringed individuals, among which only one bird lived as long as ten years, six reached eight years, and 18 lasted seven years.[1]

Framed between irresistible knit-and-purl downy young, a parent Red-throated Diver epitomises motherhood. As soon as her offspring fledge, they are left to find their own way in the world. Photographed in Iceland, there is a good chance that all three migrated separately to Ireland. Nature prioritises instinct above learning. Even before they can rely on memory, young have to find a flyway they did not know they knew — except by instinct drawn from the nave of childhood.
PHOTOGRAPH: EINAR GUDMANNS

However, size and life expectancy do not always correlate. For small seabirds, such as storm-petrels whose average weight is just 28g (1 oz), there may be no end in sight because they face almost no natural enemies. Fitting metal rings to seabirds provided a false impression of longevity. The rings, unlike the wearers, perished due to corrosion in saltwater. Over time, replacement rings have revealed that one European Storm Petrel, ringed as an adult in Wales in 1974, was at least 37 years of age when re-trapped in 2011.[2] Because European Storm-petrels do not start to breed until they are around five years old, the actual age of ringed adults is no more than an educated guess.

Species that expect to live long are in no rush to breed and have no need to lay large clutches. Irrespective of the age of first breeding, until they have amassed the equivalent of a full year's flying time, new recruits cannot be expected to know the ropes. Even when they are part of the reproductive population, competition is stiff because only fit and healthy individuals breed. Unlike humans, as birds age they do not have the luxury of being able to taper into a less physically able state. Birds do not senesce. Beyond one year of age, it is fair to say that all are at Formula 1 standard. Death constantly weeds out those that fail to escape predators, never mind the vicissitudes of food supply, weather, parasites and disease. The chances of a rookie winning a last-man-standing contest against a more experienced elder are never going to be good.

Adults, whether collectively or individually, are canny. To reduce losses of chicks in colonies, breeding is synchronised. By concentrating production in a surge of abundance, adults ensure that the proportion of young lost to predators is minimised in the limited time available. When it comes to furthering the chances of personal survival, older hands draw upon experience. Anthropomorphic parallels are apt because it would appear that, just like us, birds learn by their mistakes. A study into the influence of age on the breeding biology of Common Terns in a colony on the coast of Massachusetts, USA, revealed that, although the birds' ages ranged from two to eighteen years, a large majority selected a mate of similar age. Although some of the most fecund pairs were comparatively young, it transpired that birds aged five to eighteen preferred to nest near the highest margin of the colony, well above the normal limit of high tide. Pairs whose partners were younger – mainly from two to four years of age – occupied lower sites. In some years, most of their nests were washed out by high tides that occasionally occurred in July.[3] Such an outcome, in the eyes of veterans, must have seemed like building a sandcastle on a beach and expecting it to last. Much more remarkable, the risk of flooding was remembered by individuals that had experienced it sometime in the past.

Can birds recall their past and retrieve information from it? Could an adult figure out where it is, based on the route it took in a former migration even if displaced by, say, inclement weather that propelled it to a different place? If so, the attribute would equip it with backup information not available to a juvenile embarked on a maiden flight controlled purely by instinct.

Researchers first began to suspect that birds possessed sophisticated memory capacity when, during 1937, adult Sparrowhawks deliberately transported during autumn migration from Heligoland, a German island in the North Sea, to Silesia (south-west Poland), did not resume their flight in the original direction but set off on a new compass bearing aimed more or less directly at their winter quarters.[4] The discovery that birds, particularly adults, were able to orientate themselves to a specific location and, in so doing, override compass bearings that they had previously followed – in other words, demonstrate homing ability – became a hot potato for German and Dutch ornithologists. In 1939, W.H. van Dobben hit upon the idea of catching and ringing 600 Starlings migrating through Holland in autumn and transporting them to France, where they were released.[5] The intention was to displace the birds from their chosen route in the hope that, if some were recaptured, homing ability would be demonstrated. Alas, the outbreak of the Second World War brought the experiment to an end before results were obtained.

Starlings, when they fledge, are unspotted. Juvenile plumage is plain and mouse-coloured. Once they become independent, youngsters upgrade all the feathers they grew in the nest and replace plain with spotted plumage. During summer, as moult progresses towards the head, the transition between old juvenile kit and emerging new adult-like attire produces a bizarre contrast. When the moult is complete, the precise shape of the white flank markings can be used to determine if the bird is a one-year-old or older. On youngsters, the pattern approximates to a heart (or half-moon) shape; on adults (overleaf), the white markings more closely resemble a V (or divided chevron). Viewed close up on a bird caught for ringing, the difference is a reliable and quick guide to a Starling's age.

An adult male Starling. Although several subtle criteria can be used to determine the bird's age and sex – females of all ages have a brown iris – the pattern of white markings on the flanks provide an easy method to assess age.

The project was resumed in 1948. Once again, the guinea pigs were Dutch Starlings, thousands of them. This time the displacement was to Switzerland. Three release points were chosen: Basel, Geneva and Zurich. It was considered crucially important to conduct separate releases of adults and first-years. Because Starlings migrate in flocks, it was felt that the young might be influenced by adults and follow their lead. All birds were ringed and their age – whether adult or young – was determined by several methods. One handy criterion proved to be the shape of the white tips on the breast feathers. In adults, the tips tend to take the form of a V; in youngsters, the white tip is more heart-shaped.

Starling populations across northern Europe are obliged to migrate because snow, frozen ground and short daylight reduce access to food. Millions head in a south-westerly front from north-east Europe through the Netherlands to winter in northern France, southern Britain and Ireland. From 1948 to 1957, Dutch bird-catchers, mainly directed by Albert Perdeck, ringed more than 19,000 Starlings near The Hague. Around 7,500 were released at the capture site to act as controls and 11,500 were flown to Switzerland.[6] Perdeck and his colleagues had a hunch that there might be a difference in homing ability between young and old. He speculated that only adults could compensate when they were displaced. What happened?

The releases yielded 354 recoveries. After the displacement, juveniles and adults did indeed hold to different courses. The adults, after initial departures south-west – repeating the heading that they had been following when trapped – changed direction and flew north-west. In other words, they made an adjustment and aimed for their planned wintering destination. Subsequent ringing recoveries in north-west France and Britain proved that they made it. The juveniles, on the other hand, maintained a similar bearing to what they had been following when captured in Holland. During the winter, ringing recoveries of juveniles came from south-west France and the Iberian Peninsula.

The experiment was of great importance because it demonstrated that both instinct (the initial flight in a south-west direction made by all age classes departing north-east Europe) and learning (recognition by adults that they were off course and knowing how to make a correction) play a part in migration. Quite how the adults came to realise that they were off course remains, to this day, a mystery. If anything, the experiment upgraded appreciation of homing skills because the displaced youngsters, having survived their first winter in unplanned – albeit suitable – areas, returned home to traditional breeding areas in north-east Europe but, over subsequent winters, adjusted their route to return to the 'new' winter quarters, that is, the areas they reached following artificial displacement. As well as Starlings, the Dutch researchers trapped 1,250 Chaffinches (900 adults, 350 first-years) that migrate through Holland – many from Scandinavia and some of which travel on to spend the winter in Britain and Ireland. They too were transported to Switzerland. Just three were recovered: a major disappointment. But the same pattern found in Starling recoveries was suggested: two juveniles in southern France and an adult in England.

Before jumping to the simplistic overview that juvenile migrants are incapable of correcting for displacement and are likely to continue, automaton-like,

In Ireland and Britain, two Starling populations are present in winter. Local breeding birds are resident and remarkably sedentary. From over 10,000 ringing recoveries of Starlings ringed during the breeding season in Ireland and Britain, 80 per cent of movements were less than 20km (12 miles). In stark contrast, Ireland's winter horde comes from across northern Europe, including Russia. Pulses of birds, already in flocks, arrive across the North Sea during late October and migrants destined for Ireland push west rapidly. It is these Starlings – and not local residents – that coalesce to form spectacular roosts. Departures occur in the second half of March and involve en masse emigration by sizeable flocks after a final overnight roost. Back on mainland Europe, vast flocks of eastbound migrants assemble in late March and early April to roost in parts of near-continental Europe (such as Denmark) before embarking for final breeding destinations ranging from northern Norway to the Ural Mountains and the shores of the Caspian Sea. Most, however, hail from the Baltic States. The accompanying image was taken near Slieve Croob, County Down, where a conservative estimate of 250,000 Starlings spend the night in a small coniferous plantation.

along an innate bearing, it must be borne in mind that, had the birds drifted off course in the wild – as opposed to being transported in a vehicle or aircraft from which they could not see the outside world – then they would have been able to log the extent of their displacement and, ultimately, known the measure of correction needed to retrace the route and get back on course.

Echoing the Starling experiment, in 2014 Danish scientists attached miniature satellite trackers to eleven adult Cuckoos caught in Denmark and displaced over 1,000km to Spain, well away from the birds' known migration routes.[7] During previous years, the birds headed east from Denmark before swinging south-east through the Balkans. After that, choice of route varied. Most crossed the Mediterranean, arrived in Libya and continued south over the Sahara. Irrespective of itinerary, they finished up in Central Africa. Upon release in Spain, it became clear that the Cuckoos knew they were 'off piste', a situation they attempted to correct by dispersing north-east – as though orientating towards Denmark, where they were last in the wild. One continued all the way to Poland; another flew east to the Balkans. In both cases the birds returned to stopovers used on previous migratory flights, even though they were backtracking. The remainder headed south from Spain and, one by one, rejoined the track of former routes to Central Africa. Because none had previously commenced migration from as far west as Spain, all nine that headed south were obliged to recalibrate their position from a novel starting point. Some returned to stopovers scattered across Africa, suggesting that, once there, they tapped a familiar way-marker. This behaviour not only confirmed navigational awareness but also the importance of suitable habitat at stopovers, allowing the bird to rest and feed for the next leg of its journey.

The conclusion is that adult Cuckoos can amend migratory trajectory over vast distances, so long as they know the whereabouts of breeding and wintering grounds. Another salutary point is that, had the research been conducted using artificial planetariums to test for migratory direction, none of this astonishing GPS information would have emerged. Of course, Cuckoos lay their eggs in the nests of other birds and juveniles grow up without any contact to siblings or biological parents. Ergo, the young Cuckoo has no one to follow during migration. Flying alone at night, it relies entirely on instinct. To succeed in reaching its winter home in Africa it relies upon a genetically determined programme that embraces three criteria: direction, duration and distance. Not surprisingly, tracking results from juvenile Cuckoos showed that, on their first trip to Africa, youngsters travelled faster and straighter than adults, guided by an innate migration programme. Only through time did they tweak the route, optimising it through experience.[8]

12. Inborn ability
Enigmatic homing skills

Sir, two hounds, a dog and a bitch, were sent by rail from Bective Station, County Meath, to Galway, a distance of 160 miles. The bitch returned to kennels within a week and the dog a few days later.

ALBERT A. LAVERTY

It is ironic that so much that has been discovered about bird migration has been derived from studying the homing ability of pigeons bred from wild Rock Doves – birds that do not migrate but stay in the same neighbourhood for most of their life. Consequently, it is rare to get a pigeon that can home from a long distance at a first trial. Training a racing pigeon involves taking it a short distance from its loft and releasing it to fly back, then taking it farther and farther away as its training proceeds. To improve homing ability – remember, the object is to win prizes, not conduct navigational tests – the bird is taken in the same direction each time so that it learns the way back home. If a trained pigeon is taken to a location on a compass point far removed from its traditional route, the chances are that it will become lost or not return until days later. Bad weather, particularly fog, causes pigeons to go astray or become grounded. Various notions have been propounded in attempts to explain what possible beacons are used to navigate long distances. Sense of smell was one theory. The jury is still to decide if that has merit. Another suggestion was that pigeons sense the Earth's magnetic field and somehow used it as a means of orientation. That idea seemed to bite the dust when small, magnetised bars (that counteracted magnetic force) were fitted to the wings of one group of pigeons and unmagnetised bars to another. The results showed that both groups homed successfully and led, as recently as 1968, to a premature assertion by a leading authority: 'we may conclude that birds do not orientate with reference to any magnetic stimuli … and suggest that visual stimuli are of paramount importance.'[1]

The results of homing experiments using wild birds leave pigeons waving a white flag. In tests, adults from a range of species were captured and translocated during the breeding season. Adults were chosen because it is hard to imagine a more potent tug at parental heartstrings. Furthermore, by checking the nest location, it was easy to record return times. Manx Shearwaters made ideal candidates. They nest in burrows, the sexes share incubation over a period

A young Manx Shearwater at its burrow entrance at dusk contemplates the world for the first time. For Ireland's breeding population, the annual cycle begins in March, when adults return from the Argentine shelf and arrive in the north-east Atlantic by following prevailing winds that swing them close to the West Indies, then north and into the west wind belt that carries them east. Once they arrive in home waters, females disappear for a few weeks to fatten up in preparation for laying a single egg that weighs 15 per cent of the bird's body weight – the equivalent of a human mother giving birth to a four-year-old! By June, the youngster hatches. Parents feed the chick nocturnally and synchronise their feeding routine to ensure that junior's nourishment is paramount. In August, the adults leave and no longer feed the chick, which starts to lose weight. Weight loss triggers metabolic processes and the final stages of development. Behaviour changes too. The big baby, now fully grown with a cloak of new feathers sprouted from a coat of down, comes out of its burrow and exercises by flapping its wings. When it is ready to go, it seeks out a short runway and launches into flight. Genetic programming does the rest. Confirmed by tracking results (www.oxnav.zoo.ac.uk), the juvenile follows an inherited direction straight to the South Atlantic off the east coast of Brazil. The journey takes ten days or a little longer, an average of 1,000km per day. The haste of offspring to reach winter quarters is corroborated by reports from Argentine fishermen who occasionally see birds with tufts of 'baby fluff' still on the crown.

lasting nearly two months, and their large single egg can withstand chilling for at least a fortnight if both parents happen to be at sea.[2] In 1953, Manx Shearwaters caught at colonies on the island of Skokholm, off the Pembrokeshire coast in Wales, were transported to various parts of Europe and North America. One freed in Venice returned to its burrow in less than a fortnight. It is not known if it flew directly over land or followed the Mediterranean coast and returned via Gibraltar. Another was despatched to Boston, USA. It arrived back on Skokholm twelve days later, ahead of a letter posted to confirm its release. The transatlantic distance was, in a straight line, 4,800km (2,980 miles). Irrespective of its actual homeward route, the bird still averaged at least 400km (almost 250 miles) per day.

Other experiments using land birds yielded equally memorable results. In 1958, at the University of Michigan, USA, sixteen Purple Martins were transported distances up to approximately the length of Ireland from nest boxes located at the university's biological station.[3] One was back with its chicks in little more than eight hours, and flew the 390km (234 miles) return leg during the night, maintaining an average speed of 45km/h (28 mph). Under normal circumstances, Purple Martins are daytime migrants. Although the research certainly underscored homing ability, it is unfortunate that the point was proved by exploiting the faithfulness of adults to offspring.

Some of the longest displacements involved Laysan Albatrosses in the Pacific Ocean.[4] Fourteen of eighteen adults returned to Midway Atoll, the nesting quarters in the central Pacific, within 30 days, having been transported between 2,116km and 6,629km (1,314 and 4,119 miles) to six locations, each at a different tangent to the breeding place. All showed an extraordinary ability to return, post-haste, suggesting that they did not spend much time searching but knew instinctively where home was. The quickest covered 5,148km (3,198 miles) in ten days after release off the coast of Washington State, USA. Its mean speed was 515km (320 miles) per day.

The mystery of how birds and many other forms of life – from whales to ants – find their way has puzzled people for centuries. Indeed, it seems as though Homo sapiens might be the odd one out. Could it be that modern living has led to us losing an ancestral sense we once had? Some latter-day scientists wonder if awareness of the Earth's magnetic field might have been the 'base sense' that developed before other senses.

By the nineteenth century, exploration of our planet had become increasingly thorough. Arctic breeding grounds of European winter visitors were discovered and reports from returning African expeditions revealed the Dark Continent to be a vacation destination for many birds of European summer. The question of what guided birds during migrations that outstripped preconceived notions grew more tantalising. In Germany especially, lines of enquiry into the phenomenon started to bear fruit. A handful of bird observatories were established. The jewel in the crown was the North Sea archipelago of Heligoland. Here, Heinrich Gätke (1814–1897), secretary to the British governor (the territory remained in British hands until exchanged for Zanzibar in 1890) spent half a century marshalling the first full understanding of migration's ebb and flow. Gätke's grasp of the scale of movements was framed by his realisation that the birds embarked on journeys based on some kind of inherent global positioning awareness. Awed by their ability, he felt humbled: 'Man, in spite of his senses and intellectual faculties, is not able to continue moving in a straight line for even as much as a mile in darkness or fog; whereas birds fly every autumn, without signs or landmarks, from the far east of Asia to the west of Europe, and from the North

Cape of Scandinavia to the south of Africa.'[5] As the full force of avian date-keeping hit home, Gätke began to suspect that, for both adults and independent inexperienced young, the migrants possessed a time-honoured flight plan that might as well be chiselled into a slab of marble.

Alexander von Middendorf (1814–1894), of German extraction although living in Russia, was a contemporary of Gätke. He undertook 'voyages of investigation' deep into Siberian tundra, always with a mind 'towards solving the problem of bird migration'. Middendorf, whose contribution to current knowledge has been largely overlooked, made two spectacular insights. One involved human navigational ability; the other was an educated guess at how birds orientated in high latitudes.

In travels across endless tundra that appeared featureless, Middendorf was accompanied by Samoyed people, members of a semi-nomadic Mongol tribe, who lived along the shores of the Arctic Ocean. Samoyed genealogy can be traced to Central Asia, from where families migrated to the Arctic with their beloved dogs (treated like family members) in the first millennium. Living among the Samoyed, Middendorf began to realise that they possessed an instinctive capacity for finding the right way, similar, he thought, to the faculty peculiar to birds and other animals. He formed the opinion that humans, if born into an unbroken contact with the natural world, inherited a directional sensibility – an ability tantamount to primal knowledge.

He recounted the experience in his Siberian journals:[6]

> Overjoyed at having at last discovered that Samoyede [sic] men possess, like animals, the capacity to orientate, I endeavoured to draw out from them the secret of their art and pressed them on every opportunity. They, however, only looked at me in a stupefied manner and were surprised at my astonishment. They averred that their sense of direction was an ordinary every-day occurrence and self-evident; whereas, on the other hand, my inability in finding the way seemed to them quite incomprehensible. At last they completely disarmed me with the question: 'How is it that the little Arctic Fox finds her way on the great tundra without ever going astray?' So there I was, once more perplexed on the unconscious performance of an inherited animal faculty.

In order to corroborate personal observations and turn them into irrefutable facts, Middendorf put his scholarly qualifications to work. He tested Samoyed path-finding skills against his compass. On one occasion, travelling with a group to a known location, he was convinced that they were wrong. His compass proved that their bearing was somewhat awry. Then this happened: 'after insisting that

Samoyed people live semi-nomadic lives on the flat wilderness of the north Siberian plain. During the nineteenth century, Alexander von Middendorf, a scientific explorer besotted with solving the puzzle of bird migration, lived with the Samoyed and discovered that they found their way by sensing something which they felt but could not describe. Middendorf surmised that they had to be experiencing the pull of Earth's magnetic field. He went on to reason that, for birds and other animal life, magnetism was the foundation of navigational ability.

my compass should be followed, I soon discovered that the compass, but not the directive sense of the Samoyeds, had deceived me. It was the former, not the latter, which, owing to the proximity of the magnetic pole, had been drawn to an unexpected extent out of the right direction, and I recognised to my shame that I had done these good people an injustice.'

Middendorf's travels in high latitudes also prompted him to think that migrant birds, northbound in spring, might use the magnetic North Pole as a constant against which they calibrated position, much like a mariner taking a compass reading from the sun. This idea was revolutionary. Middendorf realised that many migration routes followed directions other than north–south. He maintained the validity of his hypothesis by arguing that 'birds are persistently conscious of the directions in which the magnetic poles lie, as well as of the angle of deviation of their flight from these directions, and regulate their course accordingly … thus the bird is itself a complete magnet, marking out its course from a chart of its own inner consciousness.' Although Middendorf was aware that the principle could hardly apply in autumn, especially to naïve young birds heading south to winter quarters that lay beyond the influence of the magnetic North Pole, his logic made sense because it did not attempt to solve a problem by a formula more complicated than the problem itself.

As well as the direction of migration, Middendorf was fascinated by its timing, which seemed to connect northern Europe with Russia, especially in spring. Instead of bedlam he found order. He organised cooperative monitoring across Russia and correlated the advance of spring migrants by plotting the birds' arrival dates on maps. When these were presented to the Imperial Academy of Sciences in St Petersburg in 1855, the nature of bird migration as a broad-front continental movement was established for the first time.[7]

13. Nature's magnetic signpost
Higher laws

. . . .

In 1831, James Clark Ross, just thirty-five years old, located the place at the edge of the Boothia Peninsula in Arctic Canada where his dipping needle, a sensitive instrument used to measure the vertical angle of the earth's magnetic field, pointed straight down, and he had planted his country's flag at the magnetic North Pole.

NATHAN PHILBRICK

You do not have to be a scientist to know the properties of a magnet. One end, let's call it the north end, is a plus. The other end, or south end, is a minus. Place two magnets together and, when the two ends facing each other have the same sign, they repel each other. When they have opposite signs, they attract. Why is this? To answer that question you *do* have to be a scientist. Although it would be nice to know the answer, I cannot supply it. However, when upscaled from a child's horseshoe magnet to a pervasive global force, the implications are profound. By extension, it is coined geomagnetism. Our global magnetic field originates from electrical currents flowing at Earth's iron-rich core. Although we tend to be oblivious to this 'invisible' natural force, it protects us and amounts to an enveloping 'magnetosphere'.

In the mid-twentieth century, astronomers first observed the phenomenon of solar winds. The temperature in the Sun's upper atmosphere is millions of degrees Celsius. Gas explosions are frequent and free electrons and protons escape into space. Blown towards Earth, this solar wind of charged particles is largely deflected by our magnetic field. However, because the magnetic field is weaker at polar regions, some particles penetrate our atmosphere. The interplay of dissipating forces produces the dancing lights of the auroras that occur in the high latitudes of the northern and southern hemispheres. Hence, our home sits like a rock in a current. The damaging solar rays, capable of eroding planetary atmospheres and leaving them rarefied and lifeless – like Mars – are deflected away by the magnetosphere.

Magnetic fields are not, however, unique to our planet. On the moon the magnetic field is weak and complex. Furthermore, unlike on Earth, there is no single directional flow pulsing along a single axis; numerous lunar magnetic poles align in multiple directions. Our magnetic poles lie close to the geographic poles in the Arctic and Antarctic. Whilst the current is generated at Earth's

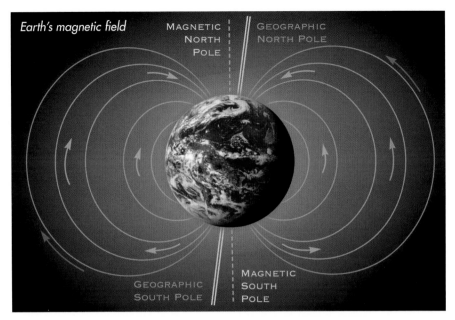

Lines of magnetic force encircle the Earth and run through its heart from pole to pole. In simplified terms, the field lines sprout from the magnetic South Pole at a 90-degree angle and then curve back – like segments of an orange – and are drawn into the magnetic North Pole, again at a 90-degree angle. When the lines reach the equator, they are parallel (horizontal) to the Earth's surface. Birds sense the change in the angle of the field lines at different latitudes (called the inclination angle) and use it to navigate. Basically, they interpret inclination angles to tell which direction is poleward and which is equator-ward.

core, it aligns itself roughly north–south. This much is easy to visualise. Like a dog constantly chasing its tail, the magnetic force arcs up from the magnetic South Pole and wreathes around the planet, flattening out at the equator, then curving down to the magnetic North Pole located in the Arctic. Here, as in the Antarctic, the 'contours' of the field are at their most precipitous. Although the magnetic field is symmetrical, its angles relative to Earth's surface are not. The field lines are steep at the poles and shallow at the equator; this makes it possible to differentiate their angle of dip or 'inclination'. Furthermore, the strength – pull – of the magnetism varies. It is roughly twice as strong at the poles as it is at the equator. While these properties are not real physical entities that we, as humans, can see or sense, they are useful devices to describe the direction and magnitude of the magnetic field at any locality on Earth. Do these forces form the basis of a global positioning system?

Coordinates for a location on Earth are usually given in terms of latitude and longitude. Latitude is a real measurement fixed by the shape of the planet. Beginning at a zero-degree parallel on the equator, the measurement increases until it becomes a right angle (90 degrees) at the geographic poles. Mariners can gauge latitude fairly readily by the length of the day, or by the height of the sun or stars in a fixed position above the horizon. Columbus followed a straight

Earth's atmosphere and magnetic field protects us from damage generated by radiation from the sun. A solar wind of charged particles is largely deflected by the magnetic field. However, because the field is weaker at polar regions, some particles penetrate Earth's atmosphere. The interplay of dissipating forces produces the dancing lights of the auroras that occur in high latitudes at both ends of the planet. The magnetic field has been weakening gradually for roughly the last 400 years but the process has become more pronounced in the last two centuries. In fact, scientists are aware of 'small patches of anomaly' where the field's polarity is reversed. If these intensify, it is not too far-fetched to imagine a global shift occurring. The outcome would be a switch in the polarity of the overall field. The process will not happen quickly. It could take over a thousand years, maybe more. During the 'flip' poles could become localised, even at the equator. Also, instead of one main axis, there may be two or three axes. In effect, Earth's magnetic field starts to wander. The effect of this on animal navigation is unclear. However, at some future time, the process will happen — and has done so several times in the past.

PHOTOGRAPH: EINAR GUDMANNS

path across the Atlantic when he 'sailed the parallel', a tactic that he thought would take him to the Indies, his goal. Had the New World not lain in his path – hence, West Indies – he would have circumnavigated the world in the same latitude. Longitude is a meridian line (a great circle) running from pole to pole. It lacks a logical starting point. Placement of the prime meridian has changed through history and politics, rather than geography, ultimately settled the line at Greenwich in London. Longitude chimes with the world's rotation. Since Earth takes almost 24 hours to rotate (in fact, a day lasts 23 hours and 56 minutes), one hour marks $\frac{1}{24}$ of a complete spin of the planet. Put another way, one hour equates to 15 degrees out of the 360 degrees involved in a full revolution.

Mariners used the stars to determine longitude and latitude at sea very effectively. On cloudy nights, use of a magnetic compass became their main means of navigation. While navigators such as Francis Drake could tell magnetic north from magnetic south, no one knew how a compass worked. Not until 1600, when William Gilbert, a physician to Queen Elizabeth I, published his book De Magnete, was it proposed that a magnetic compass functioned by aligning itself with the magnetic force of the planet.[1] That novel insight blazed like a comet and led to a realisation that Earth itself was a gigantic magnet. Gilbert's discovery also explained why a compass needle did not align with true north, because the magnetic North Pole was not the same as the geographic

A growing body of research suggests that dolphin and whale migration routes make use of Earth's magnetic field for navigation. Recent experiments with dolphins appear to demonstrate that the animals possess 'magnetoreception' – meaning they can sense magnetism and use it as part of an innate GPS.

North Pole. In other words, there was an inexact congruence between the physical Earth and its three-dimensional magnetic orb. Almost like a parallel universe, the grid lines of the magnetic field mirrored but did not precisely overlap the geographic framework of latitude and longitude. Because Earth's magnetic axis (called a 'dipole') is tilted at about 11 degrees to its geographical axis, a compass needle points away from true north. This deviation became known as 'variation'. In effect, the alignment of a magnetic compass needle, although a single motion, has two components: one is horizontal (variation from true north) and the other is vertical (inclination polewards). In time, navigators became adept at checking the magnetic meridian of their compass against astronomical calculations of true north. To confuse matters further, the magnetic poles are not static. That fact added to navigational problems and led to global collaboration in mapping the intensity of magnetic fields.

Alexander von Humboldt (1769–1882), a German polymath, made significant contributions to our understanding of geomagnetism. Appreciating that it was a global force and determined to learn more about 'the mysterious march of the magnetic needle' he inspired a chain of observation stations across Russia and galvanised an international 'Magnetic Crusade'. In 1802, travelling south along the Andes from Bogotá to Quito, he came close to the equator. Here, his measurements showed how the magnetic field decreased. That much he expected. Amazingly, his readings continued to drop well south of the equator. Not until he reached Cajamarca in Peru, 7 degrees south (830km/515 miles beyond the equator), did his compass needle turn from north to south: he had discovered the magnetic equator.[2]

Throughout the nineteenth century, as nations dispatched expeditions to fill in blanks and extend the known world, interest mounted in finding Earth's second magnetic pole. It had to lie somewhere in the icy wilderness beyond the Antarctic Circle. Seafaring explorers, tempted south at the prospect of finding a fabled great southern continent, had to contend with dangers enunciated by Coleridge: 'And now there came both mist and snow / And it grew wondrous cold / And ice, mast-high, came floating by.' The quest became like a last act in an ancient tale. Although the magnetic South Pole was eventually pinpointed in 1909 by three members of Ernest Shackleton's *Nimrod* expedition, in January 1840 the crew of *The Peacock*, one of a squadron of American ships charting the Southern Ocean, sighted a solid barrier of ice that dashed their hopes of pushing further south. The vessel had reached a realm of perpetual daylight at 66 degrees south. Just as eerie was the behaviour of the ship's compasses. The needles were almost useless because of their proximity to the magnetic South Pole and its vertical force field emanating from the very foundations of the planet. An object as small as an iron button on a sailor's uniform was enough to swivel a compass needle. One of the officers correctly attributed the phenomenon to 'the polar attraction acting in nearly a perpendicular direction upon a horizontal needle'.[3]

Why, at each magnetic pole, is there not a monument to the intrepid explorers who discovered them? The reason is simple: the poles move. The magnetic North Pole is moving in a nearly straight line in a north-westerly direction at a rate of approximately 55km (34 miles) each year. Its counterpart, the magnetic South Pole, is not tied to the same rate of movement or direction. For the moment, it moves less. Changes in Earth's magnetic field sometimes make headlines, particularly studies anticipating the timing and likely impacts of the next reversal in geomagnetic polarity. A preamble to such an event is a weakening in the field, a tendency that has become more pronounced in the last two millennia. A century ago nobody knew that magnetic field reversals occurred until geologists discovered that reliable records of periodic reversals were stored in rocks.[4] Existing rock strata also exert an influence. Where iron-rich deposits occur, the local magnetic field departs from the average regional value. The result is a magnetic anomaly, revealed only by instrumentation. Overall, the tug of Earth's magnetic field is very weak. For comparative purposes, its strength near one of the poles – where the field is strongest – is around $\frac{1}{500}$ that of a fridge magnet.

There is order in nature and Earth is part of a continuum with nothing but the unknown. The sun and the stars have, for millennia, provided mankind with information enabling guided movement. The nature of our intelligence is such that it is stimulated by the will to understand. Consequently, we are always keen to establish explanatory relationships between phenomena. When scientists first thought about how animals navigate over long distances, it was logical to consider that they used the same cues as us. The sun and the stars, yes; but Earth's magnetic field too? Yet the properties of geomagnetism provide a holistic orientation framework for any organism that can perceive them. Never mind birds that see the sun and the night sky, what information systems are used by migrating fish and other life forms whose eyes never see daylight or the great star factory and whose travels must, therefore, tap a different force of the universe?

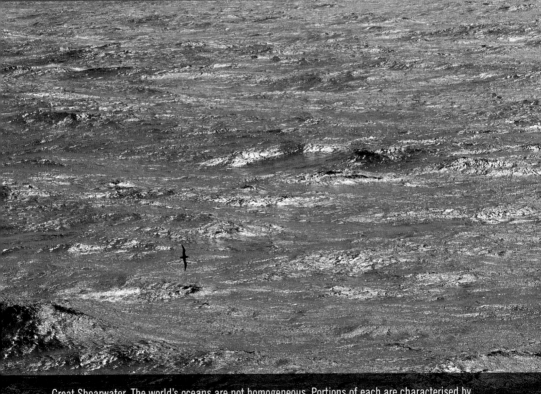

PART TWO
MECHANISMS OF
NAVIGATION

Great Shearwater. The world's oceans are not homogeneous. Portions of each are characterised by peculiarities of climate. The distribution of seabirds depends on this environment, which changes continually with the seasons. Seabirds need land for only one thing: a place to breed. Many roam the oceans and seldom see terra firma. Off Ireland, the species that make the greatest journeys are those which visit us from the southern hemisphere, among them Great Shearwaters. To a mariner without instruments, the open ocean is a trackless desert. We marvel at the ability of seabirds to navigate and fly home to a remote breeding station. Great Shearwaters breed exclusively on the islands of Tristan da Cunha, in the roaring forties, 2,400 km (1,500 miles) from the nearest land. How do they find their home islands, which span an arc of less than a quarter of a degree of longitude – a mere 33km (20 miles)?

14. Earth's magnetic field
The genie of the animal kingdom

Who knows now if she knows
her depth or direction;
she's passed Malin and
Tory, silent, wakeless,
a wisp, a wick that is
its own taper and light
through the weltering dark.

Seamus Heaney

Life on Earth sits atop a molten furnace. During earthquakes, shockwaves travel directly through the centre. By interpreting how waves are modified by the core's properties, scientists deduce that far beneath us lies a sphere of metal bedrock about the size of the moon, encased within a 'Russian doll' outer core about the size of Mars. The bulk of the magnetic field is generated in the outer core that acts as a massive dynamo powered by the Earth's rotation and the planet's long-term cooling, producing ceaseless currents in the fluctuating core. It seems nothing short of miraculous that anything ever came to exist on the surface of this fiery screen: hot, dark and smothered in gas and dust. Estimates are vague, but around 4.5 billion years ago the molten surface began to cool. Water formed. Clouds and oceans took shape. Oxygen filled the atmosphere and, over the next few billion years, microscopic single-celled organisms fused and became multicellular. The great clockwork of evolution had begun. To begin with, life was restricted to the seas. Not until around 530 million years ago is there evidence that centipede-like animals began to explore the world above water.[1] All the while, a magnetic field underpinned our brave new world.

In murky primordial waters, blueprints for the animal kingdom were contained in bacteria. And among their cell composition, iron was included. Perhaps the iron inclusions served as magnetic dipoles that conveyed a 'magnetic moment', thus orientating the cells with respect to Earth's magnetic field? If bacteria possessed the power of movement, then they could align themselves along a magnetic axis. In theory, that would mean Earth's magnetic field found an echo in living organisms.

Except when volcanic eruptions occur, we do not see what lies just a few kilometres beneath our feet. During earthquakes, shockwaves go directly through Earth's core. By interpreting how waves are modified by the core's properties, it can be deduced that the inner core is solid metal (iron-nickel alloy) and about the size of the moon; the outer core is molten and about size of Mars. Earth has a magnetic field that protects our planet from the solar wind and its damaging radiation. The bulk of Earth's magnetic field is generated in the outer core that acts as a massive electromagnetic dynamo powered by Earth's rotation and long-term cooling of the planet, losing heat from the centre and creating currents within the molten, constantly fluctuating core. Like a huge bar magnet, the magnetic field has strength and a direction that, in present time, is aligned fairly close to the geographic poles. Hence energy flows from the magnetic South Pole to the magnetic North Pole. Humans cannot sense the pull of Earth's magnetic field – but birds and most other living organisms can. For many years it has been suspected that this might help to explain the magnetic compass that birds seem to possess, and that allows them to migrate by using Earth's magnetic field. The idea is that the geomagnetic field, despite being so weak, somehow influences the rate of some biochemical process in the brain, so that the neural signalling differs depending on how the bird is orienting in the geomagnetic field. Probably, all this is true.
PHOTOGRAPH: EINAR GUDMANNS

Studying single organisms and expecting to discern 'group think' was not on any scientist's mind until clusters of microbes were observed to move with a common cause. Something was afoot. Refreshingly, in 2010, Ronald T. Merrill, emeritus professor of Earth and Space Sciences at the University of Washington, communicated the thrill of that discovery in layman's terms: 'In the late 1970s, Joe Kirschvink was in my office peering through an optical microscope at bacteria he had collected in the mudflats of Lake Washington. He wanted to demonstrate that bacteria could sense the magnetic field. While

I looked through the microscope, he reversed a strong hand magnet next to the microscope. The bacteria immediately reversed course and began to swim in the opposite direction. These bacteria were sensing the magnetic field!'[2]

In fact, an earlier study had unequivocally revealed effects of Earth's magnetic field on bacteria.[3] The response, because it was sensory, coined a new epithet: 'magnetotactic'. Subsequent research even showed that, south of the magnetic equator, magnetotactic bacteria swam in the opposite direction, thereby chiming with the field's upwards (north-facing) component in the southern hemisphere and downwards (south-facing) component in the northern hemisphere.

The beauty of studying the nuts and bolts of the behaviour in relatively unsophisticated life forms meant that mechanisms understood at this level might become applicable on a grander scale. Through being deprived of sunlight or a view of the firmament at night, the bacteria could not tap other stimuli to determine direction. Researchers established that, within a single bacterium, crystals of magnetite served as receptors by reacting to the faint torque of a magnetic field. Magnetite, or ferric-ferrous oxide, is an iron oxide – commonly referred to as iron ore – and is the only mineral that is a natural magnet. As the crystals attempted to rotate, their orientation was detected by the bacterium.[4] Analogous to lead filings creeping towards a magnet, the crystals were the tail that wagged the dog.

Unfortunately for ease of human understanding, nature does not do simple. Geomagnetism may be a pulse felt by most of the natural world but it is not the only 'true path'. There are others. Mud-bound microbes are sensitive to a magnetic murmur, yet they are eyeless entities, devoid of other perceptions. Additional rhythms orchestrate timing. Every day the sun transits the sky, describing an arc that varies with respect to season and latitude. After sunset the heavens, pricked with stars, rotate around a fixed point. Logic suggests that, given aeons of time and evolution, the animal kingdom would figure out how to navigate the planet by tapping not just the insinuating pull of Earth's magnetic field but also the clues visible overhead. It did. But we are still short of unravelling the complexity of disparate approaches. Indeed birds, because they can fly, are able to integrate multiple cues and shift between them. At this stage, jumping straight into discussion of avian orientation systems would be to overlook feats of magnetic navigation by other animals. Rather than mangle a difficult subject, it is wiser to try and comprehend how these operate.

If, metaphorically speaking, the possession of a geomagnetic sense could 'help the blind see', a good place to look would be among purblind, soil-living animals. Mole rats spend almost their entire existence in tunnels about a metre or more below the surface. Some have slits for eyes. Others have a thin layer of skin covering their eyes, rendering them effectively blind but still light-sensitive. They retain an ability to perceive a shift from dark to light because brightness may indicate a tunnel being opened by a predator (or, conversely, an accidental collapse brought about by a large herbivore), thus warning the occupant not to approach an opening too closely. In fact, mole rats respond to illumination by plugging tunnel walls.[5] Although they occasionally glimpse flashes of light when pushing excess soil into mounds above ground, researchers proved that this exposure did not negate geomagnetism as their means of orientating in a subterranean world.[6]

By creating artificial adjustable magnetic fields in an eight-armed maze containing sleeping nests and food chambers, researchers discovered that when the magnetic field was altered by 180 degrees, all in a group of 33 mole rats changed quarters by the same angle. A control group of 30 did not experience the experimental shift in magnetic field direction and did not move accommodation. Although the direction-sensing mechanism remained a mystery, the animals' behaviour showed that they responded to a change in the horizontal component of the magnetic field – that is, a change in *compass direction*, as opposed to a change in the magnetic field's *inclination* (dip angle). Despite the limited vision of mole rats, another 'to see or not to see' question arose concerning their eyes' sensitivity. Some scientists suspected that the retina might be involved in aligning magnetic orientation. In 2006, investigations pointed instead to the cornea.[7] Small particles resembling magnetite were found embedded in its outer surface. To determine if the particles registered geomagnetism, the corneas of 42 individuals were anaesthetised and the animals' behaviour was compared with 40 controls. Those with anaesthetised eyes could no longer sense Earth's magnetic field, whereas the ability of the control group was undiminished. The researchers concluded that mole rats were probably using the magnetic particles in their corneas as sensory conductors.

We use three criteria to characterise the Earth's magnetic field in a choreography that fuses intensity, inclination and – as deployed by mole rats – a 'compass-bearing' horizontal component based upon polarity. Confusingly, this horizontal component is often referred to as 'declination'. With more than one calibration option available, mobile life forms are presented with a choice. So we should not be surprised if different preferences are made or, indeed, if some navigation systems combine more than one criterion.

Magnetic lines, just like supposed paranormal ley lines, encircle the planet's surface regardless of land or sea. Geomagnetic force does not discriminate between terrestrial and marine life forms; its perception is available to all. Loggerhead Turtles migrate from their nesting grounds on sandy beaches between North Carolina and Florida and undertake a transoceanic migration, gradually circling the tropical waters of the North Atlantic before returning to the American coast. Initially, they swim along the Gulf Stream to the North Atlantic Gyre, which rotates around the Sargasso Sea. Jellyfish hotspots within the gyre's gentle circulation provide abundant food but straying outside its

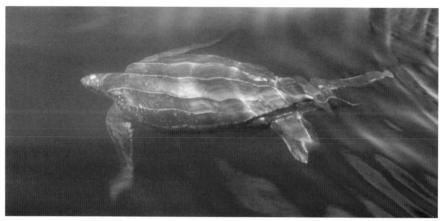

Ireland's continental shelf is a vital feeding ground for hundreds of Leatherback Turtles – the largest of all living turtles and the fourth-heaviest modern reptile, bar three larger species of crocodilians. All the world's marine turtles travel enormous distances before ultimately returning to the sandy beach where they hatched. Swimming in the sea and not being able to calibrate navigational ability by reference to celestial cues, they rely on Earth magnetism to guide them. The map reveals the travels of a Leatherback Turtle tagged off the coast of County Kerry.
PHOTOGRAPH: IAN SLEVIN

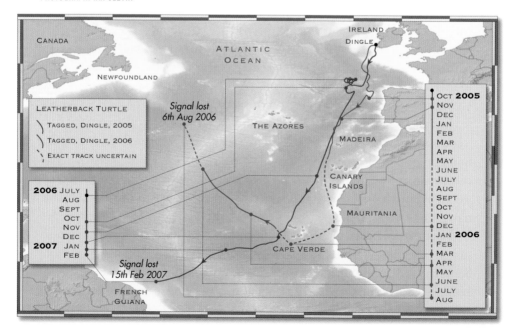

confines risks displacement into cooler seas where food is scarce and currents are strong enough to sweep some turtles to Ireland.

Although Loggerhead Turtles can grow to more than a metre in length, they are dwarfed by Leatherback Turtles, which are more than double their size. The sudden appearance of an ET head emerging, periscope-like, among swells is baffling until the animal's car-bonnet carapace breaks the surface. Leatherbacks are at home in colder waters and roam widely. Perhaps 400 or more feed on Ireland's continental shelf.[8] One tagged in Ireland passed the Canary Islands and then spent three months between Mauritania and the Cape Verde Islands before heading north-west over the North Atlantic Ridge towards the Newfoundland Grand Banks.[9] Marine turtles can match or exceed a human lifespan. They have been in existence for 100 million years. In that time they have not only learned to steer by referring to geomagnetism but also to travel along migratory pathways by using regional magnetic markers signalling changes in swimming direction at crucial geographic boundaries.[10] However, none orientated in accordance with horizontal components of the magnetic field. Instead, they took a bead from the field's inclination. Hatchlings were tested in darkness in water tanks surrounded by a system of magnetic coils that could invert the vertical component of the magnetic field, as well as shift it in a horizontal plane. Only when the field was inverted did the hatchlings change their swimming direction. Altering the field's horizontal component – in other words, its polarity – had no effect. The hatchling turtles, when 'interrogated' in the laboratory and presented with fields characteristic of different parts of the ocean, showed responses that mapped their hardwired migratory route.

The mysterious migration of silver-bellied eels from Ireland to the Sargasso Sea caught the imagination of Seamus Heaney. He immortalised their journey in 'A Lough Neagh Sequence'. Scientists have speculated that they use Earth's magnetic field because, during experiments, they orientate in a particular direction to magnetic north. The orientation varied with water temperature. In cool water – below 12 °C – they orientated in an appropriate migratory direction but in warmer water they diverted at a right angle. In effect, they stopped migrating. The abruptness with which they quit serves them well because, when cool water returns, they know to resume migration by reversing the right angle.[11] Information gained by demystifying migration could come to the rescue of nature itself. Understanding how eels migrate might help in the management of a national fishery. With eel stocks down to under a tenth of historical levels, Ireland should do more than simply ban commercial fishing.[12] For how much longer will eels muscling down the Shannon finish up being minced by the ESB's hydroelectric turbines?

15. Evidence of magnetic perception in birds
Global superpower

> *At that time people found it hard to imagine a mere bird possessing such a sophisticated sense.*

Roswitha Wiltschko

Homing pigeons are famous for their ability to return to their lofts. They became the 'laboratory rat' of choice for research into animal navigation. During the 1970s pursuit of the topic was remorseless. In 1977 the world's leading investigators attended an international symposium on 'Animal Migration, Navigation and Homing' at the University of Tübingen in Germany. Although suspicions abounded that the Earth's magnetic field appeared to be involved in orientation, previous trials had failed to confirm the magnetic sensitivity of homing pigeons.[1] That is not to say experiments did not record behaviour consistent with a geomagnetic sense. The main problem was reproducing the same results by other researchers or, indeed, by the same pigeons when faced with different weather or other environmental conditions. A repeat of one experiment required the birds to be released from a specific loft. It appeared that they were so highly tuned to the local 'magnetic topography' that they needed time to adjust to the different conditions of a new release point.[2] Although scientists suspected that homing pigeons and, by extension, birds in general, used a variety of interchangeable and complementary compasses – such as the sun, stars and possibly smell – the inescapable conclusion was that they deferred to the most appropriate cue when circumstances dictated. This meant that, probably, magnetism was used.

Two American researchers, Charles Walcott and Robert Green, were convinced that homing pigeons were guided by the sun on clear days but that, flying in solid overcast – when the sun was obscured – the birds relied upon a magnetic compass as backup. In 1972, they devised an ingenious test. In dull weather they placed tiny battery-powered magnetic coils around the birds' heads. On some, the polarity of the batteries was reversed, producing an opposite magnetic field. They predicted that, under grey skies, the birds fitted with reversed polarity batteries would fly in the opposite direction to home, whereas those with batteries aligned in the correct polarity would return to the loft. Remarkably, that is precisely what happened.[3]

Homing pigeons aside, the scientific establishment had not embraced attempts that sought to link magnetic orientation with migration in wild birds. The dominant view was that Earth's magnetic field was extremely weak and too faint to serve as a reliable guide for a bird on the move, especially across hemispheres. Gauss, its unit of measurement, had to be upscaled several hundredfold before it matched the pull of a humble fridge magnet. Yet one scientist, Wolfgang Wiltschko, had the temerity to suggest otherwise: 'since the sensory basis for the perception of the magnetic field by birds is still unknown, investigating behavioural responses to different types of magnetic fields appeared to be the best approach to gain more information about how birds' "gaussmeter" might function.'[4] Wiltschko had the knack of asking vital questions for which answers were unavailable.

The first studies on magnetic orientation by migratory songbirds involved Robins studied in Germany, at the University of Frankfurt, in the late 1950s and early 1960s. The initial work was performed by Professor Friedrich Merkel, who tested Robins in covered orientation cages. At migration time, birds exhibit a state of travel unrest – *zugunruhe* – and indicate their preferred direction by jittery, restless hopping. The agitation corresponds with natural behaviour. Hopping becomes most pronounced at night when the migrant should be on the wing.[5] The actions, therefore, elaborate a bird's motivation. Provided with an inkpad perch at the centre of a funnel-shaped cage lined with blotting paper, the bird's choice of direction is shown by its footprints (these days researchers tend to use thermal paper or electronic devices). The apparatus, known as an Emlen funnel (below) after its American inventor, Steve Emlen, enabled captive migrants to be tested under a variety of conditions – from planetariums whose star patterns were artificially controlled, to pitch dark steel vaults where not even radio signals permeated the walls.

Professor Merkel observed that, despite excluding all known external stimuli, the experimental Robins were still able to orientate their nocturnal hopping in more or less the correct direction. Wolfgang Wiltschko was a student of

Emlen funnel. To test a migrant's preferred direction of travel, the sides of a mesh cage are covered with blotting paper and the bird's perch is an inkpad. Restless and fluttering, its feet reveal which way it planned to fly.
PHOTOGRAPH: JONATHON BLAIR / NATIONAL GEOGRAPHIC CREATIVE

Merkel. He upped the ante considerably when he undertook tests in which he altered the direction of magnetic north within the orientation cages by placing magnetic coils on their periphery, allowing him to adjust the field's polarity. He found that the Robins shifted their hopping preferences accordingly.[6] Scepticism stalked Wiltschko and Roswitha, his scientist wife. They realised that one of the major difficulties in orientation studies was that the scientific approach of experimentally manipulating factors one at a time did not work. This was because the subjects could exercise arbitrary choice and ignore one system in favour of another. Such a response did not mean that the bird lacked a particular ability – such as magnetic sensibility – rather, it simply did not use the ability in a test situation.

Eventually, perseverance paid off. A breakthrough was made when it emerged that, although a bird's magnetic sense could be disrupted by manipulating the magnetic field, in order to elicit a response the field's intensity had to fall within the bird's normal sensory range. Furthermore, because the bird in the course of its migration history would routinely have registered other field intensities, these fell within its memory. Basically, it was as if the bird had a dial for certain radio stations between which reception amounted to unintelligible static. Wiltschko stated: 'the birds seem to have to adjust to each intensity separately. Under natural conditions adaptation to different intensities must occur, albeit in very small steps over a number of days when the intensity gradually changes during a bird's migration flight. [Therefore] birds seem to be able to use only those magnetic fields with which they become familiar.'[7] Revelations continued when the Wiltschkos discovered that bird compasses were not sensitive to the polarity of the magnetic field. Rather, they detect the *inclination* of Earth's magnetic field (see Chapter 13, p. 93). When tested in a horizontal magnetic field (no dip angle, as at the magnetic equator) Robins seemed confused and hopped in random directions.

One question raised by sceptics related to trans-equatorial migrants. They would, presumably, become unable to navigate at the magnetic equator because the field loses it dip. Northern-hemisphere species wintering south of the equator would encounter ambiguity because, south of the magnetic equator, the dip angle reverses and the innate rule that worked in the northern hemisphere should, in theory, send the bird back towards the equator. Using Garden Warblers as a test case, the Wiltschkos countered.[8] The species is a long-distance migrant, heading from Europe into Africa south of the equator. Wiltschko kept some Garden Warblers in captivity and tested their orientation in autumn. They hopped south. After a time, to simulate an expected arrival at the magnetic equator, he placed them in a horizontal magnetic field. Next, he tested them again but this time he put them back into the original magnetic field where they had been hopping south. Incredibly, they reversed their orientation. In other words, they began hopping towards magnetic north. In the real world, in order to continue to fly into the southern hemisphere, the birds had shown that they needed to change from flying in the direction in which Earth's magnetic field lines incline upward, to flying in the direction in which they flatten out and then dip downwards. In that decision, the dip angle is, literally, pivotal. Wiltschko showed that sequential exposure to a horizontal magnetic field apparently 'recalibrates' the bird and causes it to reverse its response to the inclination of the magnetic field. As for the matter of the polarity of Earth's magnetic field and its periodic reversals in direction, Wiltschko noted that a compass based upon inclination angles rather than polarity would continue to function and would not be affected by such switches. The evidence was irrefutable and the results pointed to more, not less, navigational sophistication.

Today it is widely accepted that birds integrate directional information from the world about them – the path of the sun across the sky, the rotation centre of the starry sky and the inclination of Earth's magnetic field. As the body of migration research grows, it has become clear that species differ in the way they prioritise each set of environmental cues. Although they possess sophisticated navigation systems, the birds require optimum weather conditions for their successful use. For Sanderlings, whose high-latitude breeding grounds are located within 15 degrees of the geographic North Pole, the relatively steep inclination of the magnetic field in polar regions probably demands very precise bearings to be taken, especially as the field lines cluster at the magnetic pole. It is possible to imagine the globe of Earth steepening as all the meridians of longitude converge. Soon, you conceive, the Earth must 'level out' under the arcing force of the gravitating magnetic field. For Sanderlings – and other migratory birds heading this far north to breed – it seems that navigational decisions made at departure time are of critical importance and are only made under clear skies. In experiments conducted in Iceland, where Sanderlings stop off before departing for breeding areas in north-east Greenland, departures were invariably delayed during overcast conditions, indicating that a combination of celestial and geomagnetic information is needed to determine an appropriate migratory orientation.[9]

16. Light, magnetism and the avian eye
The eyes have it

Having thus examined the many inadequate theories that seek to elucidate the wonderful faculty possessed by migrants of discovering the correct migratory path, and after considering the phenomenon for more than 50 years at a spot so ideal as Helgoland, I still cannot offer a satisfactory explanation.

Heinrich Gätke, 1895

Heinrich Gäkte was a man who could differentiate between reliable information and superstition. A century later we are in the enviable position of knowing most of the external cues that birds use to find their way – such as the pull of Earth's magnetic field, patterns of polarised light in the sky (more on this later) and the rotation of the night sky around a stationary Pole Star. But how do birds sense these things? The discovery of ferro-magnetic materials in the bodies of bacteria and some animals (see Chapter 14) could explain the foundation of magnetoreception in these groups of species. Debate on how birds sense Earth's magnetic field has, in the past, also centred on the use of magnetised grains found in the heads of pigeons. However, another hypothesis has gained ascendancy in recent years, based on processes

MAGNETORECEPTION – A CRASH COURSE

Magnetic sensing – magnetoreception – is a type of sensory perception. It is thought that humans might at one time have possessed such an ability but it apparently has become redundant.

Recent scientific studies have demonstrated that many living organisms perceive magnetic fields. Magnetism is a force of nature and is generated by Earth's metallic, molten core. Because Earth's magnetic field has a steady axis, it can be used for orientation. Although, in terms of polarity, Earth's magnetic field arcs from the magnetic South Pole to the magnetic North Pole, its field lines are not uniform in inclination. The lines are steeply angled at the poles but become almost parallel to Earth's surface at the equator (see illustration on p. 93).

A wide variety of life forms, from fruit flies to fish and turtles, perceive and utilise geomagnetic field information. Migratory birds provide the best example of truly global navigation based upon an innate magnetic sense. In birds, magnetic sensing occurs in the eye and a compass guide is derived by sensing the inclination angle – not the polarity – of Earth's magnetic field. The ability is light dependent, meaning that the bird can register the magnetic field only in certain wavelengths of light. Research shows that blue, short-wavelength light, is needed. Under normal circumstances, birds are sensitive to only a narrow wavelength band but – given accommodation time – can adjust to wavelengths of slightly higher or lower intensity.

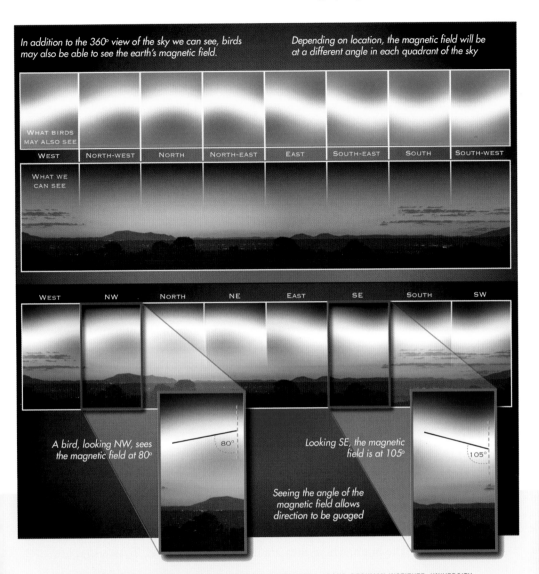

In addition to the 360° view of the sky we can see, birds may also be able to see the earth's magnetic field.

Depending on location, the magnetic field will be at a different angle in each quadrant of the sky

WHAT BIRDS MAY ALSO SEE

| WEST | NORTH-WEST | NORTH | NORTH-EAST | EAST | SOUTH-EAST | SOUTH | SOUTH-WEST |

WHAT WE CAN SEE

| WEST | NW | NORTH | NE | EAST | SE | SOUTH | SW |

A bird, looking NW, sees the magnetic field at 80°

80°

Looking SE, the magnetic field is at 105°

105°

Seeing the angle of the magnetic field allows direction to be guaged

BASED UPON IMAGERY BY THEORETICAL AND COMPUTATIONAL BIOPHYSICS GROUP, BECKMAN INSTITUTE, UNIVERSITY OF ILLINOIS AT URBANA-CHAMPAIGN

The biological process that facilitates a bird's magnetic compass has eluded researchers for decades. The two main concepts for avian magnetoreception are a magnetite-based model and a radical-pair model. The former suggests that the compass is founded by small particles of magnetic-sensing magnetite located in the head. The latter idea contends that the compass may operate through a chemical reaction in the eye, involving radical-pair molecular reactions to wavelengths of light – a 'radical pair' being a pair of molecules, each of which have an unpaired electron. The physics involved in this molecular manoeuvring is difficult to grasp[1] but the upshot provides a vital spark that creates an image projected onto an inner screen within the bird's vision. What might the bird see? At present that remains a mystery. One possibility is that the bird's visual field is modified through a 'magnetic filter function', which operates like a graduated photo filter, emphasising the cardinal direction.

involving the perception of light. Although certain animals probably register light through the pineal gland (the 'third eye' located on the rear crown) and despite the fact that the same organ is known to be substantially involved in producing melatonin, a hormone that is believed to play an important role in the development of migratory activity in birds,[2] the avian eye has emerged as a more likely locus of sensory ability. Across the natural world, eyes and the vision they generate are not uniform. Unlike humans, most primates can only sense two distinct wavelengths of light: they do not see colour as well as we do. In contrast, birds have four channels and see more than we do. But how, among their spectral inheritance, might migrants discern pathways that guide them on migration?

The magical effects that are the power of sight are produced by the internal mechanisms of the eye. To grasp what is going on it is important to describe something of the orb's workings. It is therefore necessary to engage with the language of science in order to understand current thinking on what birds see that we do not.[3] The eye is a lens system that focuses light entering the eye through the cornea onto the retina through a crystalline lens. The transparent cornea is the 'window on the soul' that brings the real world into view. In humans (and some birds) the lens is rigid and made of dead cells whose blood supply is cut off at birth. Our eyes are embedded in muscles that flex and move the eye in all directions. Shifting focus between near and far is termed 'accommodation'. Birds' power of accommodation is superior to ours and, depending on species, is achieved by expanding or contracting the lens itself, which is malleable. The need for extensive and rapid changes in accommodation for airborne insectivores such as Swallows is obvious. The space between the lens and the retina is filled by a gelatinous substance, the vitreous humour. The retina is packed with receptors, which convert light into electrical signals that are transmitted along nerve fibres to the brain, where they are interpreted as vision. To oversimplify,

The position of the eyes on a bird's head correlate with lifestyle. The eyes of predatory species – such as owls and hawks – are directed towards the front of the face. Snipe, because they probe, have eyes placed to look along the line of the bill. In common with other birds whose eyes are located on the side of the head, the eye is set in a crease to facilitate peering behind. If danger threatens, Snipe freeze and keep watch by looking away. They can do this because, with eyes set high and backward, they have more effective binocular vision of objects to the rear than in front.

the retina contains two different types of photosensitive (light-sensing) cells, called cones and rods. In humans, cones are sensitive to red, green and blue. In birds, they are also sensitive to ultraviolet.

The general construction of a bird's retina is orthodox enough. However, it outranks the human retina in sophistication because of a greater complexity of components. Not only are the rods and cones more numerous and tightly packed than in other vertebrates but the layers of conductive cells are unusually abundant – so much so that the avian retina is up to twice as thick as in most vertebrates.[4] A further refinement is the presence of coloured oil droplets in the retina's cone cells. Until recently their function was unknown but investigations undertaken by different groups of researchers established that the droplets act as light filters and that each responds differently to specific wavelengths of light.[5] By the 1970s, when it was realised that pigeons could discriminate polarised light and that other species could see ultraviolet light, researchers began to speculate that such perceptions might be of use in migration and orientation. Previously, ultraviolet in the wax blooms of berries and in the arrangement of veins in the blooms of flowers, which served as beacons of colour designed to attract foragers, was believed to be the only benefit of registering ultraviolet in bird vision. Although the penny took a while to drop, by the end of the last millennium some in the scientific community wondered if birds had a knack of orientating by the 'light' of Earth's magnetic field. Sometimes the best questions to ask are those that lack answers.

One study that led to a giant leap in understanding had a serendipitous beginning. American geneticists working to unravel the genes that determined eye colour in a species of fruit fly *Drosophila melanogaster* found that the insects sensed a magnetic field. Fruit flies like sugar, small quantities of which were placed at the end of long tubes. The insects could be conditioned to find it by manipulating the magnetic field using metal coils. Confronted with a

choice, flies only crawled along tubes containing sugar that were placed in a magnetic field. Ultimately, even when no sugar was present, they entered the tubes placed in the magnetic field and ignored other tubes.[6] But how did the flies sense the magnetic field? By using filters the researchers controlled the wavelengths of light used in the experiment. They found that the flies sensed the magnetic field only when ultraviolet light was present. They also proposed that a protein – cryptochrome – present in the insects' eyes served as a light-sensing 'photoreceptor'. Because cryptochrome 'told' the flies about the presence or absence of the magnetic field, it was not only a photoreceptor, it was also – crucially – a magnetoreceptor. French scientists brilliantly confirmed cryptochrome's magnetoreception qualities by carrying out similar experiments using mutant *Drosophila melanogaster* whose eyes lacked cryptochrome. These mutant flies could not be conditioned to the presence of a magnetic field, while others with cryptochrome could. The conclusion was inescapable. Cryptochrome was necessary for the flies to sense a magnetic field.[7]

This discovery had far-reaching implications. For one thing, it was already known that birds' eyes possessed cryptochrome. That fact prompted speculation about the existence of a biochemical process capable of relaying information about Earth's magnetic field from the eye to the brain and generating an image. Ornithologists engaged in migration research had puzzle pieces that, if shaken loose and assembled in the right order, might clarify how birds sense the magnetic field and show that the faculty could be activated by exposure to certain wavelengths of light. Although a bit of a mouthful, a 2007 paper entitled 'A visual pathway links brain structures active during magnetic compass orientation in migratory birds'[8] succeeded in assembling a physiological model. The paper's title can be seen as the remark that opened up the subject to a wider scientific audience and although we know that birds perceive Earth's magnetic field, we still do not know what they see. From a lay perspective, trying to imagine how chemical reactions induced by light transmute into a visual pattern capable of serving as a direction marker is like trying to conceive the supernatural.

In plain language, how do scientists believe the system works? The mechanism involves the interactions of excited states of molecules with Earth-strength magnetic fields. Basically, cryptochrome molecules react when bombarded by ultraviolet light, an action made possible by a process known as the radical pair hypothesis, a complicated concept that can only be understood through quantum chemistry. Mining through the science is difficult, especially when the aim is to produce a simple analogy that encapsulates the complexity of a process operating at subatomic levels. For a start, what is a radical? Within the hazy

Eyes provide living organisms with the ability to sense the spectrum of light bathing Earth. That spectrum consists of a range of electromagnetic frequencies. The portion of light varies among species. Within the human retina, we detect light with three types of photoreceptor cone that are sensitive to red, green and blue light. Although we also have a blue photoreceptor – which can register some light in the ultraviolet wavelength – the eye's lens and cornea filter out these wavelengths before they reach the retina, presumably to protect against damage. The avian retina is, on the other hand, designed to let through ultraviolet light. By accessing this extra 'channel', birds – as well as most invertebrates and some other vertebrates – see differently. Plumage reflectance is one area where appearance is affected. In ultraviolet, the sheen of the blue crown of a male Blue Tit (right) is used in courtship as a guide to health. Males with the best lustre are preferred by females. Because offspring tend to inherit parental attributes, female Blue Tits paired with less 'attractive' males produced more female young than males – favouring good-looking daughters over dull sons![9]

world of atomic structure, flux occurs. Electrons spin around atoms, preferring to travel in pairs. Unpaired electrons are relatively unstable and seek other 'free' electrons to combine with. To do so, they momentarily shift orbits. In that 'free radical' moment – before they recombine with a new electron – infinitesimally small energy bursts occur. Such moments generate 'photo excitation'. In their short lives free radicals may form transient radical pairs which are sensitive to magnetic fields. The system can work if it contains a fixed array of radical pairs that are functionally linked to light-sensitive pigments.

Talk of fixed arrays of photo pigments immediately describes the retina. And, in the new millennium, experimental support has been found for the notion that birds have a magnetic compass located in the retina.[10] If a compass based on

Oily droplets present in certain cells in the avian retina act as light filters and respond to specific wavelengths of light. Within the droplets a protein called cryptochrome serves as a light sensor, or photoreceptor. Vitally, cryptochrome also reacts to a magnetic field, thereby also making it a magnetoreceptor. In a nutshell, the cryptochrome molecules react when bombarded by ultraviolet light and, through a chemical chain reaction, generate a visual determination of the inclination angle of Earth's magnetic field – which a bird perceives. Although our species can put men on the moon and splice genes, we still cannot see Earth's magnetic field.

the radical-pair mechanism is present in bird retinas, it appears that the photo pigment involved is cryptochrome. Cryptochrome is expressed in birds' retinas in a group of nerve cells, and has the right dynamics to produce the radical pairs needed for magnetoreception. Of course, the retina is a kaleidoscopic array of cells and how cryptochrome triggers the required directional sensitivity is not clear. Bird head movements might be necessary to 'focus' the sense of direction. Watch a bird tilt its head and you will notice that it does so in a manner resembling click stops on a camera rather than a continuous smooth movement. Could it be that each tilt creates a pause that facilitates some kind of calibration? Certainly, evidence that cryptochrome-containing nerve cells in the retina are capable of connecting with visual centres in the brain is now well grounded.[11] Therefore, it is quite feasible that migrants can 'see' the right direction to follow to a chosen destination.

Birds' ability to find their way is uncanny. We know that they use a variety of tricks, most of which are preprogrammed into successive generations by parents that pass on a tried-and-tested genetic codebook. We have a fair idea of the contents but experiencing the sensations that the codebook contains is still outside our sensory ken. Some things we can appreciate, such as the rotation of stars around Polaris, which migrants use as a celestial maypole. Other avian path-finding techniques leave us groping for analogies. Tapping Earth's magnetic field for direction is the natural world's masterstroke. Human head-scratching took centuries to assemble compasses capable of figuring fine degrees of polarity. Arguably, birds are still one step ahead because their magnetic compass is based not on the polarity of the magnetic field, but on the inclination of the axis of the field lines: a failsafe system that will still function when Earth's magnetic field reverses, as occasionally happens. Getting to grips with the circuitry inside a bird's skull is another challenge. The connections that crackle from eye to brain and guide birds on migration are deemed so sophisticated that nuclear physicists consider them based on quantum mechanics – 'it may be that the way some animals navigate during migration … require quantum explanations if they are to be understood'.[12]

Our brain is divided into two hemispheres that deal with different types of detail. This discovery was made in the nineteenth century by a French physician, Pierre Broca, who studied the brains of patients with language disorders and established that damage in one part of the brain exclusively affected speech. Over time, understanding grew and it was realised that the left and right hemispheres of the brain act as separate information highways. The effect is called 'lateralisation' (also known as sidedness) and until a few decades ago it was widely and incorrectly assumed that only humans possessed the faculty. The process is now known to occur widely in the animal kingdom, including invertebrates. Fruit flies prioritise odour messages received through two separate antennae and nematode worms allocate one brain hemisphere for sensing odour and delegate taste perception to the other.[13] Similarly, eyes can multitask. Most birds' eyes are placed on either side of the head, enabling, for example, pigeons to use one eye to pick grain at their feet while using the other to watch for predators. Yet, in trials featuring pigeons, when it came to discriminating grains from a confusing pebble background, visual 'asymmetry' – that is, searches using just one eye – outscored binocular vision.[14]

Researchers suggest that lateralisation confers several advantages. For one, brain capacity is freed up by avoiding duplication of functions in two hemispheres. In birds, lateralisation embraces more than detecting food while simultaneously checking for danger. In a growing number of species, scientists have discovered that the magnetic compass is lateralised in just one eye.[15] The right eye is favoured. Given that cryptochrome – the protein that mediates directional information about the geomagnetic field – is present in *both* eyes, it seems that lateralisation increases the brain's processing efficiency. As if to prove a point, young birds, during the first year of life, orientate using either eye but gradually confine the function to just the right eye and, therefore, the left hemisphere of the brain: implying that left/right differences in the brain require a developmental period.[16] Although science-speak hits the nail on the head – 'differential development of visual cortex correlates with specific recognition memory' – if birds could speak they might put it another way: why find the way with two eyes when one will suffice?

17. Star patterns and orientation
Celestial pathfinders

· ·

Tonight the west is full of clouds;
The east is full of stars that fly
Into the cloud's dark foliage,
And the moon will follow by and by.

W.H. DAVIES

In springtime in eastern North America the night sky crackles with calls. The source is millions of songbirds, many hailing from Central and South America and bound for breeding quarters in Canada. Anonymous twitters have the emphasis of phonetics in italics; other notes are barely audible and make you wonder how many more are beyond human hearing. Staring at the moon with binoculars reveals moving specks silhouetted like shooting stars in negative. Some species use calls exclusive to nocturnal migration, meaning that sound and picture can be united on the same bird in daylight. More important facts that need shape are those explaining how the heavenly horde knows the way. Dusk departures carry with them all the conviction of prophets who have burned their bridges. Many aspects of migration are inherited and are, therefore, under genetic control. In a way, this is galling: migrants are born knowing. But what powers do they use to divine routes in the dark?

Nocturnal migrants generally set off at dusk. We classify the close of day as vespers: a half-light transition in which the going down of the sun yields to moonrise and the emergence of stars. In our mind the process conjures images of bedtime. For birds intent on migrating, nothing could be further from the truth. The switch from sunlight to celestial light sources – horizon glow, the moon and the stars – presents navigational opportunities. For centuries, humans have used star patterns like a map of runic monuments. By taking a bead off Polaris – the stationary North Star or Pole Star – navigators had a constant reference for other constellations in an all-over pattern that changes with the seasons and, indeed, latitude: 'such as even poets would admit perforce, more practical than Pegasus the horse'. (Robert Frost, from *A Star in a Stone-Boat*).

Of course, it is just a coincidence that there happens to be a bright star (Polaris) close to the celestial North Pole. The real apex at the centre of star trails is the celestial North Pole and it is around this that Earth's rotation can be gauged (see photograph on facing page). The southern hemisphere is not as

In this moonlit image of Himalayan peaks, concentric star trails denote the position of Polaris, the 'north star', around which the night sky rotates. In reality, Polaris sits close to the true point of rotation – the celestial North Pole. In the image, the trails recorded in the time exposure include a bright blob-shaped arc of movement made by Polaris itself around the invisible nodal point of the celestial North Pole. Hence, it is the mountains on Earth that move – not the stars. (L–r): The three main peaks are Annapurna South, Hiunchuli and Machapuchare.
PHOTOGRAPH: JIA HAO

fortunate. The only star that comes close to being equivalent to Polaris is Sigma Octans which, although only one degree away from the celestial South Pole, is too dim to see except under optimal conditions. Because the stars move in the sky, the fact that we have a 'north star' and not a 'south star' is a transient phenomenon. In many thousands of year's time, the situation might be reversed.

For migrants, steering by the star pattern is, therefore, a possibility. Although there is a wealth of evidence to show that they make use of it, caveats apply. In Arctic regions, where many globetrotting shorebirds breed, the sun never sets in summer. Juveniles, reared in perpetual daylight and programmed to migrate south in autumn, would not experience much darkness until close to the time of their departure – around the middle of August. Research has shown that once they (and young of many other species) experience night and see the night sky, they engage an innate ability to acquire stellar insights as a navigational aid.[1]

Much of the early experimental work on star navigation was carried out by German ornithologists Franz and Eleonore Sauer. Their approach was to note the directional tendencies of caged migrants exposed to star patterns under a natural sky during migration.[2] Among the species used were Garden Warblers

Lesser Whitethroat – a common visitor across Europe but a scarce visitor to Ireland – was among several migrant warblers tested to see if inborn directional preferences could be manipulated experimentally. Unlike most European summer visitors, such as Whitethroats that migrate south-west in autumn, Lesser Whitethroats travel south-east, before changing to a southerly bearing in the eastern Mediterranean.

and Lesser Whitethroats, selected because they follow dissimilar migration routes, depending on their home range in Europe. Garden Warblers migrate south-west. Lesser Whitethroats take a different line: they leave Europe on a south-east bearing, turn south-south-east in the eastern Mediterranean and reach north-east Africa by finally veering south. When exposed to the star pattern, Garden Warblers exhibited default south-west tendencies in autumn and – the expected corollary – north-east preferences in spring. In addition to wild-caught birds that were held for the duration of experiments, the researchers raised young Garden Warblers in incubators. Deprived of ever seeing the night sky or meeting adults of their own species, they behaved appropriately when exposed to the night sky for the first time. This astounding result was one of the first to demonstrate that migration information – coupled with the ability to orientate – was inherited. Memory retention was also confirmed when a wild-caught Lesser Whitethroat, kept in darkness during its first autumn and spring and placed in a 'Euro-centric' planetarium in the second autumn of its life, responded immediately by hopping south-east. Proof that its inborn compass was unerring was verified when, presented with simulated skies depicting more southerly latitudes, it altered course and, at 15 degrees north of the equator, headed due south.

The thrill of discovery needed to be tempered. Some efforts at repeating the work were unsuccessful. Nonetheless, in attempting to dissect the research, no conclusions destroyed the core finding: provided enough of the night sky was visible, migrants were able to use stars as a guide. Contradictions persisted, however. In 1961, experiments in Germany using wild-caught Robins demonstrated that, even under conditions when stars were excluded, the birds showed restless behaviour corresponding with southwards migration in autumn and, at the end of a starless winter confinement, northward urges in spring.[3] Although perplexing, there was no need to throw the baby out with the bath water. North American Indigo Buntings, tested in planetariums, maintained an appropriate southerly migratory direction under an autumn sky but when the artificial star pattern was reversed by 180 degrees, the birds changed their directional preference to the north.[4]

The departure point for inspiration was the obstacle. The breakthrough came when tests showed that, rather than memorising constellations, birds responded to the rotation of the night sky around a fixed point. Polaris was the beacon. To appreciate its significance, you need to envisage Earth lying at the centre of the firmament. As the planet spins, its axis not only aligns with the geographic poles, it also intersects with Polaris. Hence, by extension, there exists an axis of celestial rotation that, invariably, accords with geographic north. Constellations move across the sky but their shape remains the same and, crucially, they maintain a constant position relative to Polaris. In experimental conditions, birds learned to recognise invented stars anchored around a single conspicuous star, a surrogate for Polaris. The evidence became overwhelming when researchers reared Indigo Buntings under an artificial sky with the bright star Betelgeuse (in the constellation Orion) as the point of rotation. The nestlings reorientated themselves on Betelgeuse and, when subsequently tested, treated it as Polaris.[5] Birds' knowledge of the night sky is, therefore, not innate. It depends upon seeing a rotating field of stars and pinpointing Polaris by the simple expedient of 'the star that stays still'.

Scientific enquiry, having established the way birds searched for cues in the night sky, was still left with a lot of solid information that needed to be reconciled. A magnetic sense was also embedded in avian guidance systems. Was one sense dominant? Perhaps the two were interconnected? Moreover, might there be yet other senses at birds' disposal? If so, which of several potential compasses achieves overriding importance at a given time? This topic became the subject of investigations in so-called 'cue-conflict' experiments. Birds were presented with two or more orientation cues at once. Forced to choose between them, their decisions could be monitored. It turned out that as well as celestial and geomagnetic cues, the sun – or rather sky polarisation patterns produced by the sun's position – amounted to Cupid's bow for direction seekers.

18. Skylight polarisation and navigation
Here comes the sun

That sunset, borne on waves of ether,
I cannot begin to comprehend,
Whether it is day's end, or the world's,
Or where the deepest mystery ends.

ANNA AKHMATOVA

The sun has rhythm. In the morning, it breaks in the eastern sky like an egg. By day the hoisted chalice arcs into the west. Its movement amounts to a trail of golden Braille that provides a compass direction and a sense of time. We use it for those sundial purposes. Surely the rest of the animal kingdom does too? Establishing that birds might use the sun as a combined compass-cum-clock was a tall order. In Germany, at the end of the Second World War, Gustav Kramer resumed work on trying to discover a 'sun-orientation mechanism' that he suspected existed among Starlings.[1]

Kramer designed a circular aviary with an opaque ceiling and sides, along which six shuttered windows were placed symmetrically. The bottom of the aviary, complete with annotated compass points, was made of Plexiglass, making it possible to observe bird behaviour from below. Once inside the aviary the only source of light was sunlight entering through the windows. In an attempt to exclude potential recognition of landmarks, positional awareness or even Earth's magnetic field – nothing was left to chance – the contraption was moved to different localities, rotated and surrounded with sufficient quantities of iron to make a compass needle oscillate wildly. Starlings in a state of migratory restlessness – *zugunruhe* – were used in the experiments. The captives' daily activities reflected the regime of others in the wild: migration in the morning waned towards the afternoon, when migrants switched to foraging behaviour. Kramer soon discovered that the birds showed a marked preference for one sector of the aviary. Because all known possibilities had been eliminated, he guessed that the sun was being used to orientate.

The next stage, therefore, was to try moving the sun. All the window shutters were repositioned and large mirrors attached to each, mounted at an angle of 135 degrees. The effect was to alter the apparent location of the sun as seen from inside the aviary. Following the adjustment, the birds took up a new position. Kramer changed the direction of the artificial sun several times.

'The sun shone, having no alternative, on the nothing new.' (Samuel Beckett)

Over how many aeons of time has the sun marked the passing of a day on Earth? As well as a guide to time, its daily pageant is a guide to place. Birds are cognisant of its clockwork and use it as both a timepiece and compass.

PHOTOGRAPH: KATHRYN McGEEHAN

And, every time, the Starlings responded. When sunlight was excluded the birds' orientation became haphazard. The conclusion was inescapable: when restless and motivated to migrate, the birds followed the sun. To test for a sense of timing, the Starlings were trained to locate food behind blinds. In keeping with foraging activity in the wild, food was provided only in the afternoon – in other words, at a time of day marked by a specific position of the sun. A final manipulation involved presenting food behind only those curtains that corresponded to the appropriate position of the sun – whether real or artificial – in the afternoon. Once again the birds' actions were convincing. Not only did they use the sun as a compass, they also used it to gauge time. Somehow, they had an inbuilt chronometer that compensated for the sun's movements across the sky.

Kramer had proved an important principle. He was, nonetheless, cautious: 'it seemed obvious that the sun orientation in its effectiveness was comparable to a compass … yet the function of a sun compass was strained beyond reason by believing that it enabled the bird to maintain its direction even during the night, once the setting sun or its vanishing glow had set the bird's bearings at take-off.'[2] Kramer's conservatism was justified because subsequent research proved that birds use the sun only as a compass;[3] it is not part of the wherewithal used for establishing their position on an inherited map indicating where to go from where they are.

It is important to draw a distinction between the two different types of orientation ability possessed by birds. The first is a compass sense that utilises a range of phenomena, such as magnetism and light from the heavens, whereas the second is a map sense: the savvy to determine from a compass where a destination lies, be it a breeding area or winter quarters. By analogy, if you were turned adrift somewhere on the world's oceans with ample provisions and a compass but no map, you would remain hopelessly lost. A compass only takes you so far, without a map you do not know where land lies. Birds have devised elegant and ingenious solutions to the problem of compass navigation but science is a long way short of understanding how their psyche prefigures a journey map. It is deceptively easy to link 'map' and 'compass' in a couplet. However, the two are massively out of kilter. Determining a compass bearing is like looking at a watch to tell the time; devising a map is like making the watch. Watches are mechanical constructions. Birds' maps are genetically encoded living cells responsive to complex chemical signals induced by forces that still defy comprehension.

Tragically, Kramer died when just 49. He was prescient in recognising that the vanishing glow of the setting sun might provide a directional cue that amounted to another compass. Before the Second World War, Karl von Frisch established that, unlike human eyes which register light in three wavelengths – red, green and blue – bees also see ultraviolet, the light responsible for sunburn.[4] Birds possess the same faculty. In addition, birds and insects are able to see polarised light. Blue sky is full of polarised light. We do not notice it because our eyes cannot distinguish between it and ordinary light. However, to birds and other life forms, polarised light is special. Bees use it as a means of establishing the sun's position when it is obscured by cloud. Birds, however, use the pattern of polarised light discernable at dusk and dawn as a motive power enabling them to behold a celestial axis whose end points denote north and south.

What is polarised light and why might perceiving it be important for migratory birds? Other than polarised lenses in sunglasses that remove glare and make the sky a deeper blue, most people are unaware of polarised light. Light travels in waves. If you watch waves moving across water, you notice that an obstruction – a stone, for instance – disrupts the wave train and causes wavelets to go off in various directions. Light from the sun is affected in the same way by the molecules that make up Earth's atmosphere. The process is known as *scattering*. If Earth had no atmosphere to scatter light, the sun would appear white and rise and set in a black sky.

Light acquires its colour from its wavelength. Red light has a long wavelength; blue light a short one. The 'white' light from the sun is a combination of all the colours in the spectrum from red, through orange, yellow, green, blue and indigo, to violet. Wavelength decreases as red bleeds into the next colour in the sequence. Our ability to resolve colour stretches only as far as blue; birds and other life forms register very short wavelength ultraviolet light. Earth's

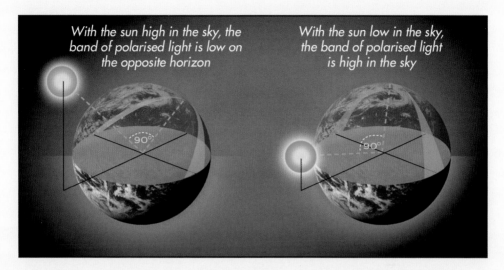

With the sun high in the sky, the band of polarised light is low on the opposite horizon

With the sun low in the sky, the band of polarised light is high in the sky

The sun's rays are made up of light of different wavelengths. When sunshine illuminates Earth, the planet's atmosphere scatters the light particles – called photons – and creates a band of strongly polarised light at 90 degrees (perpendicular) to the sun. Although this 'band of maximum polarisation' is invisible to us, birds and other life forms are able to detect the pattern, which follows the sun across the sky. Therefore, by observing the band's position, birds are able to use the end points as a navigation reference – even when the sun is obscured.

The final four images (below) are photographs of the sky at sunset taken with a fisheye lens that captures a 180-degree view. The first and third images were taken with a polarising filter attached to the lens, enabling the position of the band to be distinguished by the human eye. In the natural sky (first photo), the band runs like a shadow from north to south. Although the band's presence is unaffected by clouds, they reduce its visibility when viewed from below. Hence, when the sky becomes cloudy (third photo) the band is less clear-cut, even though the polarisation pattern remains stable. Photos 2 and 4 are representations of how those same images may appear to birds. Experiments have shown that birds' eyes possess a heightened sensitivity to polarised light. The degree of polarisation, enhanced in different colour channels, makes the band's position much clearer.

PHOTOGRAPHS BELOW: JUSTIN MARSHALL

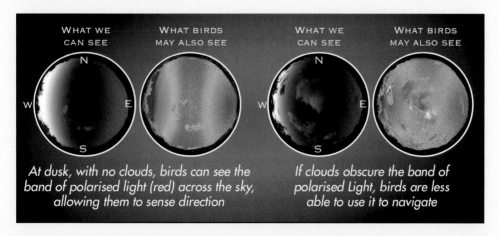

WHAT WE CAN SEE   WHAT BIRDS MAY ALSO SEE   WHAT WE CAN SEE   WHAT BIRDS MAY ALSO SEE

At dusk, with no clouds, birds can see the band of polarised light (red) across the sky, allowing them to sense direction

If clouds obscure the band of polarised Light, birds are less able to use it to navigate

'That late in the season, the light went quickly. It was sunny one minute and dark the next ...
the mountain range was canted against the afterglow, and for a while it seemed unimaginable
that anything could lie beyond the mountains, that this was not the end of the world. The wall of
pure and brassy light seemed to beat up from infinity. Then the stars came out, the Earth rumbled
downward, and the illusion of an abyss was lost.' (John Cheever)

Just after sunset, in air clear as glass, a blue velvet curtain follows the sinking sun. During
daytime the sky is blue because, as light from the sun reaches us, particles in our atmosphere
scatter the different wavelengths that make up sunlight. Blue light has a very short wavelength
and is scattered most. Because of this, it colours the sky blue. Earth's atmosphere not only
scatters the light particles – it also polarises them and creates a deeper blue band perpendicular
to the position of the setting sun.

atmosphere acts like a weak polarising filter. Particles within it – predominantly
gaseous oxygen and nitrogen – are most effective in scattering the shorter
wavelength portions of the light spectrum. So as white light from the sun passes
through our atmosphere, short wavelength blue light (as well as indigo and
ultraviolet light that fall outside our eyes' colour sensitivity) is scattered by
atmospheric particles, whereas longer wavelength light (red, orange and yellow)
passes through the atmosphere without significant alteration. Scattering of the
shorter wavelength light illuminates the sky with the one colour – blue – that
we can see from the shorter wavelength light scale. In fact, ultraviolet light is
more easily scattered by atmospheric particles. Imagine, therefore, what the sky
must look like to birds and other life forms that are sensitive to ultraviolet?

An elementary fact arises from the great clockwork of the sun's daily passage across the heavens. Although invisible to us, a 'band of maximum polarisation' exists. The band is bound to the sun's path and is, at all times, perpendicular to its position. Because the band is visible even when the disc of the sun disappears over the horizon at dusk (and just before it rises in the morning), it serves as a reference. And because the band's axis is north–south, it can be detected by birds – most likely in the ultraviolet range – and used to locate true north.

Most nocturnal migrants initiate their journeys shortly after sunset. Researchers felt that key decisions about which way to fly were made at that time. In North America, Ken Able and his colleagues demonstrated that, at sunset, the visual cue was not the sun itself, nor the residue of a bright glow illuminating the western sky and denoting where the sun went down. Instead, it was found that birds looked at patterns of polarised light in the sky.[5] By testing birds in orientation cages covered with large sheets of polarising material between sunset and the time the first stars came out, the researchers were able to show that the birds responded to manipulations of the polarised light. By changing the axis of the polarisation band, the birds' orientation shifted accordingly. The coup de grâce was delivered when depolarising sheets eliminated the pattern and rendered the birds unable to select a direction.

The scientists' discovery, although momentous, needs to be set in a real-world context. In a very clear sky, the polarisation band is clearly defined. More typically, although still distinguishable, its edges blur in hazy or cloudy conditions. Fuzziness develops because of the presence of suspended particles or water droplets in the atmosphere. These depolarise light and scatter it.[6] Nevertheless, if the sky is not entirely covered in cloud, the patches of open atmosphere that are visible from Earth's surface retain the polarisation characteristic of their relationship with the sun.[7] Thus, birds that rely on celestial polarisation can continue their migration activities, either by sticking to a bearing that they took before visibility became reduced or, en route, avoiding cloud and seeking out areas of clear sky. Because the polarisation pattern 'times out' roughly an hour after sunset but then returns – weather permitting – about an hour before sunrise, a migrant would be well advised to maintain a constant course. This would provide a check on position vis-à-vis the location of the polarisation band at the end of the night. Indeed, radar studies confirm that, except when benighted by adverse weather, dusk-to-dawn flight paths follow a single bearing.

Taking into consideration that birds tap magnetic, stellar, sunlight and sky polarisation cues to orientate, a means of integrating all of these into a 'horses for courses' hierarchy seems feasible. In theory, a migrant could calibrate its magnetic compass (telling it where it is in relation to the magnetic field's inclination) against a north–south polarisation pattern, verifiable at dusk and – after an overnight flight – at dawn, that would equip it with the equivalent of a GPS with built-in checks. To the human mind, that revelation feels like a piece of copper wire inserted into the brain and briefly attached to the electricity supply of a nuclear power plant. In a flash, it becomes possible to imagine cue combinations that permit birds to cut migratory cloth to suit.

Birds probably use information from several compass mechanisms and put greatest emphasis on whatever cues are most reliable in the conditions prevailing, switching from one to another, if alternative cues are available. Scientists have investigated the interplay of orientation mechanisms in attempts to understand how birds rationalise the various options into an overarching reference. Some results found a hierarchical system with magnetic cues taking priority. Researchers in North America reported that Grey-cheeked and Swainson's Thrushes, shy pint-sized versions of Song Thrush that breed in boreal forest and winter in the tropics (see p. 12), used polarised light patterns at sunset to calibrate their magnetic compass.[8] Migrants were trapped during migration and housed in specially adapted cages with a view of the sky. However, when the birds were resting prior to departure at sunset, magnetic coils surrounding the cages enabled scientists to change the magnetic field by 90 degrees. The altered magnetic field was turned off after sunset, restoring 'normal service'. Therefore, after sunset, the birds' sensitivity was to Earth's normal magnetic field. A control group was not subjected to the shift in the magnetic field. Almost uniquely for an experiment of this sort, the birds were not tested in artificial conditions but were released and tracked in the wild by radio transmission. The results were astounding. The group whose magnetic field had been altered before sunset changed their flight direction by 90 degrees relative to the control group that did not have the magnetic field direction 'reset' at sunset. The experimental birds reverted to normal orientation again on succeeding nights. The findings suggested that the thrushes were calibrating the direction of true north relative to the local magnetic field by using the polarised light pattern at sunset.

Results of 'cue-conflict' experiments involving other birds were different. Rather than the research being flawed, discrepancies are possibly due to variations between species. Because birds do not share personal moments with us, a complication could be the 'mental predisposition' of migrants. Equipped with several alternatives, an individual may opt to render one system redundant temporarily, creating the misleading impression that an aptitude is lacking.

19. Other beacons
Seabirds and odour trails

....

29th September 1997. Rossan Point, County Donegal.
We glimpsed and then saw fully the majesty of the Great Shearwater
movement ... with party after party going by, looking for all the world
like lines of kites strung on endless twines, so regularly spaced were
the birds and so synchronised their movement.

D.I.M. WALLACE

Seabirds live, to us, a lonely existence. Pelagic species may be out of sight of land for a year or more. Yet they can return unerringly to tiny and remote breeding islands after long migrations or, if feeding young, commute vast distances between foraging areas and nesting burrows. Curiously, trials that fitted magnets to shearwaters and albatrosses to disrupt perception of Earth's magnetic field had no effect on the birds' homing ability.[1] However, because certain navigation systems can be 'put on the long finger' and only deployed when needed, scientific studies do not rule out the possibility that seabirds – especially marine species that travel in the dark or under conditions where visibility is limited by fog or dense cloud cover – are sensitive to Earth-strength magnetic fields. What other sensory ability might they use?

Like mustelids – the mammal family that includes stoats, weasels and martens – petrels, shearwaters and albatrosses are renowned for a strong, musky – but not unpleasant – scent. The aroma perfumes plumage, nest material and even eggs. The same species have external nostrils stacked at the base of the bill. Although ornithologists refer to seabirds that possess the protuberance as 'tubenoses', the precise explanation for this external arrangement of the nostrils remains a mystery and may be unrelated to odour detection. That said, it is hard to deny a 'nosing the air' role for a structure encased by a pelt of plumage and running like paired moraines directly into the soft tissue of the skull. The birds rid themselves of excess salt ingested from their diet by extruding brine solution through the nostrils: perhaps this is the primary function? James Fisher, a long-standing seabird authority, considered that the nostrils were an anatomical adaptation for preening, since they are found only in species that produce stomach oil, discharged through the nostrils during preening.[2] Stomach oil is, in effect, 'distilled' fishy quarry, stored in the foregut. The bird converts what it catches into a space-saving liquid asset whose energy is higher than the undigested food: almost equalling the caloric value of diesel oil. This is a liberating advantage for species that forage over huge distances to provide food for chicks, or require a concentrated reserve during long-haul flights in search of rich pickings.

Skellig Michael is one of two islands that lie about 9km (5 miles) off the coast of County Kerry. Little Skellig is pebble-dashed white with breeding Gannets. Skellig Michael is larger and juts out almost vertically from the North Atlantic like a colossal shard of rock flung by King Kong. Despite its remoteness and inhospitable conditions – such as lack of soil and flat ground – monks inhabited Skellig Michael for hundreds of years. Some time in the twelfth century the monks moved away and left a legacy of stone beehive cells, oratories, a church and graveyard. Come nightfall, large numbers of Manx Shearwaters and European Storm Petrels flutter around the serpentine pathways and monastic remains before scuttling over the ground and disappearing into cavities. During daytime surveys designed to enumerate part of the breeding population, a reliable method of pinpointing an occupied nook was to sniff for a musty fragrance at gaps in stonework.[3]

Not surprisingly, because petrels, shearwaters and albatrosses have some of the largest 'olfactory bulbs' among birds, they have a highly developed sense of smell. In all birds, air is inhaled through two external slit-like nostrils located on the top surface of the bill. In most species there are three chambers inside the bill's upper mandible. The first two moisten the inhaled air; the third is housed at the base of the bill and contains the conchae, comprising bone, cartilage and tissue. Conchae cells disseminate odours and relay information to the brain. The more sophisticated the conchae, the larger their surface area and the greater the number of scent-detecting cells. The part of the brain responsible for interpreting smell lies close to the base of the bill. Bulbous in shape, it is coined the olfactory bulb. In Fulmars – despite their superficial resemblance to gulls, they are members of the petrel family – the olfactory bulb has twice as many cells as rats and six times as many as mice.[4] Might such an acute sense of smell embrace more than known capabilities – such as locating food at several kilometres' range – and perhaps facilitate navigation by odour recognition? Evidence that, in some cases, homing is based on smell was shown in the 1970s when it was discovered that Leach's Storm-petrels breeding on islands in the Bay of Fundy, Canada, invariably returned to their nesting burrows from an upwind direction, indicating that they followed a scent plume.[5] When the olfactory (smell-detecting) nerve of some birds was rendered inoperative, they were unable to relocate the breeding colony.

Fossil records of fulmar-like seabirds extend back over twenty million years. 'Our' Fulmar is the only representative of its genus in the northern hemisphere. Others live in the Southern Ocean and it was from here that colonists spread into the North Pacific. The Atlantic population probably colonised its ocean from the North Pacific across the Polar Basin. Fulmars, therefore, know their way around the world's seas. Although superficially gull-like, they fly like their cousins – the albatrosses and shearwaters. All these seabird groups share an external 'tube-nosed' nostril located, in the case of Fulmar, on the ridge of the bill. The nostril's function is not fully understood. It could have multiple roles. If aroma detection is one, then a navigational ability linked to sensing marine foods (such as zooplankton) by smell is a possibility.

It is possible to fabricate the tang that pervades the sea and bottle the chemical substance. Known as dimethyl sulphide (DMS), it is used commercially as a food preservative. In the world's oceans, DMS is released from the bodies of phytoplankton when they are eaten by zooplankton, small floating or weakly swimming organisms that drift with currents and make up the food supply upon which almost all marine life depends. Because the sea is overlain with DMS, might its distribution reflecting feeding hotspots provide seabirds with a worldwide olfactory reference – akin to the stale smells from some enormous laundry? Where phytoplankton accumulate, such as where currents mix or at upwellings (rising columns of cold water), predatory zooplankton co-occur. And, as zooplankton consumes phytoplankton, DMS is released.

Carried downwind to seabirds, the vapour constitutes a sensory contrail tantamount to a dinner gong. The plume can be detected night or day, in fair weather or foul. To find it, seabirds embark on exploratory crosswind sorties; once they pick up the scent they follow it upwind to the source. Because wind and wave action can deflect or weaken DMS's airborne strength, seabirds in pursuit mode adopt a zigzag course, casting from side to side in order to

The 'smell of the sea' can be distilled into a chemical form (dimerythl sulphide, or DMS). It derives from the breakdown of phytoplankton when they are consumed by zooplankton. In effect, DMS serves as a dinner gong for everything higher up the food chain. Fish oil spread on the sea has the same effect and its DMS vapour trail draws in storm-petrels from many kilometres away that feed by supping up the droplets. In the photograph (taken at a 'chum' slick several kilometres south of Fastnet Rock, County Cork) all bar two are European Storm-petrels. Two Wilson's Storm-petrels — slightly larger and with an isolated grey diagonal across the middle of the upper wing — are left and right of the centre.

maintain contact with the odour trail. By cross-checking albatross flight paths against stomach monitors (that recorded when food was swallowed), scientists confirmed that the birds followed odour plumes to prey in approximately half of their feeding activities.[6] Until recently, what was lacking was evidence that albatrosses, shearwaters and petrels were able to detect DMS at concentrations encountered under natural conditions, especially as the smell density was a million times lower than previously reported odour sensitivities for birds.[7] By

using heart rate monitoring and blowing air with or without DMS over the nostrils of burrow-nesting seabirds, researchers demonstrated that the species tested reacted to the whiff of DMS at minuscule levels on a par with those experienced at sea.[8]

The discovery that seabirds are drawn to DMS could not have been more timely. The world's oceans are polluted with plastic debris that is ingested by hundreds of species of organisms, from zooplankton to seabirds and baleen whales. How such a diversity of consumers can mistake plastic for their natural prey is not fully understood. But in 2016 researchers demonstrated experimentally that marine-seasoned microplastics produce a DMS signature.[9] The results suggest that plastic debris emits the scent of a marine 'information chemical' creating an olfactory trap for susceptible marine wildlife.

Evidence that albatrosses, shearwaters and petrels inhabit two worlds – visual and olfactory – is incontestable. Members of these seabird families have lengthy chick-rearing periods that can last from six weeks for small petrels to nearly a year for the largest albatrosses. Many species nest in burrows and come ashore only in darkness. So it is no surprise that smell outranks visual and auditory stimuli. In the dark, breeding partners recognise each other, as well as their offspring, by scent, not sight or sound.[10] As one bouquet binds the birds to thoughts of home, another leads them to their prey. A sense of smell underpins their universe. A logical extension of this lifestyle is that, as individuals mature, they develop an ability to navigate by scent. It is not clear to what degree other orientation cues – such as geomagnetism, stellar rotation and polarisation patterns – integrate with olfactory navigation. Although use of olfactory navigation has been controversial in other bird families, especially in experiments using homing pigeons that distinguish a range of airborne scents and use them as markers, in the marine environment DMS is linked to a food source tied to predictable oceanic features of high productivity. For seabirds that can connect health and home by following their nose, olfactory navigation has everything.

As always, knowledge is king. Once seabirds become acquainted with the migratory journey that connects breeding quarters with wintering grounds, they memorise details of everywhere in between. Because they do not travel by express, nowhere blurs. Over time their remembrance amounts to a Filofax of dates and places covering stopover sites. Species whose bailiwick crosses hemispheres accumulate an amalgam of information of global proportions. Long forays from one ocean to another become calendar customs. At a species

Skuas are pirates, harassing other seabirds and stealing their food. For this reason, pirate and prey are linked – although the relationship is hardly loving. Bound for winter quarters in the South Atlantic, this young Long-tailed Skua is yet to learn powers of pursuit. Raised among habitat consisting of a covering of birch scrub and crowberry-dominated heath, youngsters fatten on berries before disappearing into the Atlantic. Of all skua species, Long-tailed is the most maritime.
PHOTOGRAPH: BRUCE MACTAVISH

level, because Homeric wanderings have, for millennia, met with success, epic journeys are repeated by individuals, who distil the experience and tailor it to suit.

Long-tailed Skua is a sublime seabird that sees little of darkness. Ribbon-tailed adults settle to breed on the tundra in June but switch hemispheres in autumn. Populations breeding from the Canadian Arctic to Siberia trek to the South Atlantic where they concentrate in two areas: the Benguela Current off the coast of Namibia and the Falkland Current, off Argentina's continental shelf. Although all commute through Ireland's latitude, their chief thoroughfare is the broad Atlantic far from land. In May, westerly gales sometimes deflect northbound migrants inshore. Nose to tail, the flocks resemble sinuous columns of vertebrae, visible from headlands along the Wild Atlantic Way. In autumn, juveniles meander south, seemingly blasé when compressed along windward coasts during inclement weather. For up to five years researchers tracked 38 Long-tailed Skuas drawn from Greenland, Svalbard and northern Scandinavia. They discovered that, during winter in the South Atlantic, some birds confined themselves to one current whereas others visited both: a switch entailing a flight of 5,200km (3,200 miles).[11] Intriguingly, individuals could be consistent in choice of winter quarters between consecutive winters and then flexible between other years. What prompted site shifts was not clear. Most likely, the response was due to local conditions, possibly food abundance. The greater discovery was the birds' savvy in knowing about the existence of alternative wintering grounds. This meant that a long-haul migrant, reliant on finding food at the opposite end of the planet from its breeding range, had knowledge of two winter homes and could, if circumstances dictated, use one or other or both.

More remarkable yet, tracking results from fourteen Cory's Shearwaters (which hail from the Mediterranean and blue-water archipelagos in the eastern North Atlantic, such as the Azores, Madeira and the Canary Islands) revealed a population-wide awareness of several disparate winter ranges – the north-west Atlantic, Canary Current, Brazilian Current, central South Atlantic, Benguela Current and Agulhas Current.[12] Five individuals, a significant proportion, changed their main wintering quarters in successive years. This included two birds that switched from the South to the North Atlantic. Although some birds were faithful, year on year, to set wintering quarters, others switched ocean basins within hemispheres and even switched hemispheres. The study uncovered previously unknown flexibility in choice of wintering site. Was there an explanation for the wanderlust? Researchers did not find any evidence of a link to age, sex, repetition of previous years' routes or even when movements were plotted against known changes in oceanographic conditions in the

Cory's Shearwater, until they are old enough to breed —
at around nine years old — behave like prodigal sons.
In that time the adolescents visit and memorise all
parts of the species' known range.
PHOTOGRAPH: JOE PENDER

wintering areas. Although two birds left areas where food availability decreased,
three others left areas of food abundance. However, one statistic hinted at the
reason for the birds' behaviour. In common with all seabirds, Cory's Shearwaters
are long-lived. Most do not begin to breed until they reach nine years of age.
Before then, youngsters disperse and accrue knowledge of foraging opportunities
available across the non-breeding range. It seems that, in the course of not
one, but several concurrent 'gap years', adolescents sample the species' known
universe. That much was suggested by the only young bird tracked in the study.
Before its fifth birthday, it changed its main wintering area from one year to the
next and clocked up a staggering 108,000km (67,000 miles), during which time
it flew to the outer limits pricked out by its forebears.

20. Statistics of slaughter
Oops!

FOG
A vagueness comes over everything,
as though proving colour and contour
alike dispensable: the lighthouse
extinct, the islands' spruce-tips
drunk up like milk in the
universal emulsion.

AMY CLAMPITT

Although evolution has taken birds' migratory capabilities to dizzy heights, bad luck cannot be eliminated. There are stories to tell about the calamities that scupper journeys honed over millennia. For the voyagers that were dazzled and then mowed down by the Kentish Knock Lightship on a miserable Halloween night in 1952, it is easy to reconstruct the logistics of death:

31st October 1952. Kentish Knock Lightship, southern North Sea. Starlings, Skylarks, thrushes and finches travelled west all afternoon until sunset. Weather conditions were good. At midnight the watch reported that the wind had dropped and that the sky had suddenly become overcast and that birds had arrived at the lantern. Numbers increased rapidly and by 01.30 hours the weather had deteriorated and light rain had begun to fall. By this time the rigging, masts, decks, in fact all available perching places, were covered with resting birds. Thousands more circled the lantern and flew up the beams of the revolving light. Many hit the lantern glass resulting in terrific mortality. At times stunned and dead birds dropped into the sea and onto the deck continuously. Just before dawn they were so numerous that, as I stepped on deck, my head and shoulders were covered with birds seeking resting places.[1]

The night's observations are of interest because it is unlikely that many birds would have set out in the type of weather they met en route. Departures, almost certainly, would have been made several hours earlier. The range of

Echoing the events at Kentish Knock lightship in October 1952, Martin Grimm witnessed a similar deluge of migrants when working aboard a research vessel in the Baltic, located roughly 30km off the north German coast, in October 2015. Most were finches – Chaffinches, Bramblings and Siskins – travelling south for the winter. Over the preceding three days, strong southerly winds and rain had halted departures from Scandinavia. Calm, clear conditions set in during the afternoon of 18 October. The change in the weather was seized upon by the bottled-up birds and an exodus ensued. But that night heavy drizzle gave way to fog. Sitting in a pool of brightness, the ship's lights dazzled waves of migrants that swirled around and around, like moths. Martin wrote: 'the birds became disorientated and they tried to land anywhere – on the deck or any perch, even if that was myself or others who were watching the multitude falling out of the sky. Strange things happened. Robins, Dunnocks and Goldcrests rested and even slept immediately next to Sparrowhawks, which were also among the flood.' To view video of the event, visit Youtube and search: 'Mass Bird Migration in the Baltic Sea – 1'.

PHOTOGRAPHS: MARTIN GRIMM

A Swallow's sleek lines may fit an aerial lifestyle but weighing not much more than a CD, the sylph can be plunged into crisis by powerful crosswinds. Swallows migrate relatively low in the air and feed as they go. Unlike most other migrants, they carry little fat in reserve. As well as being susceptible to squally weather on sea crossings that occasionally sweep them miles off course, desert storms in Africa can ground migrants for days and prevent them from feeding. Little wonder that the species is reported dead in the Sahara more than any other bird.

species indicates a pulse of migrants crossing from the Continent bound for Britain and, quite possibly, Ireland. Often during October the birds' area of origin – Fenno-Scandia and the Baltic – is normally under the influence of anticyclonic weather systems. Eastern Britain, too, comes under the same influence, but the western seaboard of Europe is always liable to be affected by low pressure moving in from the Atlantic. To a degree, this is what happened to those that foundered. Having flown into bad weather and lost sight of the firmament, the sea and sky merged and turned into the colour of lead. The stars disappeared, like sparks turning to smoke. Ordinarily, with one frame of reference down, another directional autopilot is engaged. Alas, other navigational options were snuffed out when, blinded and disorientated, many splintered their bones against a light in the darkness.

As in autumn, the drift that some migrants undergo in spring can be considerable. One June, a British-ringed Swallow was recovered 320km south-south-west of Ireland during a spell of strong south-east winds ahead of a weather front sweeping in from the Atlantic. In another spring, two Swallows ringed in Ireland during strong southerly winds were recovered within the following fortnight in France and Germany. Each had corrected for its displacement. Demonstrating that even large birds are unable to withstand adverse wind, in April 1978 a Scottish-ringed Osprey was found on a boat in the Denmark Strait (between Iceland and Greenland) after prolonged south-east winds over the north-east Atlantic.[2]

Wildlife can adapt to change but only at its own pace; citizens of the natural world cope badly with human-contrived novelty. When, in the past, swarms of birds dashed themselves against lighthouses, the scale of loss was insignificant because the supply was abundant and populations could withstand the hit. Measures were taken that reduced the carnage. Hugo Weingold, who carried on the work of Heinrich Gätke at Heligoland, designed 'bird protection lights' by floodlighting lighthouses and adding perches to prevent bedazzled migrants from repeatedly circling buildings and dropping from exhaustion.[3] Ironically, the subsequent growth in light pollution has probably diluted the fatal attraction of a single beam that, on a black night of inclement weather, concentrated birds from a radius of many miles.

Bird migration is a movable feast and nobody knows the overseas perils faced by Ireland's transient visitors who, for a variety of reasons, must come and go with the seasons. Increasingly, global migratory bird populations are being bled white by new hazards that cull their ranks in transit to or from breeding grounds. Although the fate of North America's nocturnal songbird migrants seems far from our pattern of experience, we have little inkling of the dangers that 'our' birds encounter once they disappear over the horizon. For all we know, unreported deaths of European species from collisions with tall buildings straddling migration routes could be on a par with similar devastation in North America, as explained in Canada's Fatal Light Awareness Programme: 'Birds are declining due to human-built structures. Collisions with windows are now a leading cause of migratory bird population decline. Many migrate at night and light from our cities is confusing them and inadvertently drawing them in. If they do not die at night, they can collide during the day. Why? Because they are exhausted and find themselves in a maze of deadly mirrors.'[4] Although collisions with buildings, power lines, wind turbines and other man-made contrivances destroy great quantities of birds and other wildlife, the major cause of decline is habitat loss or, increasingly, food loss due to the deliberate or inadvertent onslaught on insects at the behest of modern agriculture's Dr Jekyll and Mr Hyde agrochemical companies.

During migration seasons, skyscrapers in cities such as Toronto, New York and Chicago constitute death traps. An estimated five million migrants, representing about 250 species, fly through Chicago alone. The city's Department of the Environment estimates that tens of thousands of birds are killed each season. Chicago Audubon Society, a conservation charity, was told by one skyscraper manager that, on some nights, 'birds were cleared by the shovelful from the roof'.[5] In fact, a conservative estimate puts the number of birds killed annually in the USA by striking windows at 100 million.[6] Awareness of the slaughter has

It is estimated that, every year, nearly one billion (1,000,000,000) birds are killed in North America by colliding with brilliantly lit skyscrapers and glass-fronted buildings. The photograph shows the casualties picked up in downtown Toronto during the autumn migration of 2008.
PHOTOGRAPH: JIM RICHARDSON

led to action, notably in Chicago, where lights are turned off during migration seasons. The scheme has been a success with not only bird lives spared, but electricity saved too. What are the prospects for similar steps in other parts of the world where new skyscrapers are set to ambush European migrants over the Gulf of Arabia and elsewhere? At Batumi in Georgia, a key migration location on the eastern shore of the Black Sea, beneath a new high-rise hotel located on an otherwise low-rise coastal plain, several dead and injured migrants were found in September 2014.[7] Nearby, another high-rise abomination was scheduled to join the first bird slayer.

The unintended but deadly consequences of light pollution might be reduced as cities across the world retrofit their illuminations with new, energy efficient LED lighting – or just switch lights off. Another twist in the fate of migrants that stray into the path of modern living has been the discovery that man-made electromagnetic waves present in cities and conurbations are capable of disrupting birds' ability to sense Earth's magnetic field. It seems ironic that, no sooner than biology's trade secrets of navigation have finally been understood, modern telecommunications can potentially undermine natural networks critical to direction finding. It is as though the dignity and ingenuity of nature is being overcome. A scientist who attempted to delve deeper into the nature of birds' magnetic sense stumbled onto the problem.[8] Henrik Mouritsen, working at the University of Oldenburg in Germany, planned to study what part of the brain songbirds used when they made navigational decisions. Following in the footsteps of previous investigations, he installed wild-caught Robins in cages and waited for them to exhibit migratory restlessness at the onset of spring and autumn. As anticipated, Mouritsen's Robins grew restless but their movements were random and showed no clear orientation. Something was interfering with their innate migration sense. Research ground to a halt until a colleague suggested the installation of electrically grounded metal panels that would shield the birds from certain wavelengths of electromagnetic radiation. The shielding worked. The Robins immediately behaved as expected, sensing the magnetic field.

Mouritsen's unintended experimental glitch established a connection between electromagnetic radiation and the Robins' ability to tell direction. Additional research confirmed that man-made electromagnetic waves present in urban areas curtailed the birds' detection of the magnetic field. The origin of the radiation was not a single source and the frequencies were not specifically produced by mobile phone or high-voltage transmission lines. Rather, the combination of everything that runs on electricity produces an 'electro-smog' capable of masking the weak signal strength of Earth's magnetic field, birds' main planetary compass. Fortunately, for now, rural areas are outside the reach of this insidious hum of humanity.

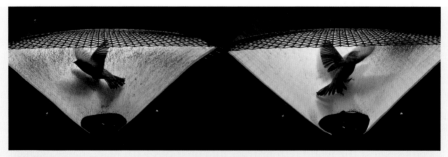

An Emlen funnel is a cone-shaped cage used in behavioural experiments that test migratory instinct (see Chapter 15). The bird's feet are wetted on an inkpad at the bottom of the cone. Footprints record the direction dictated by the bird's migratory urge. The scattered tracks on the left illustrate how an Indigo Bunting exposed to urban electromagnetic radiation loses its bearing. The unexposed bird (right) steers a clear course.
PHOTOGRAPH: JONATHON BLAIR / NATIONAL GEOGRAPHIC CREATIVE

21. Flights of Reckoning
Keeping going and youthful exuberance

I cannot believe they don't know what they are doing,
that delight is unknown to them as they gather
preparing for the long and terrible journey.
It cannot merely be all programme, hard-wire, protein
plasma, synapse, cellular. They are too expert
at elevation and elation, those twin joys.

Eva Bourke

Viewed from afar, two characteristics define Ireland's location. One is its position at the north-western fringe of Europe's continental land mass; the other is its isolation, an island whose coastline is, for the most part, not visible from elsewhere. Apart from seabirds, the edges of land masses tend to contain a limited range of birdlife; a much greater selection resides among the immensely more diverse habitats spanning continental interiors. Moreover, if you plonk yourself on an island, the sea acts as a barrier that further restricts variety. Because we live on the outer reaches of the western hemisphere, the law of diminishing returns reaches a minimalist conclusion. In keeping with the paucity of native Irish mammals – Ireland received its fauna from the rest of Europe via Britain and the supply of colonists was interrupted by changing sea levels that cut off land bridges – our suite of birds is provincial rather than cosmopolitan. Some birds, resident in Britain, are incapable of reaching us. Ptarmigan and Black Grouse never got this far west. And, with flight capabilities on a par with other game birds, they never will. Others behave like landlubbers, even though a jaunt across the Irish Sea could be made as a day-return excursion. Several species of titmice – Marsh Tit, Willow Tit and Crested Tit – as well as woodland specialists such as Nuthatch, are averse to crossing expanses of water, especially when they cannot see an opposite shore.

Luckily, there is a silver lining. In autumn, migration propels vast numbers of northern-hemisphere birds south, then back again in spring. Many are programmed not to stop until they penetrate wintering destinations in the southern hemisphere. Their journeys, although genetically determined, are influenced by several factors, notably weather. For Ireland, an island located along a continental margin, the chances of intercepting transitory visitors are excellent. Little wonder that, each year, the range of visiting species exceeds

Nuthatch

In Britain, echoing the expansion of Great Spotted Woodpeckers, Nuthatches have spread north since the Second World War. From about 1940 the species advanced through north Wales, Cheshire and Lancashire. Yorkshire, Northumberland and the Lake District came next. Scotland took longer to reach – possibly because intervening treeless areas deterred potential colonists. Sea crossings are the bird's Achilles heel. Because Nuthatches now breed in south-west Scotland within sight of County Down, Ireland may yet fall. The bird is pretty, and several attempts were made to introduce them to Scotland and Ireland.[1] Some were liberated in the early twentieth century in County Sligo, County Tipperary and possibly elsewhere.[2] Fortunately, the introductions failed, giving both the Scots – and possibly us – the chance to witness a natural event, untarnished by human interference (unlike the release of non-native Red Kites).

the birds that call Ireland home: either because they breed or spend the winter in our absurdly mild climate. Another feature of Ireland's geographical situation is that the variety of birds reaching its shores come not just from neighbouring lands but from up to several thousands of kilometres away.

If weather is one factor affecting the sweepstake of migration, the experience of the birds themselves is another, especially in autumn, when many recruits are embarking on maiden long-haul flights. The learning curve of youth is steep but can come to an abrupt end for some, weeded out by failing to reach a destination, even if through no fault of their own. Ideally, all migrants should have emergency strategies for when things go wrong – such as when over the sea, they might reverse direction and retrace the route or, if the wind is too strong to double back, continue downwind on the same heading until land appears. In the real world, unlike in experiments when artificially displaced, juveniles that drift off course experience the terrain over which they fly and can commit it to memory.[3] In this way they can fit minor defeats into victories. We can all relate to being in the wrong location at the wrong time but, as we shall see, some misplaced migrants pose questions that suggest they miscue because they are also in the wrong frame of mind.

The vast majority of migrants that make off-piste appearances are youngsters that have not yet made it to their first birthday or belong to immature ranks. While most small songbirds breed in their first year, populations of larger species contain teenagers that will be shunned as breeding partners until all vestige of underage plumage has been upgraded through a series of moults. Even then,

Mediterranean Gull

Bucking a gloomy 1960s forecast predicting extinction, 'the species has a very limited distribution [the bulk of the world population bred in one colony in the Black Sea] with an unmistakeable relict character, and is probably in the course of becoming extinct',[4] Mediterranean Gulls turned a corner and expanded west. Aspiring first-time breeders formed the vanguard. In the initial stages of range expansion, mixed pairings were commonplace — usually with Black-headed Gulls — resulting in small numbers of hybrid offspring. However, as more recruits arrived, the increased availability of pure breeding partners ended the 'hybrid era'. More than a dozen pairs nest in Ireland, yet the species was unknown this far west until the 1960s.

they need to wait their turn at traditional haunts or seek pastures new. For this reason, range expansions are fuelled by Young Turks that show initiative. If a species enjoys a boom across Europe, the ripple of success can reach Ireland, as happened with Collared Doves and Mediterranean Gulls. However, the infantry of each was rather different. Juvenile Collared Doves, which within a matter of weeks upgrade their first body feathers to those of an adult and are capable of reproducing, immediately search for living space. Each April and May new recruits arrive on Irish offshore islands unsuited to nesting. Who knows how they fare? There are few facts to record – except that offspring from somewhere regularly reach Iceland.

Around the turn of the millennium, Mediterranean Gulls established a nesting toehold in Ireland. Unlike the blitzkrieg colonisation achieved by high fecundity rates among first-generation Collared Doves, Mediterranean Gulls' tipping point took years. A random trickle of wandering young grew

Stonechat

Young songbirds are born with most of their wits about them. They have to be. For this young Stonechat, parental care amounts to around a fortnight in the nest, followed by the same in the great outdoors. After that it is shunned.

steadily over two decades until romance blossomed. Because the birds' wing markings testify to age, it transpired that initial partnerships were not among old hands. Rather, it was members of slowly maturing generations that led the way. Among the waves of would-be colonists, mixed pairs in which one of the couple was a Black-headed Gull, were not uncommon. The any-port-in-a-storm behaviour indicated a declaration of intent but once strength in numbers was in the ascendant, hybridisation ceased. Hence wanderlust with an eye to range expansion is a fact of life. Likewise, the chances of bumping into an out-of-range youth are increased when the latter is embarked upon one or more gap years. Seabirds, the longest-lived of all birds, are the slowest to breed. Until they do, like mariners of old, they 'run the meridians' and knit themselves knowledge of the world's oceans. One adolescent Cory's Shearwater clocked up more than 70,000 sea miles in travels before its fifth birthday.[5]

Whether they like it or not, most birds are born free spirits. Comparatively few individuals mate for life and many long-term partnerships are trysts that come together annually only on the breeding grounds. For the vast majority of youngsters, independence is thrust upon them not long after fledging. Songbirds, in particular, receive a short initiation before being left to fend alone. Because smaller species suffer the highest mortality rates, two broods in a breeding season are commonplace to offset losses. To ensure that some progeny survive to propagate the species, adults are forced to play the percentage game. Just how short a shrift the new generation gets can be gauged from a twenty-year study involving over 1,000 ringed Stonechats on Jersey: 'the fledging period or, more strictly, the period for which the young remain in the nest after hatching, varies between 12 and 16 days. When the young leave the nest, they are fed by both parents for four or five days, after which the female withdraws and starts building a new nest for the next brood. About ten days after departure, the young begin to be seen as they hover in search of food about the territory. The male shepherds them and keeps them together. A few days later, however, he begins to chase them out of the territory and, now well fledged, they disperse. The male then joins the female, either to accompany her as she builds the nest or to resume territorial defence as she incubates.'[6]

Future hopes are pinned upon youngsters that, a mere 30 days after hatching, are regarded as good to go. Acquiring wisdom is a hard road and, in spite of the production-line start, offspring are not automatons. For newly minted migrants, the world is their oyster and they seem to be born already knowing a lot of what lies ahead. Uncertainty is not part of their psyche. Because the overwhelming majority migrate solo at night, they cannot draw strength of spirit from companions. Loners may attempt to make contact with airborne peers by periodically uttering short notes – analogous to a radio operator's 'handle'. Species that travel in a loose flock maintain cohesion by using dedicated nocturnal calls and proceed in a kind of sonic chain.[7]

Although under genetic control to head off in a predetermined direction for a certain time and then to cease migration at a place they have never been before, the ways migrants set about attaining that goal are their own. Evolution loads the dice but they roll it. Preparations for migration are manifold and include moult timing, fuel provisioning and assessing weather conditions. In all such cogitations, individual choice is exercised. Young from a few species enjoy an easier start because they are accompanied. Groups such as cranes, geese and swans migrate in family units. Others migrate in flocks that confer security as well as the experience of veteran wayfinders. Research has shown that some young can be influenced in migratory behaviour by the example of others. For instance, 754 young White Storks were taken from the Baltic, where the species migrates south-east, and released at migration time in western Germany, where White Storks depart to the south-west. The transported birds were freed shortly before the local White Storks left. Based on subsequent ringing recoveries, the released cohorts followed the lead of the locals and travelled south-west, contrary to the south-east direction ingrained in their homeland population.[8]

There are other examples of inherent directional preferences overwritten by social influences resulting in established migration routes being abandoned. Waterfowl courtship activity is concentrated in the winter months. Drakes woo ducks and then migrate with them back to whence the female, not the male, originated, even if 'her place' is on a different continent. It is possible to stretch the definition of migration to include a range of behaviours that are essentially nomadic. Drought or food shortages precipitate major flights that, for some species, are part and parcel of a footloose lifestyle. Flamingos are obliged to shift nesting areas due to the fickle nature of rainfall in the sunny climes they inhabit. Taiga-nesting Waxwings undertake pan-European winter wandering in search of berries; flocks occasionally throng hedgerows in Ireland, evoking the North American name for the species – Bohemian Waxwing. Migration is a diamond with many facets, and it owes much to its setting. Although, in principle, it is a simple trait, its motivations are often complex. Whatever happens, weather events generally shape outcomes.

In certain situations it is difficult to draw the line between a migrant miscuing and overstepping traditional breeding areas or taking a chance for exploration offered by a fair wind or unusually benign weather. Termed 'overshooting', individuals follow their usual migration direction but travel too far and arrive at places beyond the species' regular breeding range. The phenomenon is most frequent in spring when stable anticyclonic conditions bring not only the usual mix of summer visitors north but also a sprinkling of the exotic. The odds of a rare species occurring out of range are also dependent upon the orientation of its migration route. In an Irish context, northbound migratory species leaving Africa bound for Spain are the most likely to feature. Not only will their trajectory carry them towards Ireland but because they are physically conditioned for a long-haul flight, they are likely to be none the worse for, intentionally or otherwise, missing their stop. Tempted north by balmy airs from the western Mediterranean come glitzy Hoopoes, Golden Orioles and Woodchat Shrikes. It is easy to attribute their arrival to a spell of fine weather – or Sahara dust – but when the age and sex of the arrivals is examined they are almost always found to be in the first year of life and are usually males, making the participants seem

Hoopoe

Hoopoes are avian exotica. Striking black-white-and-beige plumage is emphasised by a dipping, yo-yo flight. All in all, they are hard to miss. Their distinctive appearance and not infrequent occurrence on lawns – where they probe for larvae – often leads to sightings reported by members of the public. In Ireland in early spring (especially March), the preponderance of south coast records is not surprising. It is probable that arrivals are mainly migrant Iberian Hoopoes that have availed of a strong tailwind and unintentionally finished up in Ireland. Once they realise the navigational error, wayward members of the armada soon return home.

Gyr Falcons breed in northern latitudes but populations nesting in northern Greenland and the Canadian Arctic travel south with their prey – mainly seabirds such as Little Auk and Brünnich's Guillemot. Over the winter loners spend long periods at sea, where they rest on ice. Tracking results show individuals wandering over enormous distances – in some cases 4,500km (2,700 miles).[9] Synchronising with the extension of sea ice during winter, they reach a maximum southern extent in March (when a few 'overshoot' and reach Ireland). Gyr Falcons nesting in northern Greenland and Baffin Island return to natal areas in early April where the only available prey is Ptarmigan. Despite being one of the most powerful birds on the planet, the Gyr Falcon's breeding cycle is tied to Ptarmigan's population level at this critical time. For this reason, the bird's breeding fortunes, as with other Arctic predators, is 'index-linked' to the quantity of its prey.
PHOTOGRAPH: BRUCE MACTAVISH

more like foreign legionnaires rather than a random sample. Joyride over, most of them do a U-turn.

By the same token, prolonged spells of easterly winds can precipitate envoys drawn from the avifauna of Eastern Europe or the heart of Asia. The process has parallels with the arrival, in winter, of occasional individuals well beyond home turf. Snowy Owls, Gyr Falcons and various Arctic gulls, dispersing along coastlines in strong tailwinds, are prepared to drift south until they find sustenance, even if that sweeps them to Ireland. Nomadic behaviour, exercised by an individual, can lead to quite staggering wandering. Snowy Owls from the Canadian Arctic have reached Europe and a Chinese-ringed Common Redpoll was trapped in Denmark during winter.

A media-inspired fable trotted out when a *rara avis* makes headlines is that the poor thing is lost and was blown off course. Patronisation follows and the view of an ornithological 'expert' is usually cited who rates the bird's chances of ever returning home as zero. The same rationale has been used by collectors working for American natural history museums to justify killing migrants that arrive way beyond their normal bailiwick. These scientists deem the victims 'lost, probably genetically dead, vagrants'.[10] No bird is ever lost, even though a waif swept massively out of its native range and 'stranded' on a different continent might not be able to get back against prevailing winds. Young imprint on home and know where it lies. Moreover, memory and homing ability probably extend to all waypoints visited in a bird's life. A researcher, studying the habits of European Marsh Warblers on the species' winter quarters (*Acacia* groves) in Zambia, discovered that almost half the population returned in consecutive years to the same patch of thickets. With the annual mortality rate thought to be approximately 50 per cent, the scientist considered that virtually the entire surviving population returned: 'in a feat of navigation, the warblers successfully rediscover not just Zambia but the very same clump of bushes they occupied a year earlier, after a journey of perhaps 4,800 miles.'[11]

Nevertheless, given the use birds make of wind, it is inevitable that the powers of flight of some – especially small land birds at sea – can be overwhelmed by wind strengths that outstrip a migrant's speed and endurance. Of all those that stray and finish up gracing Irish soil, only songbirds that hail from North America can truly be regarded as having got here by being blown off course. As explained in Chapter 10, in autumn enormous numbers of North America's migratory land birds initially travel east across the northern part of the continent, heading for the Atlantic seaboard. They then turn southwards along the coastline towards winter quarters located anywhere between southern parts of the United States and South America. Although their departures are induced by relatively clear and settled conditions associated with high pressure, the changeable nature of Atlantic weather is capable of throwing a spanner in the works, as documented by Alan Durand on the *Mauretania* in October 1962.[12] Migrants beset by deep cloud and strengthening westerly wind ultimately find themselves at the mercy of fast-moving fronts whose direction of travel is north-east. As conditions intensify, they become engulfed by cloud, precipitation and wind. Disorientated, they can drift far out to sea, ultimately completing a transatlantic crossing in a following wind. Because the most vigorous depressions cross at high speed – some in less than 48 hours – displacement is rapid and occasionally multiples of migrants are caught up. Evidence suggesting that those slingshot onto our side of the ocean are bona fide and not ship-assisted comes from the range of species involved. The most frequent, notably Blackpoll Warblers and Grey-cheeked Thrushes, two New World regulars in Europe, are renowned over-ocean travellers that fly from the north-east seaboard towards the Caribbean. Despite the transcontinental scale of their dislocation, most appear none the worse for wear when observed in Ireland. Why should they be? With enough fuel in the tank to go from Canada to South America, an unexpected trip to Ireland is well within their reach.

The commonest visage of America among withered Sycamore leaves on Irish headlands and islands belongs to Red-eyed Vireo. Despite being the most frequent North American songbird in Europe, its occurrences often seem unrelated to Atlantic weather – although detection rates often lag behind arrival dates. The plot thickens because there are very few reports of the species alighting on ships. None was recorded by Alan Durand on 100 transatlantic voyages that recorded 58 species of American land birds during 1961–65.[13] Of all New World aeronauts, Red-eyed Vireo is almost the only species to penetrate, probably in a gigantic transatlantic leap, the European mainland and the Mediterranean. With such flying prowess it is not impossible that some might make it home.

Understandably, migration seasons are times of the year when unexpected appearances are most likely. In autumn, because a new and inexperienced generation is on the loose, the chances of navigational errors or flights that, for a first-timer, amount to 'taking the long way around' are almost to be expected, especially given the likelihood of interludes of stormy weather along migration routes. Indeed, post-juvenile dispersal is designed to broaden a youngster's experience of the big wide world, especially because youthful explorations may tap areas suitable for future range expansion. So it is no surprise that, during autumn, a sprinkle of first-year migrants drawn from Britain and near-continental Europe make capricious visits to Ireland. Because all make sea crossings to get here – probably their first taste of flying for hours over inhospitable terrain – they tend to converge on the first

To a lay person, searching for displaced American birds in autumn is probably on a par with looking for a needle in a haystack – without knowing if a needle is even there. The reward is marvelling at a svelte songbird that was en route from New England to Venezuela until, for whatever reason – most likely adverse weather – it flew to our side of the Atlantic to survive. Sometimes scanning sycamore leaves is like panning for gold. This Red-eyed Vireo was on Inishbofin, County Galway, for five days in October 2016.

Red-eyed Vireo

land they encounter. Hence islands, headlands and coastlines concentrate arrivals. The strangers do not linger. They are in the grip of *zugunruhe* and sense that Ireland is not journey's end. Depending on fat levels, some take a few days to refuel. Less-stressed others leave at the first opportunity and are up and away just after dusk. To birdwatchers intent on sieving through a flurry of migrants, they represent red balls scattered on a snooker table. And, among them, lurk prized colours.

Logic dictates that those from furthest away, such as beyond the Ural Mountains marking the western boundary of Siberia, would be the least frequent and, axiomatically, the rarest. To an extent this is true but how can the presence of *any* birds from this distant region be countenanced when the standard migratory direction for birds breeding there is between east and south? Unlike North American birds caught in a vortex of wind and with no choice but to fly until they find land, migrants from Asia could easily avoid drifting by landing and waiting for suitable conditions to continue their journey. Moreover, the birds are not propelled west by weather conditions against which resistance is futile. Quite the reverse: in Ireland and Britain, the biggest arrivals of 'eastern vagrants' tend to occur when anticyclonic conditions prevail over the Continent and eastwards towards Siberia.[14] It is as though the birds' determination to continue west in a flawed direction is matched by the capacity of their brethren to proceed in the diametrically opposite direction to winter quarters in South-east Asia and the Indian subcontinent.

What was it thinking? Lanceolated Warbler breeds in Siberia and migrates south-east to spend the winter in tropical latitudes. Secretive by nature, it normally stays concealed in vegetation. Out of Europe and out of land, this young migrant was found skulking like a rabbit caught in headlights on a boulder beach in the Faroe Islands, a place from which it might never return. Because migratory direction is inherited, one plausible explanation for its out-of-range occurrence is a flawed genetic compass.
PHOTOGRAPH: SILAS OLOFSSON

Lanceolated Warbler

Although research into the destiny of those that err is fragmentary and the results limited, it seems that, even when they reach the seaward margin of Western Europe, they continue 'in reverse gear'. On the Faeroe Islands, a small selection of stray autumn migrants drawn from near-continental Europe and, based on known breeding distributions, western Siberia and north-east Europe, was trapped and, upon release, their orientations were noted by attaching small radio transmitters.[15] The aim was to infer if compensation was made for all species that arrived at a destination not on the flight path between breeding grounds and winter quarters. The results, albeit from a small sample, confirmed that the West European migrants (Willow Warbler, Garden Warbler and Blackcap) vanished in the appropriate direction – generally southwards – to regain a correct route, whereas the migrants drawn from Siberia and north-east Europe (Yellow-browed Warbler, Red-flanked Bluetail and Barred Warbler) continued north-westwards on the same wayward bearing that had, presumably, carried them to the Faeroe Islands in the first place. In other words, unless they made an about-turn, they would continue over the North Atlantic with little prospect of finding land. The chances of any making a triumph out of a mess seem slim. It was as though the errant travellers were born with, not so much a death wish, as a faulty compass in which they placed total confidence. Similar suspicions arose when, several years before the Faeroe Islands experiment,

It is difficult to imagine that a tiny green bird that breeds in Siberia and winters in south-east Asia could establish new winter quarters in north-west Africa by pioneering a novel migration route west around Europe – including Ireland. This supposition is given coherence by a Yellow-browed Warbler (Moscow ringing scheme number VF80099), caught in Kaliningrad (between Poland and Lithuania) on 2 October 2016 and trapped six days later at Brownstown Head, County Waterford. Throughout the period, easterly winds prevailed over the bird's route and it flew west, clocking up 1,863km (1,158 miles) between the catching site and trapping location. Because it is not known when it left Kaliningrad or arrived in Ireland, its daily rate of travel cannot be deduced. However, whatever the details, it did not hang about.

Yellow-browed Warbler

Siberian migrants that arrived in autumn on an island in the Baltic were tested in orientation cages and also orientated towards the west.[16]

Given the broad geographical scale of the birds' navigational error, the phenomenon is known as 'reverse migration'. In effect, the migrants are describing a complete reverse of their traditional route or, to a certain extent, are setting off in a direction appropriate to spring, not autumn. Might, therefore, their mistake be as simple as responding in the wrong direction to a seasonal hormonal trigger? This is an unanswered question. Other migrants that err spectacularly do so, not in a full reverse, but by following a 'mirror-image' deviation. Mirror-image migration supposedly occurs when a departing migrant takes a correct bearing with respect to the north–south axis but chooses the wrong east–west side of that axis. Instead of, say, migrating south-east, the bird migrates south-west. The distance covered and the time taken is an exact parallel with the orthodox route. But the ultimate destination can, in some cases, lie in a different hemisphere.

Perhaps attempts at classifying the nature of miscues miss the point. Depending on species, a migration that began in reverse can include a final leg that chimes better with the misorientation being a mirror-reverse. For instance, small numbers of Yellow-browed Warblers, a hyperactive titch that breeds throughout the forests of northern Asia and winters in millions in the Orient, track west each autumn. During the last century or longer, handfuls were encountered each year along the shores of the North Sea. The mini annual influx passed down and across Britain and Ireland during September and October. Popular consensus claimed that the birds met a watery grave. That sentiment seems overly pessimistic. In the new millennium, Yellow-browed Warblers have been found wintering on several islands in the Canary Islands archipelago as well as Gambia, locations equivalent in latitude to the species' far-flung winter quarters in South-east Asia. Further proof that migrants in Europe are not doomed comes from several islands in the western Mediterranean (such as Lampedusa), where increasing numbers of Yellow-browed Warblers are caught and ringed in late autumn. Where do these spend the winter? In spite of a migratory malfunction, a sufficient quantity may return home safely to spread their genes and found a new, westward-looking migration. The stripy sprite has become a new kid on the block even in Ireland.

Migratory routes, therefore, are not set in stone. They evolve. We see the status quo that, for now, is successful. Mutations or a failure to inherit or implement orientation is an unknown and – probably – an underestimated element in the fashioning of routes. Strays may be scouts. Some will be lost but others could be seed corn. Consequently, in the roulette wheel of migration, any compass point might be a winner.

PART THREE
DAYS OF WONDER

Capercaillie

22. Winning the migration lottery
A great day with birds

We might say of these memorable moments of life that we were in them, not they in us.

RALPH WALDO EMERSON

There is something magical about being visited, right here in Ireland, by birds from afar. Discovering where the travellers come from and where they plan to go, opens up a vicarious experience. Fascination serves as fuel that carries the student from topic to topic, like a bumblebee seeking nectar. A desire to see new species is, however, only the beginning. Questions line up behind puzzles spanning occurrence patterns, thorny identifications and trying to be in the right place at the right time. If migration know-how is base metal, personal encounters with the pilgrims amount to gold plating. For this part of the book, the tight scientific detachment of migration theory has been set aside and, instead, I have used it as an ignition key showcasing a selection of unforgettable moments. Birds live exciting lives and every individual repays attention from a footloose reporter. What follows is a relay race of stories that are designed to link together to explore the wonder of migration.

One tale arose when a bird with a connection to Ireland – the now-extinct Capercaillie – drove me to travel to see the species in foreign forests rather than on native soil, where neither the bird nor its habitat remains. Travels on the trail of birds have always drawn me to find their essence, to discover what makes them tick and, maybe, to find out what makes me tick – when 'thought becomes the bride of stars' (Kathleen Raine).

We draw inspiration from others. One wet January afternoon in 1976 I walked into a bookshop and flicked through the recently published *Natural History of Cape Clear*. I had never been to the place, an island off the diametrically opposite end of Ireland from my Antrim home. The slim volume contained almost no photographs but the words painted such vivid pictures in my head that, the following September, I borrowed the family car and flew south. The book's author, J.T.R. (Tim) Sharrock, did not know what he started. Although I blame him for influencing an impressionable young man and turning him messianic, I am delighted that he has allowed me to quote his stirring words:

I was the only observer at the newly founded Cape Clear Bird Observatory in October 1959, and the first few days of the month were rather dull. There were hardly any migrants on 7th October; only a Ring Ouzel and a Red-breasted Flycatcher. Next day, a strong south-east wind blew up. Rain set in from lunchtime. Perseverance in wet weather produced a Turtle Dove, two Blackcaps and five Goldfinches: a poor haul. I had no reason to suspect that things were going to improve, and conditions were impossible.

This was the day of a general election in Britain. Having no radio, I invited myself into the warmth and comfort of Father Walsh's house for the evening. We sat up together, chatting, drinking raspberry-cordial-and-beer shandies, and listening to the election results. At 0300hrs, I returned to my cold sleeping bag in the bird observatory, noting that the wind had reached gale-force and that the rain was torrential.

I rose late in the morning. The wind roared outside and it still poured with rain. As I cooked and ate breakfast, I could hear the wind moderating. I ventured out around 0900hrs, by which time there was only the lightest breeze, the rain falling vertically. At once it was clear that many migrants had arrived. I kicked myself for sitting up the previous evening and staying in bed so long.

The trees in the garden were full of Blackbirds, and Robins seemed unusually numerous. I walked quickly up the glen, the island's main valley, noting warblers in patches of gorse where they normally do not occur. Overhead, the first Fieldfare of the autumn cruised past. The track leading to the Post Office was covered with Chaffinches and, feeding among them, an unfamiliar russet bird with a black head (ruffled to give it a shaggy crest), striking white stripe extending backwards from the eye, crescent-shaped breast band and elongated flame-orange spots along the flanks. It had pink legs and uttered a soft Robin-like 'tick' note. I watched Ireland's first Rustic Bunting for half an hour; then I hurried over to a turnip field which, earlier in the autumn, had attracted migrants. I walked up and down the rows,

A Rustic Bunting was the chief prize when a weather front swept migrants up from the Bay of Biscay.

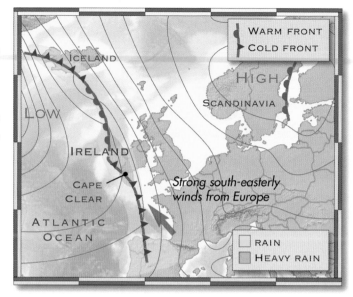

Weather map for 9 October 1959. After overnight rain and strong wind from the south-east grounded migrants on Ireland's south-west extremity, the morning on Cape Clear Island felt like Christmas.

flushing dozens of Blackbirds, Song Thrushes and Robins, plus a score of Chiffchaffs where, the previous day, there had been none.

The rain had stopped and it was calm. I returned to the garden beside the bird observatory and set three mist-nets, mainly to determine the weights of the newly arrived migrants. Many of the Robins seemed to have more yellowish breasts and paler upper-parts than the island residents. Two were soon netted. They weighed 11.5g and 12g, compared to an average of 17.9g for 67 trapped over the previous seven weeks. I concluded that they were migrants from Europe, low on fuel after a prolonged flight. Likewise, a Blackbird caught at the same time weighed 79g, compared with an average of 95g for 23 recent captures. I furled the nets and set out for Ballyieragh, the western end of the island.

Goldfinches were everywhere. Flocks were buzzing about and at one stage 226 alighted on thistles in a small field. There were more Blackbirds, Song Thrushes, Robins and a few Blackcaps, Garden Warblers and a dozen Redwings. I crossed the windswept top of Firbreaga – no Snow Buntings – and walked down slopes of soggy moorland and dry heath, a favourite haunt of Wheatears. A Linnet-like 'tchup' attracted my attention and, by crawling on my stomach over the soaking turf, I watched a Tawny Pipit at ranges down to six yards as it fed with Meadow Pipits and Rock Pipits [Tawny Pipit had been discovered in Ireland only twice before, in spring]. This revitalised me and I went to Central Bog, a hotspot of willows among reeds. The place was alive. The beds of reeds held about 50 of the yellow-breasted Robins, hemmed in by a small group of furious local resident Robins. Two dozen or more Chiffchaffs were there too, as well as six Reed Warblers.

I returned once more to the glen and, as dusk fell, re-set the mist-nets. Four Turtle Doves and four Siskins appeared in the trees, and I spent a frustrating time playing hide-and-seek with two large rufous 'warblers' [probably Rufous Bush Robins] that had white tips to their ample tails – every good day has its hoodwink.

Everyone now understands that these occasional south-east gales can deliver large falls. This particular system followed a classic approach. It brought migrants from Brittany and the Bay of Biscay in strong south-east winds, disorientating them in bad visibility and driving rain as an active weather front tracked in from the Atlantic, forcing them to continue off course until they could find land.[1]

23. Ivory Gull
Homage to a white waif

Grey sea, grey sky
two things are bright;
the gull-white foam,
the gull, foam-white.

JOHN HEWITT

'There is a period near the beginning of every man's life when he has little to cling to except his unmanageable dreams, little to support him except good health, and nowhere to go but all over the place.'[1] In 1978 I was that nutcase and I have the birdwatching notebooks to prove it. Out of university and out of work, I was birdwatching my brains out. I am glad that I did so because I can look back on the highlights. They were like passing patches of sun on the side of a rainy mountain, moments that left an indelible mark.

One episode began as a spark, not a fire. Nonetheless, as everyone knows, a spark is quite capable of igniting a blaze. In those days, instant news of unusual birds was unusual. Communications were received by telephone. If you were lucky enough to live in a home that had one, that is. The tip I received on the night of Monday 27 November 1978 was hardly hot. For one thing, the information was already two days old. Tom Ennis, a birdwatching associate, rang my parents' house and passed on word that an angler had reported a tame white gull on the wooden pier at Bangor, County Down, a place I knew well. Tom lived just ten minutes from there but had not checked out the report. For me, relying upon public transport to conduct sorties from home, the destination was two train rides and over an hour away. But I loved Bangor's harbour back then so I decided to travel there next morning.

Over recent weeks I had seen an adult Mediterranean Gull and a cream-coloured young Glaucous Gull in the vicinity, either of which might have suggested the term 'white'. No matter what the fisherman's find turned out to be, it would justify the trip. And, for the first time in my life, I could entertain a pipedream that the résumé might fit the richest prize of all, an Ivory Gull. Certainly, recent days had been chilly with winds blasting down across Ireland all the way from Greenland.

Evolution's choice of camouflage is a no-brainer but it is hard to imagine a more sublime model than an Ivory Gull.
PHOTOGRAPHS: ICE FLOES, MICHAEL CLARKE; IVORY GULL, BRUCE MACTAVISH

During my stint in academia I had enjoyed access to a university library stuffed to the gunwales with ornithological tomes. I read and read. I should also have read books related to my course of study but I never found the time. How could I divert from the likes of Edward Howe Forbush, who wrote lyrically about the birds of Massachusetts and New England,[2] including this portrait of Ivory Gull? 'Where countless crowding icebergs rear their snowy pinnacles; where dark blue, racing seas, flashing and roaring in the clear sunlight, dash their foaming crests high up the pallid slopes of crashing ice … there the snowy bird sails serene.'

Precise details of certain preliminaries have grown foggy over time. This is my line of defence against inciting truancy on the part of my young next-door neighbour, Bill Laird, who travelled with me next morning. We must have resembled Huckleberry Finn and Tom Sawyer walking down Bangor's main street towards the town's sea wall. Bill was snuggled deep inside a duffel coat and his long black fringe was cut in a Plimsoll line below his eyebrows, leaving next to no facial features for recognition by a schoolteacher at large. I sported acne-concealing long hair, resembling, I liked to think, George Harrison on the cover of *Abbey Road*. However, my

Bangor pier, 1978. The ultimate seagull-beside-the-sea postcard.

pièce de resistance was a threadbare baggy camouflage jacket that a wildfowler had given me. This was a real badge of honour, especially as it featured stains that may well have been dried blood.

As with any day in the field, the hope was for a few jolts of surprise. Waiting for a gap in traffic before crossing the seafront we joked that, if the 'white gull' was still around, we might see it from where we stood. About 200 yards away the pier's stilted wooden framework was strangely quiet. It looked cold and austere, a sphinx's fist gripping the sea. Because it was a weekday in November no one had braved the elements for a stroll. But there was life on the pier. Perched at the tip was an incongruous white dot. It did not move and was rooted like a chess piece to the spot. Bill and I ignored several changes of traffic light and assembled my rickety tripod topped with one of the few Kowa telescopes in Ireland. The dot was an Ivory Gull. We had hit the big time.

Like marines, we rushed to a better vantage point. At 50 yards' range we were on Cloud Nine. Everything that we desired was granted but the genie was peckish because it strode back and forth along the ground flicking over a brown paper bag used to carry bait. Although the bag was empty, the Ivory Gull was attracted to it by smell. My notebook was out and I began scribbling. This was a speckled youngster, not an alabaster adult; its complexion was pimpled with the ebony spots of youth. Bill and I were happy about that because we deemed a first-winter to be more attractive. Naive connoisseurs within minutes!

A footfall behind us sounded ominous. A fisherman plotted a collision course with the Ivory Gull's sanctuary. I summoned up the courage to intercept him and explained the situation. He was sympathetic, an attitude that I put down to the intimidating effect of my wildfowling kit. Maybe he thought I was armed. He stopped well short and proceeded to bait hooks. At the whiff of fish the Ivory Gull sprang into flight and sailed straight towards the fisherman, whistling as it planed down to land, light as a fairy, at his feet. He shot me a strange look but I didn't care. Bill and I were so close to bliss we could almost touch it.

Some birds feel like a messiah. Ivory Gull delivers inner heat on a cold day, eye contact with the soul and serenity born of white vestments. Airborne, the wings are raked like a tern's and at rest they resemble a bridal train.
PHOTOGRAPHS LEFT, BELOW AND FACING PAGE: BRUCE MACTAVISH

Dazed, but before losing the run of myself completely, I dashed off in search of a telephone. I decided that the enormity of the news warranted bursting into the lobby of a hotel and asking to make an emergency phone call. A bewildered clerk handed me a phone and I rang Tom Ennis at his work. The frantic conversation was overheard by several people within earshot, one of whom – a heavily perfumed, matronly figure – happened to be Bangor's mayor. She was intrigued and dispensed her civic duty by spreading the news to the mass media, including the BBC. So, over subsequent days, the Ivory Gull became a topical tourist attraction.

Back at the front, calm reigned. It was one of those sublime interludes when 'time was away and somewhere else'.[3] Bill and I watched our gift from the land of deep snow, Polar Bears and Gyr Falcons.[4] The only parallel was the intense cold. In crystalline light redolent of a gin & tonic with ice, I snapped some images when the outlander approached in the mistaken belief that we might be Eskimos about to feed seal meat to huskies. By now I was past the glib 'Ivory Gull looks like a white pigeon' caricature. I encountered elegance and a soft whistle that peaked and then declined like a descending graph. Always good at homework, I wrote everything up that night. Here are some excerpts: 'in flight, wings much longer than Kittiwake … more tapering and pointed tips … wing-beats shallow, flight light and buoyant. Called regularly when flew, less so at rest. The call was soft and mellow, disyllabic with the syllables run together, the second drawn out … *pheee-yew.*'

Watching the Ivory Gull felt like being at church. At the end of the service the two members of the congregation filed back down the pier and headed home, stealing a final peek at the monotone stranger happy in a world of colour.

24. Song Thrush traditional routes
Night moves

Quaking silent to be free
A Song Thrush peeps from filigree.
Indifferent to wind and shower
Wing-burst marshalled, it flees the bower.

A. McGeehan

When swirling drizzle descends and obliterates rocky fields, you see 'the thrush' sprigged among the sodden landscape's lumps and bumps. What looks like a small headstone has wings. Startled, the silhouette bolts for cover, swerving past the muddy shanks of cattle and disappearing inside hollow-centred fuchsias choking tumbledown stone walls. Welcome to the foggy-dewed west of Ireland! Song Thrushes are widespread here in autumn. They are not misled by wind and rain; they choose to come and retain a saturated memory of the place. In fact, by the turn of the year,

Like most songbirds, thrushes migrate at night. If autumn winds are light and the moon is bright, travellers head aloft over Britain and near-continental Europe and set a course for Ireland. Along the way, lisping notes occasionally attract peers and droplets of migrants become a stream. Without

they are often the commonest songbirds on larger offshore islands. A dearth of woodland or haw-lit hedges does not seem to bother them. The draw is top-quality worming pasture. They ditch a shrinking-violet stereotype and feed right out in the open, making it possible to savour their goofy looks and Patrick Moore eye.

Across Ireland in the self-same districts, Song Thrushes are common breeding birds. How do we know that immigrants arrive? And what of local Song Thrushes: are they inspired by patriotism to stay throughout the year? Nobody really knows. It is possible that, at least in large gardens and wooded parkland, some adult Song Thrushes maintain territories and are fairly sedentary. A three-year study of Song Thrush territorial behaviour in Oxfordshire[1] showed that comparatively few occupied the same breeding haunts from year to year. On average, males remained longer than females and about half disappeared within the year. During winter, spells of severe weather caused territories to be abandoned, temporarily or permanently. Hardly any females stayed for more than a year within the study area. New males arrived mainly during January and February, reoccupying vacated territories. In contrast, a very high proportion of females arrived during March, at the beginning of the breeding season. Likewise, most females disappeared quickly at the end of the breeding season. By calculating the proportion of each sex that disappeared from breeding territories and allowing for annual mortality (based on ringing recoveries), researchers concluded that most females chose to disperse away from the breeding area. Did they go far? More recent ringing seems to substantiate a random scatter rather than an organised migration. Some birds have covered the length and breadth of Britain and one crossed the Irish Sea from Lancashire to County Westmeath. Moreover, new territories were very seldom established by juvenile Song Thrushes that had been ringed as nestlings within the vicinity of their birth.[2] Taken together, the statistics paint a picture of a fidgety species.

The habits of Ireland's breeding Song Thrushes probably mirror their British counterparts. In which case, where might those immigrants that reach Ireland come from? A trail of evidence exists that provides the means to piece together a remarkable story. Published reports of Song Thrushes on Inishbofin, off the coast of County Galway, provide an insight into status across a microcosm of rough pasture, moor, cultivated land and sheltered gardens encompassing 935 hectares (2,312 acres).

In 1957 Robert F. Ruttledge wrote: 'Ussher & Warren [1900, *Birds of Ireland*] did not mention its presence in summer, nor did Cott in 1922 [*Irish Nat.* 31:34]. I did not see any in 1932, nor in July 1943, but in 1956 I found a nest containing eggs; saw adults carrying food and heard four in song. In December 1956 I found it one of the most noticeable birds. It was so plentiful that I was left with the impression that it outnumbered the Blackbird; it was certainly more widespread. I estimated that 50–100 were present.'[3]

Beginning in October 2006, I made numerous annual visits spanning all seasons and my findings have echoed those made by Ruttledge. Since 2013, following the removal of more than a dozen pairs of Magpies, the island's Song Thrush population soared from three pairs to more than fifteen pairs, most of which are double-brooded. Nonetheless, by late summer, when adults and juveniles moult – and become secretive – few appear in the open. At some stage emigration occurs because, by September, almost none can be found. October changes all that. Migrants arrive and can be observed at dawn, dropping like arcing tracer bullets from a brightening sky. Arrivals are furtive, restless and – the polar opposite for a species that is comparatively silent in all but song – vocal. In keeping with what seems to be an edgy disposition, most calls are analogous to those made by Blackbird but come across as more highly strung. Splutters have a tinny quality and piqued alarm calls outrank Blackbird in hackle-raising pitch. Callers are nervous yet demonstrative; they are probably using voice as a means to spread the word that they are around and looking for feeding space. As October darkens into November, the cork pops on the migration bottle and further influxes arrive. How many resettle elsewhere in the west of Ireland is unclear but by December Inishbofin's population normally exceeds 100. If cold conditions bite across Britain, numbers quickly rise and can double or treble.

Extrapolating the nationwide ebb and flow of Song Thrushes based on observations from one Irish island is no way to see the wood from the trees. A more reliable way to draw conclusions is to trace historical records. Thanks to the industry of Ireland's ornithological forebears, time travel is possible.

The mover and shaker for the first – and, to this day, the greatest – study of migration across Ireland and Britain was a Lincolnshire farmer called John Cordeaux. From 1860 he adopted the Humber Estuary and the adjoining coast as far north as Flamborough Head in Yorkshire as his birdwatching bailiwick.[4] With no library of bird books, he relied upon learned contacts, among them Professor Alfred Newton. Newton put him in touch with Heinrich Gätke on Heligoland, a tiny island off the North Sea coast of Germany. Cordeaux visited Gätke. The upshot was the formation of a Humber–Heligoland axis of comparable observations. In 1875 their findings were published in *The Ibis*, the leading journal at the time. The triumvirate of Cordeaux, Newton and Gätke joined forces with a Scot, John Harvie-Brown, and in 1878 an ambitious scheme was launched that roped in what became a total of 157 stations supplying information from around the coast of not just Britain, but Ireland too, where

Snow or severe frost changes everything. Denied access to terra firma, Song Thrushes evacuate. Unlike other thrushes – such as Redwings, Fieldfares and Blackbirds – Song Thrushes are not berry-guzzlers and flee across the Irish Sea in the hope that Irish soil is unfrozen.

A.G. Moore and R.M. Barrington were enlisted. The scheme's foot soldiers were lighthouse keepers and lightship crew members. Stationed at each 'coastal light', correspondents were asked to supply specimens, part remains and personal observations. Customised stationery and forms were designed. Barrington wholeheartedly embraced and later funded data collection in Ireland well past the project's closure in Britain. From 1881 until he published the results in 1900,[5] Barrington's army of keepers and crew members were to have less-boring days and nights. Several correspondents flowered to become outstanding field ornithologists.

The study's tactic was based upon the 'moth-to-the-flame' attraction of birds to lighthouses. Tired migrants coming in over the sea on a dark night may spot a beam from up to 40km (25 miles) away. Naturally, this leads to a greater concentration of birds landing in the proximity of the light than on the

Feeding in muted winter light, plumage tones help to age this individual. Determining the age of Song Thrushes is tricky but the bottom row of pale-tipped wing coverts shows a subtle hotchpotch of rusty hues. Forensic details aside, the fact that two types of pattern are discernible across the same band of feathers makes this a youngster. In order to clothe itself and leave the nest as soon as possible, the fledgling grew its first generation of plumage quickly and then upgraded most of it to more durable ware in late summer. The presence of some 'old kit' among the (lower) wing coverts is a hallmark of age. If you look carefully you can discern the juvenile coverts – they are slightly smaller and more brightly marked. Not until its first birthday will it moult again. After that, all its wing coverts will look the same.

adjacent coast. Sometimes the light lures them to their death, for in conditions of poor visibility they may be so dazzled that they end up crashing against the building or glass. As Barrington put it: 'the brilliant lights attract thousands upon thousands of winged voyagers, numbers of whom, when bewildered by the glare on dark nights, fly oftentimes against the lanterns with great speed, and are killed striking. The force with which they strike is immense, often smashing the thick lantern glass by such heavy species as wildfowl, where weight, added to velocity, results in a tremendous blow.' Adding to the likelihood of disorientation and collisions, Barrington discovered a correlation between casualties and lunar phases. Referring to Song Thrush specimens, he noted that 80 per cent were killed during the first and last quarters of the moon and that, during the seven years from 1888 to 1894, out of a total of 673 fatalities, only 106 (less than 16 per cent) were killed when the moon was more than half full. Correctly, he concluded that there was 'an intimate relation' between lunar phase and birds striking. Carnage was greatest in pitch-dark, especially when visibility was impaired further by rain, drizzle or fog.

In Barrington's day the Irish coast was girdled by a total of 47 lighthouses. Except for the lights of a handful of expanding cities, chiefly Dublin and Belfast, the rest of the country was in darkness. Little wonder that lighthouses exerted wondrous pulling power, the like of which will never, in our light-polluted age, come again. It is fascinating to imagine the starry firmaments of yesteryear. Until political upheaval in the early part of the twentieth century, around 95 per cent of all the productive land in Ireland was in the hands of Anglo-Irish landowners.[6] There were few roads or railways and, outside of towns and villages, it was only the big house that shone forth, creating an impressive display of status and independence in a landscape of darkness. Candles, oil lamps and – from about the 1850s – coal gas formed the sources of artificial light. All were expensive and beyond the reach of plain people, who resorted to firelight. The most elementary candle was the rushlight, made by removing all but a narrow strip of the stem of Common Rush and soaking the pith in melted animal fat. When dried, the long stem was placed in a holder that burned at a rate of around 2.5cm (1 inch) in three minutes. Although virtually free of cost, even rushlights were restricted to the better-off members of society because their manufacture required animal fat for fuel. Meat was not part of the diet of labourers and country folk in the impoverished conditions of the nineteenth century. At night, their world was illuminated by the glow from a turf fire or the uncertain flicker of burning wood.

Ireland's array of coastal lights, some of which began as entrance markers to ports rather than functioning as visible warnings against shipping hazards, contained a phalanx of ten lightships located at shoals and other hazards in the Irish Sea. Six of them lay off the east coast between Dublin and Wexford. Barrington noticed that a line drawn from lightships on the Arklow Bank (off the north-east Wexford coast) south to Tuskar Rock lighthouse, a distance of just over 60km (40 miles), would 'probably traverse the flight-line of most of the [Song Thrushes] which migrate into Ireland', an assertion based upon the locations of the specimens he received. Perhaps it is no accident this is the closest part of the Irish coast to Wales, particularly south-west Wales, the shortest crossing for migrants coming from southern Britain?

Barrington's hypothesising did not end there. He attempted to affix timing. His analysis was complicated by the difficulty of sifting reports that confused

Redwing with Song Thrush (he was aware that some keepers were confounded by the two species). He mined his data further to disentangle sightings from specimens and declared: 'the month of maximum migration is thus shown to be from 20th October to 20th November.' The sweep of movement, while concentrated along the Wexford coast, reached all parts. Although lower than the incidence of reports from lightships in the Irish Sea, west coast stations scored the second-highest number of observations, notably Slyne Head and the Aran Islands (both County Galway) and Tearaght Island, County Kerry. Compared to December, January and March, more specimens were produced in February. With hindsight, February's statistics are more likely to relate to emigrants leaving Ireland, although late-winter cold weather influxes mask meaningful interpretation. Not so Barrington's pronouncement about the end points of the migration calendar: 'it is apparently at a standstill from 10th April to 20th September, and is stronger during the first ten days of November than at any other time.'

Barrington was a pioneer whose imagination never failed to be both interested and baffled. He wrote not about birds, but about the meaning of bird migration in Ireland – which is harder. Thanks to him, the past tells us about the present. Because he was meticulous, all archives and specimens still exist and are housed in Dublin in the National Museum of Ireland. So what do we know now about the great river of Song Thrushes in the sky? Ireland's subsequent contribution to the cairn of knowledge amounts to a grass-growing silence. British observers, however, have forged ahead.

In 1960 a paper was published in *Bird Study*, the journal of the British Trust for Ornithology, discussing the origin of winter-visiting Song Thrushes to Britain and Ireland.[7] The study was based on ringing recoveries and plotted movements of birds ringed during the breeding season in Holland and Belgium and also those ringed during autumn migration along, mainly, the east coast of Britain. The researcher, M.J. Goodacre, concluded that two groups of migrants occur. She summarised the situation as follows:

There are the true winter visitors from the Belgian and Dutch breeding populations, and there are the birds that are on their way to winter quarters in Spain, Portugal and south-west France, which probably come from Scandinavia. The relatively large number of Song Thrushes ringed at bird observatories and subsequently recovered in France and Spain during the winter suggests that some Scandinavian Song Thrushes normally reach their winter quarters through Britain and that these ... pass through regularly and are not simply drifted off-course. If so, the migration route of the Scandinavian

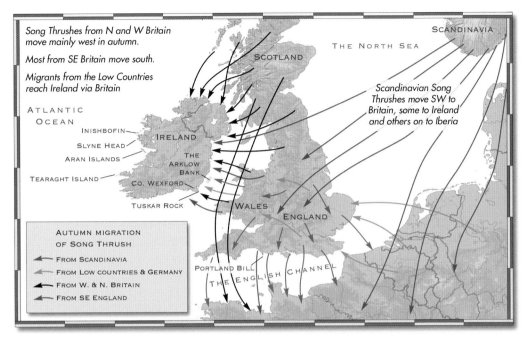

Ireland is well supplied with Song Thrushes in winter.

population crosses the migration route of the Belgian and Dutch populations roughly at right angles. This picture is further complicated by the fact that part of the British breeding population migrates to France, Portugal and Spain for the winter.

Might Goodacre's final sentence apply to the winter whereabouts of a portion of Ireland's breeding Song Thrush population too?

Portland Bill is a narrow promontory that juts out from the southernmost point of Dorset into the English Channel. In Roman times beacon fires were lit to warn passing ships of the Bill's position. Fires were not enough and down the centuries many vessels were shipwrecked until a succession of lighthouses were built. The current lighthouse dates from 1905. De-manned in 1996, nowadays it houses Portland Bird Observatory. From this sentinel position, the pulse of bird migration entering and leaving Britain is taken daily by observatory staff. But not just by day. As technology advances and improvements in bird sound identification skills keep pace, a small core of Portland observers, mainly Nick Hopper and Martin Cade (the observatory warden), monitor nocturnal traffic by recording sounds made by migrants passing overhead in the dark. Martin Cade's entry for 7 October 2016 records a particularly busy night: 'It is fascinating and frustrating in equal measure to discover just how much passes without stopping and Nick has provided yet more evidence from earlier this week. Monday 3 October was the quietest day of the week for grounded migrants, but Nick's recording gear had been deployed and his migrant totals were 607 Song Thrush calls (only 18 before midnight, but a big push between 0100hrs and 0230hrs when most were logged).' Impressive as the push was, the thrushes could have been departing from Britain or were European Song Thrushes in transit to unknown destinations. Or perhaps some were bound for Ireland? A neat coincidence was the discovery, two days previously, of 40 Song Thrushes in one clump of bushes on Hook Head, County Wexford, on the morning of Saturday 1 October 2016.[8]

Luckily, Ireland's potential Dorset connection does not end there. In *Catching the Bug*, Mark Constantine records events in a coordinated count of visible migration from Studland, overlooking the mouth of Poole Harbour.[9] His narrative for 16 October 2005 reads like an excerpt from *The War of the Worlds*:

> From the minute dawn broke, a constant stream of Song Thrushes flew past us, heading north. Not high overhead but low and often at eye-level, in sizeable flocks of 30 to 50, circling overhead before heading off north-west [inland]. We kept counting for four hours, and by the end had seen 6,205 Song Thrushes. It was to become one of the best thrush days on record in southern England. In the Netherlands, where large numbers of migrating Song Thrushes are seen annually, the largest recorded passage has been over 30,000 in a day. In the week leading up to our British record, Dutch coastal watchers saw huge numbers with a peak of over 30,000. Ringing records suggest that Song Thrushes are consistent in their habits and slowly move west across south-west Britain and Ireland during the winter.

It seems as though, for large numbers of Song Thrushes hailing from middle Europe, Ireland is a winter home. Each autumn they stream across the English Channel and then the southern Irish Sea. Many enter Ireland via the country's south-east flank and some continue until they run out of land in the far west. Barrington nailed the Irish evidence but it has taken British help to solve the mystery.

25. Wintering out
Blackcap's wrong-headed migration

*'… this had been the road of Destiny; had taken us to those
early accidents of fortune which predetermined for us all that
we can ever be.'*

WILLA CATHER

My first Blackcap (a brown-capped female) felt like a nomad forced to settle and reveal itself in winter. Food scraps probably kept it alive until its urge to migrate was rekindled by lengthening daylight in early spring. In her genes, in the secret code of her migratory programme, she intuitively knew more than ornithologists did about where home was – until German researchers solved the riddle of where Ireland's and Britain's wintering Blackcaps breed.

One cold and wet January in the 1960s I identified a Blackcap in my parents' garden. I had no idea that Blackcaps, being a summer visitor to Ireland, should not be here in winter. Although I was very young I was able to match the bird to its painting in a dog-eared copy of *The Observer's Book of Birds*, given to me by a friend of my dad's. Not only was I certain that I was right, my mother agreed. She knew less about birds than I did but mums are omnipotent. Every winter she wore a dark red coat with a furry black collar and large brown buttons resembling chocolate. She looked lovely in it, even though it was mainly worn when she brought in the washing. So she evoked

Snow White when she spread breadcrumbs and pieces of apple on the ground for the Blackcap. Back indoors, she signalled to me and we leaned against the cold windowsill, my face pressed against the glass, her hovering over me like an anglepoise lamp. My mum had a knack of generating calm in moments of expectation. We were two people with one pulse, waiting for excitement and wanting to remember it forever: the sudden flick of a bird, the lasting look, the edgy behaviour and nervous spook, the touch of a maternal hand directing my gaze through a rain-speckled window. Years later I came to realise that Blackcaps frequently showed up in back gardens in the dead of winter. Every time I see one it feels like a gift returning, a glimpse of childhood.

What was once unusual has become convention. As I grew up, Blackcaps became standard winter fare in gardens across Ireland and Britain. Watching birds at home has mushroomed and thousands of pairs of human eyes have been tapped for information. The bird's increase has been real. It was not overlooked in the past. It really is a new face at bird feeders. Based on citizen-science surveys, the ornithological mass media has charted the nature and scale of a meteoric rise. As a useful frame of reference, UK winter sightings jumped from around 22 per annum during 1945–54[1] to an average of 380 for the years 1970–77. Then, during the winter of 1978/79, approximately 1,000 correspondents in Britain and Northern Ireland (input from the Republic of Ireland was blighted by a postal strike) supplied records of a minimum of 1,714 Blackcaps.[2] Unrelenting consolidation followed and in the British Trust for Ornithology winter atlas survey of 1981–84 – covering both Britain and Ireland – approximately 3,000 individuals were believed to be wintering.[3]

Much like a historian analysing the salient facts underpinning a sweep to power, we now know that our visitors hail from Europe and that they track west in the autumn and gravitate into gardens. They do not muscle into suburbia in significant numbers until after Christmas, probably in line with the depletion of insect prey and berries over the course of winter. So, in order to survive, they switch diet and become opportunists. By January, if an interloper is guarding a bird feeder and driving away lesser mortals – as well as its own kin – you are likely to have the lodger until daylight lengthens noticeably in March. Irascibility is a hallmark. Some linger, become clockwork regulars and even start to mumble courtship arias, marking them out as young male pretenders. Others melt away. Maybe they quickly retrace their steps to home turf in time for the upcoming breeding season. By way of a spanner in the works, Blackcaps belonging to our summer breeding population that winter around the Mediterranean and in Africa – there are five ringing recoveries of Blackcaps ringed in the breeding season in Ireland and Britain and all came from southern Spain and north-

Blackcaps. Autumn migrants (two males and a female) on Inishbofin, County Galway, eagerly devour berries on a *Cordyline australis*, introduced from New Zealand in the nineteenth century. Pulses of migrants peak on headlands and islands in October. Although some may be destined to spend the winter in Ireland, the brief duration of their stay suggests that they are refuelling for destinations unknown.

The supply of wild fruits, berries and insects influences the timing of Blackcap movements from the wider countryside into suburbia. Days of plenty come to an end in December. By Christmas, Blackcaps start to become widely reported in gardens.

west Africa – begin to arrive just as the final European birds depart. In April, telling one transit passenger from another is difficult. And, it is assumed, each population remains faithful to its inherited migration route.

'The increase in the wintering population in Britain and Ireland is correlated with expansion of the north European breeding range and with larger numbers than previously migrating through Britain in autumn.'[4] Declarations such as this inform our grasp of bird migration. Does it explain Blackcap's innovative itinerary? The real story is quite different. Something happened that led numbers of European Blackcaps to fly north-west to Ireland and Britain in autumn, rather than, as most still do, head off in a broad fan of southerly directions to spend the winter in the Mediterranean and North Africa. We need to understand meaning, not means. The danger of science speaking for birds lies in allowing assertions to mask a root cause, tantamount to making a meal out of condiments. It is easy to fall into the trap of conforming to a theory that is wrong. Fortunately, if you dig deep enough and go back to 1988, the true explanation exists. Peter Berthold, assisted by Scott Terrill, was the first to get it into a nutshell. He argued that the founder members of the Irish and British wintering population developed a new migratory direction based upon an evolutionary process that, through caprice leading to good fortune, inadvertently produced a successful outcome.[5] The process, termed microevolution, involves a series of actions that lead to evolutionary changes on a small scale; that is, changes in genetic composition within a small population.[6] How might this come about?

Female Blackcap at feeder. Possession is nine tenths of the law. Blackcaps are tenacious in defence of a food resource – even if that means defending an entire feeding station against all comers.

The precision and predictability of migration tend to obscure the fact that the behaviour is actually dynamic and may change. In particular, youngsters set off 'blind' on maiden flights guided entirely by instinct. Some miscue. Perhaps the strength of an established migration strategy lies in stress-testing it by using new recruits. Occasionally changes in migratory behaviour occur on a short timescale – such as the result of navigation errors that have happy endings. However, for the individuals involved, the upshot is not reversion to a time-honoured traditional route. Instead, because the miscue proved successful, it becomes hard-wired into the bird's genetic makeup. In a sense, successful migrants really have acquired 'a code that they can live by'. A growing body of evidence indicates that in the Blackcap (and probably in many other species) important migratory traits, including the urge to migrate, departure timing, route orientation and distance, all have a genetic basis. Consequently the development of a novel migratory direction bringing European Blackcaps to Ireland and Britain is most likely an evolutionary process, unconnected with a northward expansion of the continental breeding range. Bewilderingly, the habit has become enshrined remarkably rapidly. How come?

In 1961, a Blackcap, ringed during the summer of that year in Austria, migrated to Ireland where it was found wintering when it was 'dragged in by a cat, still alive' in County Wicklow on 14 December. Twenty years later a young male, trapped and ringed at Corbally House in County Antrim on 4 January 1979, was found breeding near Triberg in Bavaria on 7 July 1981. Assuming that both birds followed a reasonably direct route, they had flown north-west to get here. These and other ringing recoveries indicate that it is European migrants that come to us for the winter and not Irish or British breeding birds that forestall migration and overwinter. Historically, small numbers of European Blackcaps wintered in Ireland and Britain. That fact is not new. What is new is the phenomenal growth in the wintering population. Apparently, some factor, or combination of factors, has altered so that a habit that has existed for some time – albeit in a relatively low frequency – is operating to amplify the wintering process.

Berthold felt that two lines of inquiry were needed to interpret the change. First, was there a relationship between the environment and the behaviour? There are correlations between weather conditions and winter survival. Global warming is producing milder winters, so prolonged cold snaps pose less of a threat. But climate change, of itself, does not account for a spike in the wintering population. However, it is probable that the increase in feeding wild birds in gardens has been a motive force. Because their diet is versatile, Blackcaps learned to exploit feeders, fruit, kitchen scraps and so on. And they are feisty defenders of dinner. The odds, therefore, favour good winter survival for those that took up the novel migration. Moreover, Blackcaps wintering in Ireland and Britain are likely to respond to lengthening daylight in early spring – surpassing the total amount of light per day in the Mediterranean region, where other European Blackcaps winter – by coming into a reproductive state ahead of birds wintering further south (photoperiod controls the onset of breeding condition, see Chapter 4). In short, advantages become a cascade. Our winter visitors

Unusually for a warbler, Blackcap sexes are easy to distinguish: a black bonnet in males, brunette in females. But not always. Before they moult in summer, juveniles of both sexes are brown-crowned. Young males are darker-crowned than females but even in winter some individuals still show a mixture of brown and black. Irrespective of crown colour, males are greyer-bodied than females.

return to Europe earlier in the spring and reap a reproductive advantage by establishing territory and attracting a mate. What is more, simultaneous waves of other early migrants are likely to have come not from the Mediterranean or North Africa, but from Ireland or Britain. The genetic implications of such pairings are seismic, increasing the likelihood that the progeny will also be predisposed to migrate north-west in autumn. If that occurred, what began as a minority migration direction would become a viable option and the genes coding for it could – presumably – increase in the population.

Berthold's second line of inquiry addressed the origin of the migration behaviour. He felt that the key lay in the existence within the population of appropriate genetic variation. He hoped to discover where a representative sample of the birds called home. That information might pave the way to test a cause-and-effect hypothesis by experiment. It had been suggested that wintering Blackcaps in Ireland and Britain were 'apparently immigrants from northern and eastern Europe'.[7] Indeed, some ringing records lent strong support to this notion, such as Scandinavian or East European Blackcaps trapped on the east coast of Britain. However, these occurred during September and October and probably represented migrants which had drifted west from their planned route through the Mediterranean. What if – as often happens – the drift was corrected and, after refuelling, the birds finally arrived where they intended? Two examples proved the point. Both were trapped on the English east coast in autumn but then flew to Lebanon.[8] Berthold marshalled what evidence he could find and it led him to believe that the recruitment area for Blackcaps wintering in Ireland and Britain appeared to be Central Europe, mainly southern and central Germany and adjacent areas.

If the assumption was correct, the novel wintering population would, in order to reach Ireland and Britain, have had to shift its original south-west migratory direction to north-west: a shift of 90 degrees, slightly less for Blackcaps breeding further north. To explain how such a shift might occur, Berthold offered this explanation: 'Continental Blackcaps show a funnel-shaped pattern of migratory direction ranging from south-eastern to south-western directions covering an angle of about 140 degrees. The western tail-end of the distribution would result in small numbers reaching [Ireland and Britain]; if these birds were previously selected against but now have much better chances of survival, the shift in orientation could have been achieved without any recent mutation.'[9]

To investigate if the migration direction had a genetic basis, Berthold and a team of researchers came to Weston-super-Mare in Somerset in December and January 1988–90. They trapped 40 wintering Blackcaps and transported them to aviaries in Germany. In March, pairs were released into outdoor aviaries for breeding. Seven pairs produced 41 young over two breeding seasons. A control group of 49 nestlings was taken from nests in southern Germany. All the birds had their migratory orientation checked using modified Emlen cages (see Chapter 15). The adults that wintered in England and their offspring orientated north-west; the Blackcaps from southern Germany – with a classic migratory focus toward Iberia – orientated south-west. The result strongly suggested that a genetically programmed north-west direction was responsible for the adults that wintered in England; otherwise their offspring would have shown a different direction.

In subsequent tests, Berthold cross-bred Blackcaps from the population wintering in England with some of the southern German birds. The resulting orientation was intermediate, further proof that migration information had a genetic basis. The high degree of 'heritability' coupled with just a small quantity of variation – in an autumn migrant's choice of compass bearing and the subsequent luck finding liveable winter quarters – appear to possess the potential to build a new nation when, out of the jaws of defeat, errant migrants unexpectedly snatch victory.

In effect, Berthold's pioneering research demonstrated not only how migration evolves but also how it can change over time. Blackcap was a good candidate because it has an almost sedentary population in parts of the Mediterranean but in northern parts of Europe it is a total migrant. Berthold hybridised Canary Island Blackcaps (resident) with Swedish Blackcaps (migrants) and was able to conduct restlessness tests that showed offspring had intermediate restlessness.[10] Therefore, migratory behaviour was under genetic influence and is inherited and passed from parent to offspring. In reality the genetic clockwork goes further because it corresponds – during the year – with the intensity, timing and duration of all migratory behaviour. Put simply, it correlates with all aspects of the youngster's first migratory 'cycle' from home to away – and back again.

I wonder if the bird of my youth made a contribution. She was a member of a small population whose fortunes were about to rise. It makes you wonder how many times in the past lone Blackcaps strayed west to Ireland in winter but never made it back whence they came, either because they perished in cold weather or died of hunger. Their genes went no further. All that changed when they discovered feeding stations in winter. More survived and because they did, they had a shorter flight back home than their peers. If, as seems likely, an earlier return to breeding areas coincided with the arrival of other Blackcaps also from winter quarters in Ireland, Britain or other parts of north-west Europe, the upshot would be reproductive isolation that, over time, increased the size of a splinter group until it became an army.

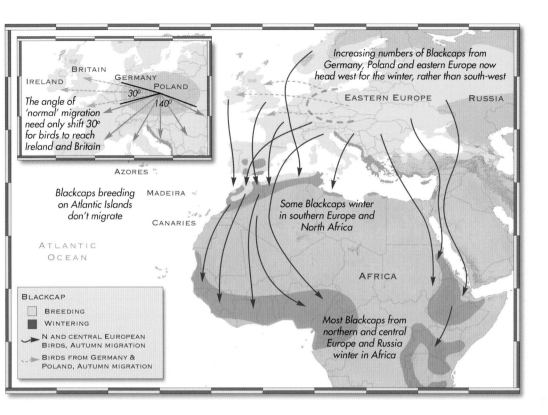

The following labels appear on the map:

Increasing numbers of Blackcaps from Germany, Poland and eastern Europe now head west for the winter, rather than south-west

BRITAIN
IRELAND
GERMANY
POLAND
30°
140°
The angle of 'normal' migration need only shift 30° for birds to reach Ireland and Britain

EASTERN EUROPE   RUSSIA

AZORES

Blackcaps breeding on Atlantic Islands don't migrate

MADEIRA

CANARIES

Some Blackcaps winter in southern Europe and North Africa

ATLANTIC OCEAN

AFRICA

Most Blackcaps from northern and central Europe and Russia winter in Africa

BLACKCAP
☐ BREEDING
■ WINTERING
↘ N AND CENTRAL EUROPEAN BIRDS, AUTUMN MIGRATION
↘ BIRDS FROM GERMANY & POLAND, AUTUMN MIGRATION

When German ornithologists Peter Berthold and Andreas Helbig puzzled over the rise in the wintering population of Blackcaps in Ireland and Britain – many of which came from Germany – they embarked upon a huge laboratory experiment to test for a genetic basis that might explain the behaviour. Blackcaps are a perfect guinea pig because, within the bird's range across northern Europe, some of the population migrate south-west and some south-east. This is referred to as a migratory divide. Through captive breeding of wild-caught migrants, 'hybrid' offspring were produced from parents that migrated in different directions. Tested in outdoor cages, the young hybrids went in an intermediate direction.

To migrate, a bird needs a compass and uses a combination of the sun, the rotation of the night sky around a fixed point provided by the star Polaris (see Chapter 16) and Earth's magnetic field. It makes sense to have major migratory factors under genetic control but Berthold's group of researchers made another breakthrough when they were able to select for migratory activity by taking birds from a partially migratory population and cross-breeding them with Blackcaps from a resident population (from the Canary Islands). These were selectively bred until, after three generations, they produced birds that were residents. Similarly, they bred total migrants from a corps of partial migrants. Hence, they demonstrated that it would be feasible for wild birds to adapt behaviour to environmental changes through genetic processes.

Based on the arc of Blackcap's migratory direction in autumn – that covers around 140 degrees – the angle of 'normal' migration need only be extended by about 30 degrees to produce an overspill of some migrants directed towards Ireland and Britain.[10]

26. Chasing Shearwaters
Birds of the ocean at arm's length

All the waves rolled by like scrolls of silver; and, by their soft,
suffusing seethings, made what seemed a silvery silence.

HERMAN MELVILLE

The Irish lose it when a heatwave hits. On the radio, Shay Byrne's early morning show becomes inundated with listeners' celebratory messages proclaiming wall-to-wall sunshine. Not since Ireland defeated Italy in the Euros has the national spirit soared so high. All this for a mere two days of heat: 18 and 19 July 2016. I was more interested in where the heat came from. A plume of tropical air crept north, a zephyr that could carry seabirds with it. Cory's Shearwaters are common over the blue waters off Iberia and can be tempted our way if the wind is at their back.

Looking west from Inishbofin, County Galway, on the day before the heat, I peered into rain that obliterated the coast. Lines of Manx Shearwaters disappeared into the murk but among them were several larger, lanky-winged silhouettes. These were Sooty Shearwaters, a species that breeds in the South Atlantic bordering Antarctica and migrates beyond the equator to feed in the North Atlantic, chiefly between Newfoundland's Grand Banks and south-west Greenland.

In late summer some Sooty Shearwaters, precisely how many is guesswork, congregate in the north-east Atlantic between Ireland and Rockall. They also

Departing in a small boat from Inishbofin, County Galway, and heading west into the North Atlantic makes you feel like a pebble tossed into the Grand Canyon.

Three Sooty Shearwaters flying among Manx Shearwaters. Although both species occur in the North Atlantic during summer, only Manx Shearwaters nest in Ireland's latitude. Sooty Shearwaters breed during our winter, in colonies dotted around the cold waters of the South Atlantic. The species could well be the world's greatest traveller. Even during the breeding season, males foraging for food have clocked up 18,000km (11,185 miles) over the course of 36 days, an average of 500km (310 miles) per day.

moult, raising the possibility that the ocean north-west of Ireland is home to more than we think. A comment in *Sea-Birds* (1954) by James Fisher & R M Lockley, indicates that this is nothing new: 'At Rockall on 17 May 1949 J.F. saw none, but from 18 to 27 June 1948 R.M.L. found them always present there, singly and up to eight together.' In autumn, a larger slice of those in the North Atlantic track south through Ireland's continental shelf.

A different story comes with each kind of shearwater. Manx Shearwaters breed in their thousands on predator-free Irish islands and spend the winter in the South Atlantic, mainly between the east coast of Brazil and the Falkland Islands. Although streamlined for a life on the high seas, the bird is maladapted for terra firma. An awkward shuffling gait and inflexible glider-shaped wings make burrow-nesting adults vulnerable to attacks from gulls and Peregrines, even though landings are made only at night. Before running the gauntlet, flocks gather offshore.

In light evening airs I could see distant rafts from shore, scattered like lead filings over a sleepy sea. Manx by the bucketful but what might be among them? If a cauldron of onshore wind and rain compressed the cornucopia closer to land, it might be possible to lift the curtain and discover what else lay among the masses. Such weather was a pipe dream. Instead, maybe I could reach the flotillas by boat?

Manx Shearwaters settled on the sea below the cliffs of Inishark, County Galway. Among them are at least nine Sooty Shearwaters.

Based on Inishbofin, the Concannon navy supplied the skipper. Seamus Concannon and I headed west in a small RIB (rigid-hulled inflatable boat). The vessel was black. That, plus its shape and rate of progress unsettled the flocks. Probably, we resembled an approaching Killer Whale. Seamus cut the engine and we metamorphosed into a lolling Minke Whale lookalike.

Manx Shearwaters are Trappists. The smooth sea seemed to chime with their silence. Each sat in the same pose and faced the same way. None bothered to feed, even though shoals of tiny fish gleamed just beneath the surface. Manx Shearwaters have a comfort zone and once that is crossed flocks become airborne. There is no panic, just an en-masse pitter-pattering lift-off. Swimming among the hordes were Gannets, Puffins, Razorbills and Guillemots. Fulmars crisscrossed the wake and juvenile Arctic Terns patrolled a few metres aloft, occasionally swooping at finny prey and maintaining a chorus of trills and staccato notes.

A veil of grey cloud removed shadows but darkened the horizon, suggesting that the Battle of Jutland was raging farther out to sea. With Ireland several miles astern we had entered a different realm. The Sooty Shearwater count went up and up. The texture of their body plumage evoked velvet. Across the back and wings, pale-fringed feather groups stood out like roof tiles. Although the body and the wing tips are dark, the centre of the underwing is silvery. Depending on the tilt of the body in flight, the linings can beam bright as a lighthouse.

It was hard to decide between taking in the grandeur of the scene or panning for gold by sifting through the cast. With so many birds, there must be a chance of something unusual? It was Seamus who first spotted the odd man out. He shouted, 'What's that big white yoke?' I spun around, sure in the knowledge that

Manx Shearwaters are flying machines fine-tuned by millions of years of evolution. Irish birds migrate to the waters east of Brazil each year.

Despite its name, Sooty Shearwater is not uniformly dark.

A glorious Cory's, the world's largest shearwater. Like a heavyweight boxer, the bird's size and bulk are no impediment to grace. Cory's are consummate fliers and their superior size generates an air that is easy-going yet impressive. Manx Shearwaters are more frenetic and – compared to Cory's – flap more and look driven.

I was not going to be disappointed. Seamus had caught a blast of snow-white underwings and belly on a banking shearwater. Manx Shearwaters have a similar pattern but the target was bigger. It was gliding among a kettle of Manx. Seamus understood instantly when I said, 'it's lazy; that means it's a Cory's!' I meant its flight action – although 'relaxed' might be kinder.

We punched the air and then tried to give chase as the flock wheeled away. The Cory's rose and fell with metronomic regularity. An average of four flaps topped up momentum and swept it high to the apex of an invisible Ferris wheel from which it slid steeply down. Encore followed encore in a kind of soporific medley. Seamus got the beat but we could not keep up with the bird. Later we found another, again uncatchable, even at 30 knots.

The voyage became a cruise. A Great Shearwater, another seafarer that travels from remote breeding outposts in the roaring forties, sat among a smorgasbord of Sooty and Manx Shearwaters. Somehow the Cory's trumped the lot. It felt like royalty, floating in flight and making me think that, hailing from hot climes and exuding idle power, the species might be more easily identified by beginner birdwatchers if renamed Mañana Shearwater.

All the world's shearwaters possess an external nostril stacked on top of the bill, at the base. A canal connects from inside the skull to the nostril. To rid itself of salt, the bird processes its food and then extrudes brine through the nostrils.

27. G is for Gull
Of Herring Gulls and hubris

When the seagulls follow the trawler, it is because they think sardines will be thrown into the sea.

Eric Cantona

Knowledge amasses from bits of evidence that lie about awaiting discovery. To organise the pieces into a way-marking cairn you need motivation. Stimuli may come from within or without. In Ireland, ornithology generally follows the lead given by Britain. A lot of inspiration comes, therefore, from across the water. Around Christmastime 1996 a one-man expeditionary force called Martin Garner crossed the Irish Sea and landed on the outskirts of Belfast. The invader spoke in tongues, '*Larus michahellis cachinnans?*' I understood a little pidgin-gull and Martin sought me out. He hypnotised me into looking at gulls – and birds generally – in a new light. I am still under the spell.

His approach might be best summed up by stating that when it comes to little-known or little-understood genres, it matters more – not less – to grasp the identification nettle. To him, it is as though the birds have been deprived of their freedom. Through being difficult or challenging to identify, they have suffered the indignity of being pushed under the carpet or shoehorned into a relationship of which they are not a part.

Few gulls rated lower than Herring Gull. The bird was trash, dirt through which you panned for gold. In Ireland, among Herring Gulls, precious metal came in just two forms: Iceland Gull and Glaucous Gull, easily recognisable pin-ups from latitudes close to the Arctic Circle. In my attempts at scrutinising other large gulls, I did not dismiss any strangers that I came across because I never saw any. And I never saw any because I was under the impression that they did not exist. Furthermore, anything unusual could confidently be assigned to Room 101 by using the get-out-of-jail card of branding it a hybrid.

The first signs that the status quo was flawed came in the late 1970s. In England, Rob Hume published 'identikits' for four types of 'Herring Gull' that wintered in the Midlands.[1] I have to admit that I did not pay close attention to the text because the lack of hard-and-fast identification criteria meant that any effort I made to look for similar birds in Ireland would not land me a 'tick' by way of a new species. That equated to pain and no gain. Every birdwatcher I

Gulls are versatile. Most species migrate and all wander. When winter bites, Arctic species are especially good at heading south. This gull – the equivalent in age to a teenager – is from the Canadian Arctic and its ilk has strayed to Ireland. What is it? What's in a name? If I said 'Kumlien's Iceland Gull', that might warn you that an ornithological iceberg lies ahead.
PHOTOGRAPH: BRANDON HOLDEN

knew in Ireland would have shared that sentiment, as would most in Britain – but thankfully not all.

Rob Hume was a prophet and Martin was an early disciple. I followed the correspondence generated by Rob's article. It was frightening. On the one hand, his findings were pooh-poohed; on the other hand the can of worms that he had opened was the size of a black hole. But he was having none of it. Rather than giving in to theories later proved wrong or mere speculation, he persisted and his observations started to clear a passage through a minefield.

By 1980 I was at least aware that Herring Gulls *Larus argentatus* came in several identifiable types. At subspecies level (see explanatory panel on facing page for definition of subspecies), Irish and British birds were *Larus argentatus argenteus*, whereas the type occurring in north Norway and along the coast of

WHAT ARE SUBSPECIES?

In essence, a subspecies is a recognisable population, usually geographically separated – such as on an island, archipelago or mountain range. Whereas a full species has a homogeneous appearance and does not interbreed with other species, subspecies are not so fully evolved and can theoretically breed with others within the same species. In other words, they are recognisable 'forms' but not sufficiently separated to be classified as a species in their own right. If the forms are not well separated but, instead, grade from one to another across the species' overall range, then the gradation in appearance is described as a 'cline'.

All species have two scientific names. The first (with a capital) describes the genus, such as *Falco*, the family to which Peregrine Falcon belongs. The second (lower case) identifies the species, in this example *peregrinus*. So *Falco peregrinus* is the full scientific name for the Peregrine Falcon. In order to distinguish a subspecies, a third word is added to the scientific name – the trinomial. The Robin *Erithacus rubecula* looks similar across Ireland, Britain and near-continental Europe (top image). However, isolated populations on Gran Canaria and Tenerife look somewhat different. Although they are still fundamentally 'Robins', their DNA shows that they are probably derived from a colonisation event that occurred when an influx of European Robins arrived some two million years ago.[2] Since then, these birds' appearance – and vocalisations – has changed. They differ by possessing a white eye-ring, a more restricted but intensely coloured breast with a brighter blue border, and a white belly (lower image). Although subtly distinctive, they are not classified as a species yet, but – in recognition of their uniqueness – as a subspecies, *Erithacus rubecula superbus*.

PHOTOGRAPH: SILAS OLOFSSON

Arctic Russia was *Larus argentatus argentatus,* distinguishable in adulthood by being (for the most part) larger, darker-backed, longer-billed and longer-winged. Here matters ended until, on New Year's Day 1981, while drooling over my first Ross's Gull (found by Guy Hamilton, aged eighteen) among a blizzard of gulls at Portavogie on the coast of County Down, I saw two Iceland Gulls that stretched the field-guide definition of that species. One was an adult that showed a grey slash among its wing tip; the other was a first-winter whose beige wing tip feathers (called primaries) were peculiarly dusky.

If British gull-watchers were struggling to establish what *Larus argentatus argentatus* looked like vis-à-vis *L.a. argenteus,* then maybe Irish gull-watchers needed to broaden their Iceland Gull *Larus glaucoides glaucoides* outlook (the subspecies breeding in Greenland) and investigate plumage variation within Kumlien's Iceland Gull *Larus glaucoides kumlieni* (the subspecies breeding in Baffin Island, Canada – see map on p. 194). I voiced my suspicion that the 'odd' Iceland Gulls might prove to be Kumlien's Iceland Gulls (hereafter Kumlien's Gull) but was met with a reaction that was destined to become familiar. In short, purportedly deep penetration of the subject – evidenced by erudite literature – was used as a block. I was faced with contemporary information dealing with Kumlien's Gull that stated 'judging from personal study of photographs and museum specimens … the pattern of wing-tip markings and their colour seems very consistent, contradicting some previous literature which speaks of highly variable pattern and colour'.[3] Ergo, the non-conformist gulls at Portavogie were lepers. Or, the solution to anything that bent preconceived rules, maybe they were hybrids?

Okay, I had tried and failed to get to the bottom of the field identification of putative Kumlien's Gulls on this side of the North Atlantic. Unless, that is, the books were wrong. Several years later I discovered that confusion had – somehow – grown. Because bird identification should not be based on opinion I decided, in January 2004, to visit St John's, Newfoundland, winter capital of Kumlien's Gull in North America. My guide was Bruce Mactavish, Canada's keeper of the keys to Kumlien's kingdom. I saw hundreds and, by and large, no two were the same. Thankfully, my curiosity had never died.

Newfoundland was gull heaven. Absorbing the wing patterns of all ages of Kumlien's Gulls was just the start of a learning curve. The variation was unnerving but more surprising was the fact that I did not see Kumlien's Gulls as simply the equivalent of Iceland Gull with random markings across a few outer wing feathers (primaries). I formed the impression that, while still elegant, Kumlien's Gull was a coarser bird than Iceland Gull. The trip was a trial run that sought to answer questions such as 'if a first-winter Kumlien's Gull with

Not all Herring Gulls are the same. Central to evolution, what begin as minor differences within the appearance of one species can, over time, lead to divergence – especially if migration route and breeding distribution bolster separation. For the moment, the European Herring Gull is a broad church. Across its overall range, the population grades in plumage and size (described as a 'cline' – see explanatory panel). But the end points are distinguishable. From an Irish perspective, the winter discovery of distinctive 'Arctic' Herring Gulls *Larus argentatus argentatus* among hordes of commoners caused great excitement. Hitherto, their presence was largely unknown and, because of a gap in identification knowledge, deemed impossible to prove. Because the plate was originally aimed at an esoteric readership, the images depict only 'Arctic' Herring Gulls *L. a. argentatus*, albeit photographed in Ireland, rather than our regular stock-in-trade – *L. a. argenteus*. To try and address this imbalance, two adult gulls (centre right) have been added to show the difference in back colour and amount of white markings in the wing tips between (at front) *L. a. argentatus* and (behind) *L. a. argenteus*.

unmarked primaries showed up in Ireland (some first-winters had, to all intents and purposes, plain primaries) how could it be identified?' The answer was that it probably could not. But that did not matter because the majority of all ages could. Numerous articles have since raised awareness on this topic.

Another question seemed less pertinent, although still troubling. At the other end of the scale, was there a problem separating those Kumlien's Gulls with the darkest primaries from a Thayer's Gull *Larus thayeri*? Thayer's Gull breeds in the Arctic in Canada and Alaska and travels a considerable distance to winter along the Pacific coast – some cross the northern Pacific and winter in north-east Asia. With such a long-range disposition, might a drifter make it to Europe? Neither Bruce nor I had experience of Thayer's Gull so the subject was filed away, although we knew it was a hot potato and we could see potential fool's gold flying around in front of us.

By the early 1990s gull-watching had become high fashion on both sides of the Irish Sea and beyond. Martin unwittingly lit a fuse when I learned that he had seen several *argentatus* Herring Gulls around Belfast in late December 2006. This was the wake-up call that I needed. In the past I had had 'UFO' experiences at Killybegs, County Donegal, where trawlers plying their trade all the way to Russia disgorge catches and boat-following gulls. Among a Herring Gull maelstrom containing Glaucous Gulls and Iceland Gulls I had spotted large dusky brutes with white-rimmed wings and less-than-normal dark in the wing tips. They had presence. The wings said 'B52' and the nature of the beast evoked a Glaucous Gull seen through smoked glass. In the absence of anything better, I declared them to be *argentatus* Herring Gulls. To me, they felt like a species with no name.

I submitted details, including photographs, to the Irish Rare Birds Committee, of which I had been a former member. They were of the opinion that the taxon was not recognisable and that the matter of determining the birds' subspecies was irresolvable because 'clinal variation occurred in the Herring Gull complex thereby rendering subspecific identification impossible'. In other words, one size and one coat of feathers fitted all. On the other hand, I reasoned that variation in Herring Gull was likely to operate like a set of paint colour cards. At one (southern) end you start small and pale-backed; at the other (northern) end you finish big and dark-backed. Such gradual stepwise variation is defined as a cline. Throw in leapfrog migration – whereby members of the most northerly populations track furthest south and mingle with their least similar cousins – and the upshot was likely to be the contrasting types that I beheld. It made perfect sense. The more I looked the more I questioned the scale of difference: three things stood out – observable differences in size, back colour and wing-tip pattern – and there was a lot more to come. Far from hanging by a slender reed, distinctions between the two types of Herring Gulls were substantial. And not just for adults.

Along with Martin, I disappeared in the family car among avalanche slopes of stinking domestic refuse at landfill sites at Belfast and Derry. One look at an *argentatus* became a departure point for inspiration. Eureka moments came thick and fast. The largest individuals were not podgy like a Glaucous Gull or heavily muscled like a Great Black-backed Gull. Although big, they were gangly and statuesque: Usain Bolt rather than Jonah Lomu. Their bills were long yet benign, reminiscent of Pinocchio or a goofy albatross. Evolution's trick in making them gentle giants was to lengthen the bill, not enlarge it. The forehead was sloping and the face stretched into a relatively narrow bill base – like someone sucking on a cigarette. The size discrepancy between individuals was considerable, more than in any other large gull. Was this male versus female or did different populations come in different sizes? Smaller birds had a more conventional bill but still retained a demure countenance because, as in the largest birds, the underside of the lower mandible was more concave than on an *argenteus* Herring Gull. January was the peak month, when up to 50 occurred. Most did not arrive until December and by early February departures were already under way. Yet even this 'dead of winter' schedule threw up physiological quirks that marked out *argentatus* from *argenteus*. Differences in moult timing meant that primaries on some were not fully grown until December. Through moult of head plumage, adult *argenteus* became white-headed in late January; *argentatus* did not and retained winter streaking until early spring, a clue to travellers nowhere near home and in no rush to upgrade plumage to look their finest for courtship in distant lands. In similar vein, hormonal activity was dormant and kept bill colour insipid yellow on most *argentatus*, whereas *argenteus* bills glowed yellow.

Herring Gull (*Larus argentatus*)

M. D486211	nestling found dead	17.7.61 7.2.65	Great Ainov Island: 69°50′N. 31°35′E. (Murmansk) **U.S.S.R.** Alveston: 52°13′N. 1°40′W. (Warwick)
M. D489299	nestling found dead	27.6.61 29.4.65	Great Ainov Island, **U.S.S.R.** Pitsea: 51°34′N. 0°31′E. (Essex)
M. E554686	nestling found dead	11.6.63 28.3.65	Great Ainov Island, **U.S.S.R.** Druridge Bay: 55°15′N. 1°34′W. (Northumberland)
O. 091846	nestling found dead	11.7.55 27.6.63	Reinøya: 70°18′N. 31°07′E. (Finnmark) **Norway** *near* Malton: 54°08′N. 0°48′W. (York)

These old ringing recoveries show that Herring Gulls breeding well north of the Arctic Circle – within the range of *Larus argentatus argentatus* – reach Britain and, as we now know, Ireland. Demonstrating that many do not stop once they encounter the edge of the North Sea, two were recovered well inland – one in the middle of England.[4]

Young *argentatus* dwarfed *argenteus* and could approach Glaucous Gull and Great Black-backed Gull in size but not structure. They were lean, long and often leggy. As with adults, size discrepancy applied. However, even for the smallest individuals, bill and head shape made detection feasible. A striking attribute was homogeneous plumage. Unlike on a first-winter *argenteus*, a chameleon would be able to blend in a second due to no contrasts or patchwork to copy, just a sea of beige plaid. Thin pale eye crescents and a variable but consistent pink bill base forged an affinity with Glaucous Gull rather than 'bog standard' Herring Gull. Other attributes built a unique animal. The upper parts were largely (or in some cases entirely) juvenile, a hallmark of a moult strategy geared to a lengthy migration. The underwings were fawn-coloured with diffuse pale webs creating light windows across the bulk of the primaries. In 2002 I committed my experience of *Larus argentatus argentatus* to print plus an accompanying plate in *Dutch Birding* (p. 189).[5]

Sometimes with Martin, sometimes solo, I went 'dump gulling' many times over several winters. Sadly, like ghosts at dawn, the birds have gone. Not because they ceased to exist but because the food supply was cut off when the landfill sites closed. Before that happened, a different bolt of lightning struck Belfast in early March 1997. It was Saturday 1 March but it came to feel more like epoch-making Ides of March. Lowering cloud created flat grey light, the perfect backdrop for viewing plumage. Martin and I latched on to a striking café-au-lait gull. It flew directly in front of us. It was alone: a ballerina entering the spotlight. Unlike *Larus argentatus argentatus*, the apparition had an English name. Like a pair of clever clogs on *University Challenge*, we blurted out the answer to the question before Bamber Gascoigne had finished asking it: we were in the presence of a first-winter Thayer's Gull. Martin reached inside his wallet and produced a picture of what we had just seen. For years he had kept the image to hand. It was from a winter issue of *American Birds*. If the likeness was uncanny, the timing was spooky. Was this meant to happen?

Years later I can reveal that, in the course of that long second, I experienced conflicting emotions. Elation mixed with trepidation. Having seen all the bedrock commoners, I knew that we were reporters who had landed a scoop. Provided we accumulated the hard evidence, then all we had to do was point up the bird's key features. I got plenty of images. Did that make me happy? Yes and no. On the one hand, the documentation would be watertight; on the other hand, challenging the establishment by claiming a Thayer's Gull was like declaring war. However, with Martin as a partner I felt safer. We could have said nothing and filed away our encounter and kept it for a distant time when the uncertainty over the status of Thayer's Gull would be resolved. Instead we went

Where to begin? Wreathing the Arctic coasts of North America and Greenland, there lives a single species of gull that either exhibits a different appearance, migration strategy and disjointed breeding range amounting to 'three types within one' (the current view of taxonomists) – or these differences point to the existence of three species that look different, follow different migration routes and do not interbreed (see accompanying map). Only adults are included in the plate; many more plates would be needed to cover the appearance of younger ages. It is sobering to see current scientific opinion shoehorn three identifiable birds into a 'one size fits all' classification. Therefore, only one species is shown in the plate – Iceland Gull. Or, in a crude attempt at clarification, the plate is a collection of 'Iceland Gull types' with each differentiated. If Iceland Gull is wine, what you see is red, white and rosé! The subject is hopelessly complicated.[6]

ICELAND GULLS (TOP THREE): PHOTOGRAPHED IN IRELAND BY AUTHOR. KUMLIEN'S (ICELAND) GULLS (MIDDLE THREE): PHOTOGRAPHED IN NEWFOUNDLAND BY BRUCE MACTAVISH. THAYER'S (ICELAND) GULL (BOTTOM FOUR): TWO ADULTS AT REST PHOTOGRAPHED BY STEVE GANTLETT IN VANCOUVER, CANADA; TWO ADULTS IN FLIGHT PHOTOGRAPHED BY AMAR AYYASH ON LAKE MICHIGAN, WISCONSIN, USA.

public in the hope that the Belfast individual might be instrumental. In Ireland as well as in Britain, previous claims of Thayer's Gull had been dismissed. Even across its home range, 'Thayer's Gull' was not considered a species – it was merely a Pacific coast cousin of Kumlien's Gull that sported darker wing tips – so it stood no chance of being identified here.

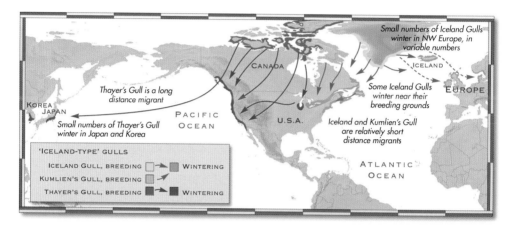

Martin Garner (1964–2016) alongside Thayer's Gull on Vancouver Island, British Columbia. If possible, proof should lie at the heart of bird identification; no one likes to make a false statement. Other disciplines have hypotheses that are tested against experimental evidence until they fail and are overtaken by new hypotheses. Having decided that the young gull we saw at Belfast was a Thayer's Gull, the best Martin and I could do was to go to British Columbia and study its peers. Bird artist David Quinn has kindly recreated – inset, from photographs – the Belfast Thayer's Gull for comparison.

In the debate that followed, several allies emerged that shared our belief that the Belfast bird was a first-winter Thayer's Gull. At *Birding World*, editors Richard Millington and Steve Gantlett promoted a renaissance in large-gull identification articles. Paramount among these was a photographic essay on Thayer's Gulls from the birds' winter homeland: British Columbia.[7] Along with David Quinn, Martin and I travelled to Victoria Island, just west of Vancouver, in late November 1997 and spent most of a week watching Thayer's Gulls. We became utterly convinced that not only was the Belfast individual safely assignable to the species but that, in March 1998, an adult found at Killybegs, County Donegal, by Richard Millington and me was too.[8] History will decide whether, with a little help from our friends, we managed to create enlightenment out of confusion. Luckily no Thayer's Gulls will read this. In 2017, taxonomic authorities were still divided on the bird's right to be recognised as a species. Whether Thayer's Gull is or is not a species (a fluid, human-invented concept) they are still entirely identifiable and exciting – a 'Martini gull' whose capricious appearance, any place, any time, anywhere, can enliven a dark winter's day.

28. A trip to Newfoundland
Olympic fliers under starter's orders

The slow
Rollover of evening, the spruce
Growing dense, gathering dark,
Standing in pools of departure.

Don McKay

From my seat near the front of the Westjet Boeing 737 at Dublin airport I spotted the young pilot when he popped his head out of the cockpit to talk to one of the air stewards. So, later, I had a face to fit the voice that crackled over the intercom. Because he said little, his words had a peculiar force; they were not worn dull from constant use. 'We should be on the tarmac at St John's in around forty minutes. Our current speed is 420 miles per hour; that's seven miles per minute. Weather on the ground is a strong north-west wind of around 25 knots. Welcome to Newfoundland.' Cue the eastern tip of

Newfoundland claws the North Atlantic with rocky fingernails grey as zinc. Glades of fog creep ashore and then vanish – leaving the impression of a land mass freshly emerged from the Pleistocene.

North America. I peered down at the ocean in an effort to compute what I saw and transpose it into the real world of a shorebird or songbird migrating over the same element. If any were heading south today they would double their speed thanks to the added zip of a tailwind. The sea was pimpled. Smudgy white wave crests appeared and then died like melted snowflakes. Each slow-motion puff faced the same way, like small boats heading for Dunkirk; a big sea was running.

Land appeared. I saw cliffs the colour of dry beetroot and a dark forest with trees resembling an army of toothpicks, part of the mosaic of rocky barrens, scrubland and spruce that smothers Newfoundland. Wilderness – what a commodity. And I was going to be among it, walking coastlines and peering into a sylvan universe beneath which the bones of mammoths sleep, undisturbed since ice passed this way 10,000 years ago. It was autumn. Deciduous green was starting to turn bronze and the birch trees massed along lakeshores and the edges of bog pools were being overshadowed by spruce and fir. The season was speeding up. By the end of my visit I would have traversed autumn. The brassy leaves would have fallen and flickered out and a coniferous deadness would prevail. Before monastic calm sets in and temperatures dip, birds will desert in droves. For the only time of the year, Newfoundland is a staging area for migrants drawn from as far away as Alaska. The island is a final fuelling stop for optimists flying out to sea and trusting that evolution's great handiwork will, once again, convey troops to winter quarters in South America.

When migration starts, the participants cannot be stopped. Instinct, nature's absolute force, commands the field. The breeding urge has been switched off and replaced by a different impulse. Over previous months a suite of songbirds that returned from the tropics to breed across North America was part of the sight and sound of spring. Spring comes suddenly across continental interiors. In the face of restless warm weather, winter retreats. Whole woodlands burst into bud and birdsong fills the morning. Waves of migrants in courtship colours decant through the night. Before early mists clear and are replaced by enamel-blue skies, the drive to produce a new generation gets under way. Those hectic days are gone. The process of finding a mate, building a nest, laying eggs, incubating a clutch and feeding young until they fledge is over. Young are now independent, adults have separated from mates and it is every bird for him- or herself. A new priority is signalled. It is time to fatten up and get ready for migration.

Unlike the spring rush to reproduce, preparations for autumn departure are comparatively leisurely. Across northern forests, mixed bags containing several species roam in flocks. Insect life is on the menu. Food is abundant and living is easy. But there is no room for complacency. Depending on the migration strategy encoded in the genes of a parcel of energy weighing not much more than a ballpoint pen, a mind-boggling flight over water is coming soon. Blackpoll Warbler is one of several small dynamos that gear up for a single giant leap. The mite will have no chance to land or find food and replenish body fat. Perversely, it cannot overeat beforehand; otherwise it will be sluggish and less able to avoid predators or zoom around foliage snatching insect prey. But it has a trick. It can convert what it eats into high-energy fuel and cram the stuff into every nook and cranny of its body, shrinking its digestive system to make room. Fully loaded, it waits for a fair wind.

There is more. Once under way, it must maintain a navigational focus all the way to Amazonian forests or Andean foothills. Upon arrival, it rubs shoulders with a whole new avifauna. In North America, at the end of the breeding season, Blackpolls Warblers team up with parties of chickadees, associates that, in the tropics, are replaced by mixed flocks containing antwrens, foliage-gleaners and woodcreepers.

Even for an old-hand adult who has flown the route before, the task is gargantuan. Inexperienced youngsters are hostage to an inherited template, a fixed programme that will, every autumn, be tested by an environment that weeds out any that err, so that only the fittest live on – although hurricanes do not discriminate and may hit all that stray into their path. Young or old, how do the pilgrims feel? Do adults revisit the very bottom of their memory? To an extent, it seems so because evidence supports the creation of an indelible GPS, consisting of waypoints visited during previous trips. However, to get started, all in the population feel the magnetic pull of Earth, the solemn magic that comes out of the dark woods and connects the birds to the stars and stirs them to fly.

I wanted to be among Blackpoll Warblers, to appreciate them among the forests in which they breed, as the beauty of a leopard should be seen through

It was early morning. Light mist still clung to lichen-covered branches and a moose had just crossed the track. If the Pine Grosbeak had been a brassy gold and grey female it might have been missed. It would have blended in. But the red male caught my eye and I knew I was there. Pine Grosbeaks are unafraid of Homo sapiens and are one of a handful of resident birds capable of seeing out winter in Newfoundland by munching the buds of coniferous trees. Pine Grosbeaks live like Thoreau – unsubjected to prevailing winds or weather, to anything they choose not to notice. The bird's two white wing-bars were missing, frayed by brushing against crusty undergrowth. This was a general, decorated in rouge the shade of cinema curtains.

Across North America, Blackpoll Warblers have an immense breeding range encompassing the continent's boreal forest from Alaska to Newfoundland. In those latitudes summer is short but the days are long. When the breeding season ends, the entire population – adults as well as the year's young – prepare to fly to Amazonia, the species' wintering grounds. During late summer, troops mass in a staging area stretching from Newfoundland to Virginia. Gluttonous eating converts insect prey to fat that more than doubles a bird's weight. Readied for departure, armies of migrants await the passage of a cold front that generates a tailwind and launches them on an epic trans-oceanic flight. In one of the greatest tests of endurance faced by any living creature, the birds fly continuously for two days and three nights to reach the north coast of South America. Not all that embark on such a high-stakes flight arrive safely. Each year a small number of youngsters, overwhelmed by adverse weather and wind strengths greater than their own air speed, fail to make it. A few arrive in Europe, seemingly none the worse for wear, but destined not to return to their native continent. Although survivors, their genes will not make the cut in the next generation: the species does not want unreliable aviators.

dappled foliage. 'Blackpoll' is a nod to the male's saucer-shaped black cap – set off by snowy cheeks – that is the acme of his costume in spring. Indeed, for the most part, spring adults are monotone. That changes in autumn, when parents and offspring look the same. Kitted out for the rainforest canopy, the entire population dons a tropical green back atop a glowing yellow chest. Two white bars slash the wing, and tail spots catch the eye when the bird flits deeper into cover – semaphore to others that it is moving. Feathers are at their best in autumn. Following moult everything is original and soft. Unlike human adults, birds can reverse the effects of ageing by sprouting a new coat of plumage. Autumn warblers have Botticelli angel faces and, in my mind's eye, I still see that first Blackpoll Warbler, in Ireland. Now, in Newfoundland, I have caught up with the past.

Some members of a species that slingshot themselves in a three-day odyssey over the western North Atlantic to reach South America are bound to come a cropper. Anticipating favourable weather is one thing but expecting benign conditions to prevail along an oceanic route crossing two hemispheres is risky.

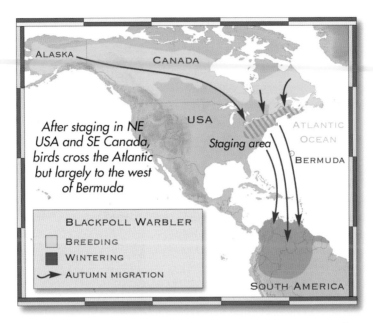

After staging in NE USA and SE Canada, birds cross the Atlantic but largely to the west of Bermuda

Staging area

ALASKA
CANADA
USA
ATLANTIC OCEAN
BERMUDA
SOUTH AMERICA

BLACKPOLL WARBLER
BREEDING
WINTERING
AUTUMN MIGRATION

September, peak migration time, is also hurricane season. Surprisingly, avoiding a hurricane bearing down on the landward flanks of the Caribbean or eastern seaboard of the United States is usually possible. Displacement is more likely when a migrant is surprised by a small, fast-moving weather front (a wave depression, see Chapter 10) tracking towards Europe or Iceland and outpacing the aeronaut's meagre speed of around 30km/h (20 mph).

That is what happened in early October 1984. I was rarity-hunting on Cape Clear Island off the coast of County Cork. On Saturday 6 October, the day I arrived, no unusual European land birds had been found. With the wind in the west that was no surprise; the hard bit was finding a land bird *from* the west. American waifs are always few and far between. And they do not sit in the open and wave at you. When I saw a quiver among foliage in a thicket of alder trees I was confused at the sight of two bright white wing-bars. Chaffinches were on the island and they have a similar wing pattern. Might that explain the field mark? Among verdant foliage, female Chaffinches become chameleons, so a green veneer did not ring alarm bells. Until I saw the true shade: parrot green. Yikes! The foreigner was moving and twisting like a shower nozzle falling from a holder. It spied an insect on the underside of a leaf and nabbed it. As it swallowed lunch it sat still and I glimpsed and then worshipped a VIP face that I had only seen before in illustrations and photographs.

For me, Blackpoll Warbler's connection with the Old World brought delight. Sadly, that is less true for those that arrive. In effect, they are shipwrecked – alive but marooned in the wrong hemisphere. Or so we think. Moreover, having achieved a solo Atlantic crossing rivalling Amelia Earhart, the displaced are classified, in ornithological terms, as 'vagrants'. That seems harsh, especially when – adding insult to injury – a consensus of ignorance declares them to be lost. In truth, they know precisely where they are and that they have blundered. But then they are, after all, children. How can we tell?

Although young and old are outwardly similar in appearance, a bird in the hand is different. Experienced ringers can determine if an individual is immature by checking the condition of its skull. Basically, youngsters have thin skulls that, because the bone has not yet fully ossified (a hardening process that is usually not completed until after autumn migration), look paler than the skull of a fully ossified adult. Applying this test, of 266 autumn migrants trapped by David Wingate for ringing on Bermuda from 1963 to 1965, 96 per cent were young.[1] Because first-time migrants are less experienced, some members of this age group are more likely to be poor navigators. Indeed, a proportion of those trapped in Bermuda had dangerously low fuel levels. Although a crude yardstick, the statistic suggests that the river of migrants pouring from a staging area encompassing eastern Canada, New England and west to Virginia is concentrated west of Bermuda.

In the late 1970s, with a view to discovering migration routes, C. John Ralph analysed the age and distribution of 42,000 autumn songbird migrants from coastal Massachusetts to inland Pennsylvania.[2] He postulated that, for any species, the main criterion delineating the edge of a traditional route was suggested by a higher proportion of young among the overall density of records. Out of all the species he assessed, only Blackpoll Warbler conformed to an over-water, direct flight to South America. However, for almost all species – including Blackpoll Warbler – he detected a 'coastal effect', whereby the incidence of young was higher along the coast than on any other part of a main migration route. Ralph concluded that, because a higher percentage of young was among the cross-section of the population sampled at the margin of a recognised route, they were, to an extent, off-piste – or worse, 'most probably the young found near the coast lack some navigational capabilities and are off course; many of them probably perish.' Could it be that, by pooling the analysis of ringing data from Bermuda and Massachusetts, Blackpoll's autumn river in the sky flows strongest off the coast of New England?

'Did you hear that?' I did. I was beside Bruce Mactavish among fir branches festooned with lichen in Newfoundland. Ahead, a wall of green girdled an abandoned quarry; alders had sprung up and airbrushed the abandoned workings. The trees were bushy, dense as an All Blacks scrum and scarcely taller than us. Bruce made *kssh-kssh* sounds to pique the curiosity of anything hiding among the numberless leaves. In response, a cacophony of alarm notes resounded like enemy fire which, invisible at first, slowly encircled the pair of us. 'That lisping note … the sharp one … that's a Blackpoll. Got it?' I had. I tried to commit the sound to

Cape May Warbler is one of several foliage-hugging warblers that come in a selection box of colours and patterns – 'small, unfrightened quicknesses, that if you shook them they'd simply flutter free in loosened gusts… eye-ringed, wing-barred, marked or cowled with dark.' (Amy Clampitt)
PHOTOGRAPH: ROBBIE BROOKES

memory and make it stick like burning phosphorus. One day I might hear it in Ireland and know the source. In truth, I could have done with more sound and less imagery but once the fireworks started I was overwhelmed. Warblers were leaping, twisting and squirrelling into view. Mesmerised by Bruce, several added angst to his racket, which encouraged more to approach. The common horde consisted of Black-and-white Warblers, Blackpolls and Common Yellowthroats. Each hit double figures within minutes. I was on Cloud Nine but Bruce kept panning for gold. He enunciated new arrivals when he glimpsed a smidgen of plumage or pricked his ears at a telltale call: 'Wilson's … Yellow-rumped … kssh-kssh … Black-throated Green … CAPE MAY WARBLER!'

We reached a muddy patch in the woods and our ways parted. It was still early morning but it felt like the end of a journey. I was that little boy again, eyes full of wonder watching bijou warblers as they busied themselves for Brazil. Each possesses an incommunicable genetic link with the past. Destiny requires them to head for a distant coast, so far beyond the curve of Earth that September has been set aside to gather the world's population safely together on another continent.

Inishbofin, County Galway, is one of several Irish islands flanked by the North Atlantic but also sitting in the slipstream of Europe. Hence migratory birds from both worlds are possible. The island's vista of untamed ocean set against hard-as-steel coast is priceless; a time warp of scenery little changed since remnants of the Spanish Armada were blown against the same shores in 1558. White sand beaches etched with sun-dried wrack containing kelp flies attract skeins of shorebirds. Globetrotters arrive – Sanderlings from Greenland, Bar-tailed Godwits from Siberia and, rarely, White-rumped Sandpipers from the Canadian Arctic. Unlike Brent Geese that breed across Canada's tundra and use Ireland as a winter home, White-rumped Sandpipers should not be on our side of the pond; the species is unique to the western hemisphere. The bird is a shrinking violet. At no time in its life does it don ostentatious plumage. But more than any other shorebird on the planet, each individual is probably migrating between breeding areas in the Arctic and wintering areas as far south as Patagonia for at least six months of every year. Southward and northward routes are not the same, habitats are switched to maximise food intake and different prey species are chosen. And, until as recently as 1998, details of where most of the population go during a major portion of their migration were unknown.

From the moment a White-rumped Sandpiper chick's down is dry, it scampers through a romper room of tundra moss and fine grasses like a mouse on stilts. Its birthplace is the Arctic and its star sign is Cancer. Its parents arrived in early June when snow still covered the ground on the north side of hummocks unwarmed by the sun. The landscape is flat and peppered with pools. Hummocks act as advertising hoardings for males, who vocalise and launch acrobatic aerial displays. White-rumped Sandpipers are speed daters. Although they have just flown from staging grounds in the mid-west of the United States to north of the Arctic Circle, they begin frenetic breeding activities immediately so that a clutch of four eggs hatches in late June or early July, timed to coincide with around-the-clock daylight and an endless supply of insects for aspiring members of the next generation. Little is known about the activities of males after they have fathered a brood, except that they leave the breeding grounds well before the females. Researchers on the coast of Labrador, where southbound migrants begin to pass through in August, discovered that, in the early waves, males noticeably outnumbered females.[3] Juvenile White-rumped Sandpipers are among the last northern sandpipers to begin southbound migration. Just before freeze-up in October, some are still feeding on muddy shorelines in Hudson Bay. For a very good reason – they are taking on fuel. Evidence supports a single flight directly over the ocean between Canada and South America. No appreciable numbers touch down along the Atlantic coast of the United States and virtually none of many hundreds marked with dye in staging areas in Canada has been found in the United States.

White-rumped Sandpipers have a peculiar shape. They are longer-winged than similar-sized shorebirds and the wings are somewhat sickle-shaped. Like aeroplane design, there is a complex relationship between surface area, weight and speed. Perhaps White-rumped Sandpiper shape is super-aerodynamic? If so, to what height might they fly? Comparable studies of mean altitude heights used by shorebirds travelling, in autumn, over the Arctic Ocean between Siberia and North America produced a mean flight altitude of 1.3km (0.8 miles), and 10 per cent of birds regularly travelled above 3km (1.8 miles) up to a maximum height of 4.8km (2.9 miles). They preferred to migrate on occasions and at altitudes with following winds; such conditions provided an average gain in speed of 16km/h (10 mph). There were also recurrent cases of birds migrating in tailwinds of gale force, between 74km/h (46 mph) and 85km/h (53 mph).[4]

As with aircraft, birds' high altitude achieves some efficiency through reduced drag but, unlike planes, the birds must operate within the limits of an oxygen-driven metabolic system. Although it is shameless speculation, might their bloodstream possess, in addition to normal haemoglobin, 'high-elevation' haemoglobin designed to extract oxygen from rarefied air? What sounds like a Jules Verne invention is, in fact, an attribute of Bar-headed Geese that migrate over the Himalaya and fly at more than 5km above sea level. The geese have at least two types of haemoglobin. One supersedes the other when, departing north from India in spring, the birds climb from near sea level to altitudes of over 7km (more than 4 miles).[5]

Although a tropical country with a shoreline lapped by a warm ocean, Suriname's coastline is not universally sandy – a lot of it is mud. East of Suriname lies French Guiana and east of there lie Brazil and the mouth of the Amazon River. Throughout the immense Amazon watershed (covering 40 per cent of South America's land mass), there are dry and rainy seasons. Because nearly half of South America straddles the equator, some part of the continent will always be under the influence of a rainy season, sending run-off to the catchment area. The quantity of water flowing down the Amazon and its tributaries is so huge

Amazon rainforest at dawn. At the end of a third night on the wing, journey's end for a Blackpoll Warbler is breakfast in the tropics.
PHOTOGRAPH: TOM McGEEHAN

that downriver water levels fluctuate by up to 12 metres (40 feet) between seasons. Enormous pulses of freshwater flow from the Amazon into the Atlantic and much of it is carried north and west by the Guiana Current toward the coast of Suriname.[6] Here, the current settles as expansive mudflats, hopeless to walk upon yet navigable by boat: 'the tidal mudflats characteristic of the Suriname coast consist of a soupy mud known as sling mud. I saw a small boat actually sail (and make headway!) on the mud far back from the low-tide line.'[7] Accessing the habitat is further complicated by mangrove swamp that stretches several miles deep along the coast. The mud soup is chock-full of invertebrates. Might that be of interest to White-rumped Sandpipers?

During August and September 1982, Brian Harrington, a shorebird researcher, visited the Suriname coast to find out.[8]

We made our way to the coast by boat near the mouth of the Suriname River. We arrived just at dusk at a very short section of coast where there was enough high ground for the Suriname Forest Service to build a small visitor camp. Soon after dawn next morning I watched flock after flock of sandpipers, many of them White-rumpeds, passing east along the coast towards Brazil. Counts I kept showed that birds were passing my position at a rate of about 4,500 per hour. A similar flight happened during the next two mornings … later in the day I was able to get close enough to two feeding flocks to see that all the White-rumped Sandpipers were adults. None appeared to be fat. In fact, none caught by Arie Spaans, who spent three years studying the shorebird migration in Suriname during the 1970s, had enough fat to fly any great distance. Arie also found that the passage [of adult] White-rumped Sandpipers is mostly completed in Suriname by September.

Brian Harrington's observations suggest that White-rumped Sandpipers, when they leave Suriname, continue east – and towards Brazil. Perhaps they do. Alex Lees, who compiled shorebird data from field observations in Brazil and nearby

White-rumped Sandpiper's autumn migration is full of surprises. In an odyssey linking breeding grounds in the Arctic with winter quarters stretching from Argentina to Patagonia – a few have even reached the coast of Antarctica – the bird's route bisects Brazil. Rather than follow the Brazilian coast south, most follow a central flyway over Amazonia to reach the coast of Argentina.
PHOTOGRAPH: TOM McGEEHAN

countries in the 2000s, is not quite so sure: 'These birds do not move along the coast towards Brazil. They are rare anywhere on the coast north of the wintering areas. I believe that the whole population heads overland in a long-jump movement. Most White-rumped Sandpipers never land – otherwise we would see them in the interior, where they are only encountered in very modest numbers.'

The distance from Newfoundland to the Suriname coast is a little over 5,000km (3,000 miles). If White-rumped Sandpipers fly at a ground speed of around 65km/h (40 mph), they would require 65–75 hours to complete the flight. But if, like most other southbound migrants, they launch their flights when assistance can be derived from weather systems, especially tailwinds that come with cold fronts arriving from the north-west, the journey time will be significantly less. But will a migrant have enough fuel? Based on the ratio of wing length to body size, weight, flight speed and fat levels, biologists can (roughly) gauge how far a sandpiper can fly. According to the energy equations used, 20g of fat would sustain flight for a White-rumped Sandpiper of 40 to 45 hours. That would not, in theory, be enough for a migrant to reach the South American coast. Yet thousands do. Either the birds are flying faster than we think or, a key factor, they time their flight to gain maximum benefit from favourable winds.

Is it time to draw breath and pat the birds on the back for completing such an epic flight? Believe it or not, they are off again. Next stop Argentina. However, rather than follow a coastal route, they fly directly south, probably pitching down to feed along the muddy edges of rivers within Amazonia.[9] Some flying machines do not stop there but continue all the way to the Falkland Islands – where it is the most abundant shorebird during the austral summer – and the beaches north of Cape Horn. An enforced windborne diversion to Ireland is probably nothing to write home about. But, for a lucky finder, it is everything to write home about.

I suppose I should not have been surprised that it was asleep. The adult White-rumped Sandpiper was nestled among seaweed on a gravel beach on Portugal Cove South, one of the last bits of Newfoundland before the horizon leans south and out to sea. The foreshore was glazed with mist making the silhouette stand out against driftwood. At dusk, it might look up at the great star factory, zip aloft to check the wind and, assuming it has at least 20g of accumulated fat under the hood, set off for Suriname. I crawled over grey gravel to try for a picture. Seal-like squirming was easy. My boots filled with stony grains. I took my time, watching for a bill to unpeel from among plumage.

One eye followed my every move. I got within range for photographs. I tried a single click, not wanting to disturb it. More shots followed. It snuggled

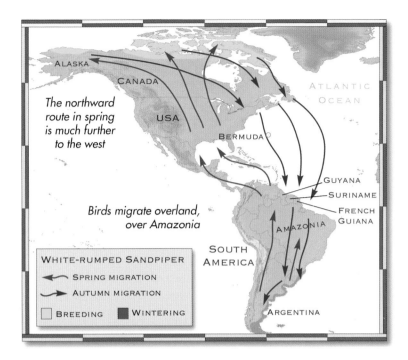

The northward route in spring is much further to the west

Birds migrate overland, over Amazonia

WHITE-RUMPED SANDPIPER
← SPRING MIGRATION
→ AUTUMN MIGRATION
☐ BREEDING   ■ WINTERING

ALASKA
CANADA
USA
BERMUDA
ATLANTIC OCEAN
GUYANA
SURINAME
FRENCH GUIANA
AMAZONIA
SOUTH AMERICA
ARGENTINA

deeper. What must it think of me? It trusts me and I am not going to frighten it. Little did it know that I had travelled thousands of miles for this moment. We exchanged an all-consuming regard that ignored everything else on Earth. I started my backwards crawl. It sensed the change of direction, which roused it to lift its head, as if to say, 'so you're not staying?' No, I was not. And, maybe later that night, neither was it.

Resting in a lee among lasagne-layered kelp in Newfoundland, this adult White-rumped Sandpiper is primed to migrate to South America. Departure is at night and out to sea – beyond the surf-roar to the far side of silence.

White-rumped Sandpiper (left) and Dunlin on Inishbofin, County Galway. For the White-rumped Sandpiper, it is the right habitat but the wrong hemisphere. Both shorebirds are juveniles acquiring plain-grey upper-parts – the new plumage is paler and more uniform, and resembles a shawl, especially where the feathers are homogenous high on the back. The remainder of the (darker) wing plumage is un-moulted first-generation kit. On White-rumped Sandpiper, the first-generation feathers are scallop-shaped; on Dunlin, the same feathers are more pointed and straight-sided. This distinction is noticeable at a much greater distance than White-rumped Sandpiper's shorter bill and neat head pattern with a level stripe running over the eye. In life, movement and shape are further distinctions. White-rumped Sandpiper has long, sickle-shaped wings (obviously longer than Dunlin) and a picky gait, probing hither and thither, rather than 'stitching' like a Dunlin. Although the white rump is diagnostic, it is usually hidden at rest – and superfluous to identification requirements.

29. Heritage lost
A ghost from history

Not one would mind, neither bird nor tree
If mankind perished utterly;
And spring herself, when she woke at dawn
Would scarcely know that we were gone.

Sara Teasdale

The Dodo is dead. Everyone knows that. Dodos evolved in isolation on the remote island of Mauritius. Although, millions of years earlier, the bird's ancestors – a kind of fruit-eating pigeon – colonised a string of Indian Ocean islands by flying from one to the next, flight became unnecessary when the population grew accustomed to living in paradise. Over time the wings shrank until they were no more than a feathery decoration. With the arrival

Contrary to popular belief, rather than an overweight ugly duckling, the Dodo was an endearing creature – a big-nosed Ziggy Stardust. This contemporary painting, by Dutch artist Cornelis Saftleven in 1638, is an original depiction, possibly based on one of several Dodos transported to Europe.

of seafarers on Mauritius at the turn of the seventeenth century, the species' trust in a benign existence was undone. Tame and flightless, the innocents were easily slaughtered. Yet, despite being as large and rotund as a turkey, one account did not consider them particularly good eating: 'her body is round and fat, few weigh less than fifty pounds ... more for wonder than for food, greasie stomackes may seek after them, but to the delicate they are offensive and of no nourishment.'[1] Dodos lived among predator-free dry coastal forest and fed, year-round, on fruit and seeds. Pigs, rats, cats and monkeys were liberated into this pristine universe. Within a century of being discovered, the species was extinct. To add insult to injury, the bird's name is a byword for stupidity and illustrations portray a podge. However, one life drawing by a contemporary Dutch painter (see above) captures a kindly countenance evoking a fledgling albatross.

The Capercaillie is Ireland's Dodo. Unlike the Dodo, its flesh made good eating. Bishop Henry Leslie, a Scotsman who was the Church of Ireland Bishop of Down and Connor from 1635 to 1661, recorded that the bird was 'very rare' perhaps, as he also remarked, because it had 'a gentle taste.'[2] There can scarcely be any doubt that the word Capercaillie, with all its many variations in spelling, comes direct from Gaelic, although seemingly Scottish Gaelic, not Irish. Following the thread of debate among linguistic scholars,[3] it appears that William Thompson, the greatest writer about Ireland's birds up to the time of his death in 1851, was right to refer to the species as 'Cock of the Wood', a derivation of *coileach feadha*, indicating Capercaillie, as opposed to *creabhar*, the Irish name for Woodcock.[4] Intrigue over the origin of the name does not end there. 'Caillie', it is commonly agreed, is an anglicised pronunciation of *coille*, the Gaelic word for woodland. 'Caper', on the other hand, might stem from *cabhar*, meaning old, that in an allegorical sense was a nod to the bird's

Male ostentation is counterposed by the female's need of camouflage. She is the one that will have to incubate eggs among undergrowth and chaperone young until they become independent. In a world of Scots Pine, her outfit matches the tree's flaky orange bark.
PHOTOGRAPH: FLORIS SMEETS

impressive stature – personified as 'the old bird of the wood'.[5] In reality, that title is apt only for an adult male. Males dwarf females and look entirely different. Female plumage is cryptic to provide concealment among branches of Scots Pine, the needles of which provide the staple diet, as well as to camouflage an incubating bird.

Males display during late winter and early spring. At first light they glide down from a roosting perch and parade at ground level, filling the air with a hiccupping tattoo that ends with a pop. Females spectate and are drawn to the finest troubadour in the district, who mates with each. Because, it is claimed, a male's voice resembles the clip-clop of a horse's hooves, not a few Gaelic scholars consider that 'Caper' is derived from *capall*, a horse. This interpretation gives 'horse of the woods'. As if to reinforce the moniker's phonetic credentials, several nineteenth century Scottish Gaelic scholars quote local sources that referred to the bird as *Capallcoille*.[6] Many bird names are, of course, down to whim.[7] Sadly, Ireland's Capercaillies disappeared sometime in the early eighteenth century. They had been part of our natural heritage for thousands of years, almost certainly since tree cover became re-established in the aftermath of the last Ice Age, about 10,000 years ago. In those distant times, humankind struggled to survive. The impact of hunter-gatherer Mesolithic people was negligible. Ireland was forested, and wood was used for everything – fuel, accommodation

What daybreak might have looked like in Ireland, *c.* 1000 BC. PHOTOGRAPH: REMO SAVISAAR

and weapons. Capercaillie remains, estimated to be around 7,000 years old, were among 79 bird bones identified at a Mesolithic settlement at Mount Sandel, overlooking the River Bann near Coleraine.[8] Neolithic farmers, who arrived roughly 5,000 years ago, cleared land for tillage and grazing. Soil studies indicate that their arrival coincided with a decline in tree pollen, and an increase in grass and cereal pollen. Agriculture was becoming a way of life. Nonetheless, in early Christian times, people lived by a body of custom that espoused woodland. Trees were valued, and penalties were imposed for cutting them down. In an economy lacking cash, cattle and timber were the main riches. Trees supplied heat, building material and even sustenance. Hazel nuts formed an important food and could be stored and eaten throughout the year.

Why, therefore, did the Capercaillie and much other forest-dwelling wildlife – wolves, wild cats and Goshawks, whose bones have all been found in Mesolithic settlements – disappear? In the blink of time between the end of the reign of Queen Elizabeth I in 1603 and the coronation of Queen Elizabeth II in 1952, Ireland's ecological framework was lost. In its place we see 'tourist board green' that has brainwashed a nation into believing that this is a natural appearance. Cultural amnesia is one thing but the extinction of flora and fauna that deprives us of a green heart is appalling. The firestorm's embers lay in the fact that ideas of 'possessing' land were not part of the native psyche until the notion became crucial during Tudor times (1485–1603). As colonisation sewed conflict with Irish society, woodland was exploited or razed. Land was cleared to make way for human plantations and farming. To boot, a military tactic was to destroy any woodland fastness in order to eradicate sanctuary for opposition. Queen Elizabeth I specifically ordered the felling of tree cover to deprive the Irish of shelter: 'the war waged on Irish soil became as much a war against the trees, against the Irish environment, as it was against anything else.'[9] Wolves were hunted and trapped to extinction. In the eyes of Lord Blennerhassett, that meant two-legged as well as four-legged varieties. In 1610, he recommended 'periodic manhunts to track down the human wolves to their lairs.'

When was the last Capercaillie seen? Writing in 1772 in the first volume of *The Natural History of Dublin*, J. Rutty states that a Cock of the Woods 'was seen in the County of Leitrim, about the year 1710, but they have entirely disappeared by reason of the destruction of our woods.'[10] For a first-hand description that describes an Irish Capercaillie, the source is a memoir written about Lord Deputy Wandesforde and the game to be found on his estate at Castlecomer, County Kilkenny, around 1640: 'this princely estate abounded with all sorts of wild fowl, particularly a most stately bird never known in England, called the Cock of the Wood, as large as a Turkey-cock, with black feathers, scarlet eyes [no doubt a reference to the vivid red wattle around the eye] and flesh more white and delicate than a Turkey's.'[11] All literature references to the species in Ireland were gathered together by Hall.[12] Environmental destruction in Ireland was paralleled in Scotland, where Capercaillies were lost at around the same time and for the same reasons: 'the destruction of great forest tracts by fire, the cutting down of the same by man, the wasting away of the forests from natural causes, by the conversion of dry forests into bogs and morasses and, from this, the decrease of the food of the species ... to get rid of wolves, a large pine forest extending from the western braes of Lochaber to the Black Water and mosses of Rannoch [as the crow flies, a distance of almost 100km or 60 miles] was burned ... the destruction of woods by enemies, thereby to remove a most important part of the national defence.'[13] Despite everything, a sufficient quantity of the Caledonian pine forest remained in Scotland so that, when reafforestation schemes began in the early eighteenth century, there was enough habitat to accommodate limited reintroductions of Capercaillies from Sweden.

If only it were that simple. Although Capercaillies are resident and live their lives in forest, evolution moulded them to fit within a specific woodland ecosystem. They seek the succulent needles and young shoots of Scots Pine. Such growth occurs at the ends of branches high on mature trees or on bushy saplings at lower elevations. Indeed, the body colour of females is a perfect match for the orange shade of stout branches that stretch beneath the crown of the tree and along which the birds walk to reach fresh sprays of foliage. For

In nature's plan, fallen trees rot and their light is freed up for seedlings, some of which have waited years to take their place. The richest stage in a wood's ageing process is provided by mature specimens, not the youngsters of 50 years and less. Trees respect their elders.
PHOTOGRAPH: STEFAN TAYLOR

the world's largest gamebird, Capercaillies are agile and feed, for the most part, among canopy and resort to terra firma only when fresh heather tips and, especially, bilberries are in season. Snow cover is not, consequently, a problem. In late spring chicks are led by mothers to damp ground where, to boost rapid growth, they feed exclusively on insects. Once youngsters switch to an adult diet, the entire species is, except for courtship rituals and ground-nesting, largely arboreal. To conjure a Capercaillie wood you need to imagine an enchanted forest dotted with sunlit clearings and the vault of a cathedral through which the heavyweights can fly without much hindrance. None of these attributes apply to modern forestry plantations.

Stefan Taylor, my half-Swedish guide, concentrated on keeping the car in the centre of the gravel track that threaded its way through dense forest interspersed with occasional bogs that shut on and off like a slide presentation. We left our base about an hour earlier (a wooden cabin with a sauna, log fire and stove, but no running water). Despite travelling through backwoods country, we were still not yet in Capercaillie habitat. To reach that, we walked. Before

Reminiscent of Breughel's depiction of winter in *The Hunters in the Snow*, female Capercaillies go into a huddle and prepare to watch the action of a displaying male.
PHOTOGRAPH: FLORIS SMEETS

hiking off-piste, Stefan double-checked that I had everything I needed to spend the night in a hide. I had not seen the accommodation, but I knew what to expect – an elegantly camouflaged but feeble tent. April in Sweden means sub-zero overnight temperatures, but all seemed to be in place to 'enjoy' being out in -10 °C. I had to be inside the hide at least 90 minutes before dark. Time was tight so dawdling to admire the Narnia-like surroundings was postponed.

Why the rush? Stefan was master of woods lore and he explained Capercaillie routine. Males have a fixed area within the forest – called a lek – which they visit around dawn every morning. Starting in late winter, they display against each other to determine rank. The dominant male then holds court and, when daylight lengthens and females come into breeding condition, the lek becomes his ballroom of romance. The trouble for me, Stefan explained, was that the male was moving around a lot – he defends about one hectare of forest – and because the display commences at dawn, he flies in to roost above the parade ground before dusk. That was why we were in a hurry. Contrary to popular belief, male Capercaillies are extremely shy and, if I was to watch the action next day, I had to be totally quiet and out of sight well before dusk. Stefan wished me luck and zipped the hide fabric shut. I was alone.

Wolves and wildcats roam these Swedish woods. I sat and peered through flimsy gauze draped over the hide's viewing ports. I wondered what creatures might, veiled by night, pad across the carpet of lichen and moss covering the ground. I had marvelled at Stefan's noiseless exit, made possible by the quilted terrain underfoot. Now I understood what nature intended mature pine forest to look like.

Ireland's Capercaillies were snuffed out when their home was trashed. Because the species does not migrate and is unable to fly across the sea, it will never return. Knowing the history, I wanted to collapse time and visit the past – and feel that I was in Ireland's lost world of magnificent birds and beasts.

No wind stirred and the air felt amplified. Evensong from thrushes sounded more reverential than normal but the backing vocals, trumpeting Cranes in a bog and Green Sandpipers 'singing' from treetops, stole the show. I watched golden shadows lengthen and turn auburn, then gutter to solemn dark green. Night was falling. I felt meditative. Not for long. Normally the sound of a downed tree is prefaced by a shout of 'timber!' The unannounced crash, therefore, was electrifying. And it was close; in fact, possibly in the Scots Pine above the hide. Stefan was right. He said that if the male Capercaillie arrived it would make one heck of a racket when it landed among branches. Game on![14]

I organised everything in preparation for daybreak. I had to know where I could reach my food, where I left the head torch and how I could access the pisspot. Everything had to be conducted in absolute silence. My biggest worry was setting the alarm on my phone. What if, instead of waking me, it woke the Capercaillie and caused it to fly? I set it for 0400hrs. At 0345hrs I was awakened by the Capercaillie. Behaving like a child on Christmas morning, it was revved up at the first glimmer of light. All hell broke loose. Its riff resembled wooden sticks being knocked together until the crazy drummer hit a high note. The rhythm was pure calypso, accompanied by a pulsating wheeze that, heard at only a few metres range, made me wonder if the hide might come under attack. I was still curled up deep inside my sleeping bag. To move was fatal – and that made it impossible to look. I lay there in the dark, transfixed and picturing the bird of my dreams.

SCIENTIFIC NAMES USED IN TEXT

Antarctic Tern *Sterna vittata*

Arctic Tern *Sterna paradisaea*

Arctic Fox *Vulpes lagopus*

Baltimore Oriole *Icterus galbula*

Barnacle Goose *Branta leucopsis*

Barred Warbler *Sylvia nisoria*

Bar-headed Goose *Anser indicus*

Bar-tailed Godwit *Limosa lapponica*

Black Grouse *Lyrurus tetrix*

Black-and-white Warbler *Mniotilta varia*

Blackbird *Turdus merula*

Blackcap *Sylvia atricapilla*

Black-headed Gull *Chroicocephalus ridibundus*

Blackpoll Warbler *Setophaga striata*

Black-tailed Godwit *Limosa limosa*

Black-throated Green Warbler *Setophaga virens*

Blue Jay *Cyanocitta cristata*

Blue Tit *Cyanistes caeruleus*

Bohemian Waxwing *Bombycilla garrulus*

Brambling *Fringilla montifringilla*

Brent Goose *Branta bernicla*

Bunchberry *Cornus canadensis*

Cape May Warbler *Setophaga tigrina*

Capercaillie *Tetrao urogallus*

Catbird *Dumetella carolinensis*

Cedar Waxwing *Bombycilla cedorum*

Chaffinch *Fringilla coelebs*

Chiffchaff *Phylloscopus collybita*

Collared Dove *Streptopelia decaocto*

Common Dolphin *Delphinus delphis*

Common Guillemot *Uria aalge*

Common (Mealy) Redpoll *Carduelis flammea*

Common Tern *Sterna hirundo*

Common Snipe *Gallinago gallinago*

Common Whitethroat *Sylvia communis*

Common Yellowthroat *Geothlypis trichas*

Cory's Shearwater *Calonectris diomedea*

Crested Tit *Lophophanes cristatus*

Crossbill *Loxia curvirostra*

Crowberry *Empetrum nigrum*

Cuckoo *Cuculus canorus*

Curlew *Numenius arquata*

Dodo *Rhapus cucullatus*

Dunnock *Prunella modularis*

European Eel *Anguilla anguilla*

Fieldfare *Turdus pilaris*

Field Sparrow *Spizella pusilla*

Fulmar *Fulmarus glacialis*

Gannet *Sula bassana*

Garden Warbler *Sylvia borin*

Glaucous Gull *Larus hyperboreus*

Goldcrest *Regulus regulus*

Golden-crowned Kinglet *Regulus satrapa*

Golden Oriole *Oriolus oriolus*

Goldfinch *Carduelis carduelis*

Great Frigatebird *Fregata minor*

Great Shearwater *Puffinus gravis*

Great Spotted Woodpecker *Dendrocopos major*

Grey-cheeked Thrush *Catharus minimus*

Greylag Goose *Anser anser*

Gyr Falcon *Falco rusticolus*

Hairy Woodpecker *Leuconotopicus villosus*

Hermit Thrush *Catharus guttatus*

Herring Gull *Larus argentatus*

Hooded Warbler *Setophaga citrina*

Hoopoe *Upupa epops*

House Martin *Delichon urbica*

House Sparrow *Passer domesticus*

House Wren *Troglodytes aedon*

Iceland Gull *Larus glaucoides*

Indigo Bunting *Passerina cyanea*

Ivory Gull *Pagophila eburnea*

Knot *Calidris canutus*

Kumlien's Iceland Gull *Larus glaucoides kumlieni*

Lanceolated Warbler *Locustella lanceolata*

Lapwing *Vanellus vanellus*

Laysan Albatross *Phoebastria immutabilis*

Leatherback Turtle *Dermochelys coriacea*

Lesser Whitethroat *Sylvia curruca*

Linnet *Carduelis cannabina*

Little Stint *Calidris minuta*

Loggerhead Turtle *Caretta caretta*

Long-tailed Skua *Stercorarius longicaudus*
Magnolia Warbler *Setophaga magnolia*
Magpie *Pica pica*
Manx Shearwater *Puffinus puffinus*
Marsh Tit *Poecile palustris*
Marsh Warbler *Acrocephalus palustris*
Meadow Pipit *Anthus pratensis*
Mediterranean Gull *Larus melanocephalus*
Merlin *Falco columbarius*
Mole Rat *Heterocephalus glaber*
Monarch Butterfly *Danaus plexippus*
Mourning Dove *Zenaida macroura*
Mourning Warbler *Geothlypis philadelphia*
Myrtle Warbler *Dendroica coronata*
Nightingale *Luscinia megarhynchos*
Nuthatch *Sitta europaea*
Osprey *Pandion haliaetus*
Painted Lady Butterfly *Vanessa cardui*
Pallas's Warbler *Phylloscopus proregulus*
Pied Flycatcher *Ficedula hypoleuca*
Pine Grosbeak *Pinicola enucleator*
Pipevine Swallowtail *Battus philenor*
Pink-footed Goose *Anser brachyrhynchus*
Ptarmigan *Lagopus mutus*
Purple Martin *Progne subis*
Purple Sandpiper *Calidris maritima*
Puffin *Fratercula arctica*
Razorbill *Alca torda*
Red-breasted Flycatcher *Ficedula parva*
Red-eyed Vireo *Vireo olivaceus*
Red-footed Booby *Sula sula*
Red Goose-foot *Oxybasis rubra*
Redstart *Phoenicurus phoenicurus*
Red-flanked Bluetail *Tarsiger cyanurus*
Red-throated Diver *Gavia stellata*
Redwing *Turdus iliacus*
Reed Warbler *Acrocephalus scirpaceus*
Ring Ouzel *Turdus torquata*
Robin *Erithacus rubecula*
Rock Dove *Columba livia*
Rose-breasted Grosbeak *Pheucticus ludovicianus*
Ruby-crowned Kinglet *Regulus calendula*

Rufous Bush Robin *Cercotrichas galactotes*
Rustic Bunting *Emberiza rustica*
Rusty Blackbird *Euphagus carolinus*
Sanderling *Calidris alba*
Sedge Warbler *Acrocephalus schoenobaenus*
Siskin *Carduelis spinus*
Skylark *Alauda arvensis*
Silver Y Moth *Autographa gamma*
Slate-coloured Junco *Junco hyemalis*
Snow Bunting *Plectrophenax nivalis*
Snowy Owl *Nyctea scandiaca*
Song Thrush *Turdus philomelos*
Sooty Shearwater *Puffinus griseus*
Song Sparrow *Melospiza melodia*
Sparrowhawk *Accipiter nisus*
Spotted Flycatcher *Muscicapa striata*
Starling *Sturnus vulgaris*
Stonechat *Saxicola torquata*
Storm Petrel *Hydrobates pelagicus*
Swallow *Hirundo rustica*
Swainson's Thrush *Catharus ustulatus*
Tawny Pipit *Anthus campestris*
Thayer's Gull *Larus thayeri*
Tree Pipit *Anthus trivialis*
Turnstone *Arenaria interpres*
Turtle Dove *Streptopelia turtur*
Waxwing *Bombycilla garrulus*
Wheatear *Oenanthe oenanthe*
Whimbrel *Numenius phaeopus*
White-fronted Goose *Anser albifrons*
White Stork *Ciconia ciconia*
White-throated Sparrow *Zonotrichia albicollis*
White-rumped Sandpiper *Calidris fuscicollis*
Willow Tit *Poecile montanus*
Willow Warbler *Phylloscopus trochilus*
Wilson's Warbler *Cardellina pusilla*
Woodchat Shrike *Lanius senator*
Wren *Troglodytes troglodytes*
Yellow-shafted (Northern) Flicker *Colaptes auratus*
Yellow-bellied Sapsucker *Sphyrapicus varius*
Yellow-browed Warbler *Phylloscopus inornatus*
Yellowthroat *Geothlypis trichas*

SOURCES OF POETRY & LITERATURE QUOTATIONS

1 The day imagination caught fire
Young, Neil. 1970. 'Helpless' from *Déjà vu* album. 1970. Atlantic Recording Corporation.

2 Types of migration
Benson, S.V. 1937. *The Observer's Book of Birds*, p. 7. Frederick Warne & Co. Ltd. London and New York.

3 The source of Ireland's visiting Blackbirds
Dickinson, Emily & Peter Washington. 1993. A winged spark doth soar about' from *Everyman's Library Pocket Poets – Dickinson*, p. 122. Alfred A Knopf. New York, Toronto and London.

4 Triggers of migratory behaviour
Cather, Willa. 2013. 'Sleep, minstrel, sleep' from *Everyman's Library Pocket Poets – April Twilights and Other Poems*, p. 71. Alfred A Knopf. New York, Toronto and London.

5 The physiology of migration
Birkhead, T., Wimpenny, J. & Montgomerie, B. 2014. *Ten Thousand Birds*, p. 118. Princeton University Press. Princeton and Oxford.

6 Assessing the weather
White, E.B. 1952. *Charlotte's Web*, p. 243. Penguin Books. London.

7 Atmospheric motion – its influence on migration
MacNeice, Louis. 1949. 'London Rain' from *Collected Poems 1925–1948*, p. 183. Faber & Faber Ltd. London.

8 Giant-leap travellers
McGeehan, T. (2009) 'Enter spring – hello summer'. Private publication.

9 Tracking through hurricanes
Raine, Kathleen. 2000. 'Nocturn' from *The Collected Poems of Kathleen Raine*. Golgonooza Press. Ipswich.

10 A hurricane called Daisy
Durand, Alan L. *British Birds* 65:435.

11 The role of instinct
Hemingway, Ernest. 1952. *The Old Man and the Sea*, p. 40. Charles Scribner's Sons. New York.

12 Inborn ability
Albert A. Laverty, letter to the Editor, *The Field*.

13 Nature's magnetic signpost
Philbrick, Nathan. 2003. *Sea of Glory*, p. 34. Harper Perennial. London.

14 Earth's magnetic field
Heaney, Seamus. 1969. 'The Return' (from 'A Lough Neagh Sequence: 6') from *Door Into The Dark*. Faber & Faber. London.

15 Evidence that birds perceive magnetic fields
Roswitha Wiltschko quoted in Birkhead, T., Wimpenny, J. & Montgomerie, B. 2014. *Ten Thousand Birds*, p. 151. Princeton University Press. Princeton and Oxford.

16 Light, magnetism and the avian eye
Davies, W.H. 1907. 'The Moon and a Cloud' from *The Soul's Destroyer and Other Poems*. Self-published.

17 Star patterns and orientation
Akhmatova, Anna. 2006. 'This land …' from *Everyman's Library Pocket Poets – Akhmatova*, p. 176. Alfred A Knopf. New York, Toronto and London.

18 Skylight polarisation and navigation
Wallace, D.I.M. *British Birds* 94:116.

19 Other beacons
Gätke, Heinrich. 1895. *Heligoland as an Ornithological Observatory*, p. 142. David Charles. Edinburgh.

20 Statistics of slaughter
Clampitt, Amy. 2010. 'Fog' from *Amy Clampitt, Selected Poems*, p. 5. Alfred A Knopf. New York.

21 Flights of reckoning
Bourke, Eva. 2016. 'Swallows' from *Fermata*, p. 45. Artisan House. Letterfrack, County Galway.

22 Winning the migration lottery
Emerson, R.W. 1876. *Letters and Social Aims*, p. 263. J.R. Osgood. Boston.

23 Ivory Gull
Hewitt, John. 2007. 'Grey and White' from *The Selected Poems of John Hewitt*, ed. Michael Longley and Frank Ormsby (Blackstaff Press) reproduced by permission of Blackstaff Press on behalf of the Estate of John Hewitt.

24 Song Thrush traditional routes
McGeehan, A. 2018. *To the Ends of the Earth*. The Collins Press. Cork.

25 Wintering out
Cather, Willa. 1918. *My Antonia*, p. 179. Houghton-Mifflin, Boston.

26 Chasing Shearwaters
Melville, Herman. 1851. *Moby Dick*, p. 193. Richard Bentley (Britain) and Harper Brothers (USA).

27 Of Herring Gulls and hubris
Eric Cantona, speaking at a press conference at Croydon Park Hotel, Croydon, on 31 March 1995.

28 A trip to Newfoundland
McKay, Don. 1983. 'Dusk' from *Birding, (or Desire)*. McClelland & Stewart Ltd, Toronto.

29 Heritage lost
Teasdale, Sara. 1918. 'There will come soft rains'. Originally published in the July 1918 issue of *Harper's Magazine*, New York.

ACKNOWLEDGEMENTS

To my wife Mairead, once again – without you, no book. In attempting to cross between watching birds and understanding the scientific explanations for how and why they migrate, I owe a huge debt to Richella Duggan, an indefatigable editor, who scrutinised the text as it emerged – fitfully and often in need of translation into English. As more and more information revealed the global extent of birds' movements – many elucidated for the first time by data loggers attached to the subjects themselves – I realised that I needed an illustrator. Michael O'Clery, by combining ornithological knowledge with artistic skills, did his outstanding best for the cause of bringing these travels to life. David Quinn, a veteran of the author's 'gull days' (along with the late Martin Garner whose influence is celebrated in Chapter 27) provided exquisite artwork at short notice.

People whose expertise I admire were kind enough to read the text, improving it and directing me to additional references. The efforts of Alex Lees, Jochen Dierschke, Nick Watmough, Julian Wyllie, Frank Murphy, Neville McKee, Eleanor Keane, Joe Furphy, Phillips Wilson, Heather Robinson and Ken and Kathy Knowles all led to a higher standard than I would have achieved by myself. For technical guidance on subjects outside my understanding I am grateful to Rebecca Holberton (University of Maine) and Thomas Cronin (University of Maryland). Cas Eikenaar and Heiko Schmaljohann, researchers connected to Heligoland Bird Observatory in Germany, answered queries and directed me to important literature sources. Diverse requests for help drew kindness from strangers scattered across many lands. In Germany, Rainer Hutterer, archivist for the Kollmansperger expedition (Chapter 5) supplied the expedition's photographs for me to use and Regina Moritz answered questions about her research into how mole-rats sense Earth's magnetic field. In North America, Bryan D. Watts supplied jaw-dropping information about the results he and Fletcher D. Smith have obtained from tracking Whimbrels. At NASA, Robert Nemiroff put me in contact with Jia Hao in China, in order that I could use his beautiful image (Chapter 17). In Ireland, Simon Berrow and Padraig Whooley tracked down a picture of a Leatherback Turtle in Irish waters (taken by Ian Slevin) that I hoped might exist. On Inishbofin, County Galway, I received great assistance from Paddy-Joe and Regina King, Seamus Concannon, Jackie Jefferson, Pat Coyne, Marie Coyne, Kieran Day and John Mercer. Frank and Anne Turpin recommended the poetry of Amy Clampitt for the opening of Chapter 20. Eva Bourke, when I heard her recital at the 2016 *Inish* festival on Inishbofin, kindly allowed me to use some of her sublime verse for the opening of Chapter 21. Then, out of the blue, Dennis Hawke made me a gift of his poetry – written specifically for the book. Amazing!

I am delighted to include captivating images taken by Alex Lees, Andy Johnson, Amar Ayyash, Arie Ouwerkerk, Brandon Holden, Bruce Mactavish, Einar Gudmanns, Floris Smeets, G. Niethammer, Jim Richardson, Joe Pender, Martin Grimm, Michael Clarke, Remo Savisaar, Robbie Brookes, Silas Olofson, Sindri Skulason, Stefan Tyler and Steve Gantlett. Among the photographers are two other skilled snappers – my daughter Kathryn and son Tom.

Two overseas trips were made for the chapters about the migration of Blackpoll Warblers and White-rumped Sandpipers through Newfoundland (Chapter 28) and to encounter wild Capercaillies in Sweden (Chapter 29). Without the help of Bruce, Donna and Ian Mactavish, Kathy and Ken Knowles and John Wells in Newfoundland, and Stefan Tyler, Kari Knight, Richard Youell and Pete Smith in Sweden, neither trip would have been successful.

Many people provided tips and inspiration – or inadvertently uttered a sparkling word or phrase that was eagerly gathered in and recycled in the book's paragraphs. I want to express deep gratitude to Angela Ross, Craig Nash, Eric Dempsey, Feargal Ó Cunneagáin, Flora Irwin, Geraldine McCartney, J. McCutcheon, Jean Wood, Joe Doolin, Julian Greenwood, Julian Hough, Kerry Leonard, K.S. Douglas, Maria Veronica Laura, Ned Brinkley, Sharon Garner, Sian Phillips, Stan Nugent, Stephanie Sim, Tess Hines, Trevor McComb and Victor Caschera.

Corncrake

REFERENCES

Chapter 1: The day imagination caught fire

1 Steadman, D.W. 'The paleoecology and fossil history of migratory landbirds.' In *Birds of Two Worlds*. Greenberg, R. & Marra, P.P. (eds), 2005. Johns Hopkins University Press, Baltimore, USA and London.

2 Voelker, G. 2002. 'Systematics and historical biogeography of wagtails: dispersal versus vicariance revisited.' *Condor* 104:725–739.

3 Ruegg, K.C. & Smith, T.B. 2002. 'Not as the crow flies: a historical explanation for circuitous migration in Swainson's Thrush.' *Proceedings of the Royal Society of London, Series B, Biological Sciences* 269:1375–1381.

Chapter 2: Types of migration

1 Snow, D.W. 1958. *A Study of Blackbirds*. George Allen & Unwin Ltd, London.

2 Bakken *et al*. 2006. *Norwegian Bird Ringing Atlas vol. 2*. Stavanger Museum; Fransson *et al*. 2008. *Swedish Bird Ringing Atlas vol. 3*. Swedish Museum of Natural History and Ornithological Society.

3 Drost, R. 1935. 'Ueber das Zahlverhaltnis von alter und Geschlecht auf dem Herbst- und Fruhjahrzuge,' *Vogelzug* 6:177–82.

4 Werth, I. 1947. 'The tendency of Blackbird and Song Thrush to breed in their birthplaces.' *British Birds* (hereafter BB) 40:328–330.

5 Baker, R.R. 1993. 'The function of post-fledging exploration: a pilot study of three species of passerines ringed in Britain.' *Ornis Scandinavica* 24:71–79.

Chapter 3: The source of Ireland's visiting Blackbirds

1 Montgomerie, R. & Weatherhead, P.J. 1997. 'How [American] Robins find worms.' *Animal Behaviour* 54:143–51.

2 Spencer, R. 1975. 'Changes in the distribution of recoveries of ringed Blackbirds.' *Bird Study* 22 (number 3): 177–190.

3 Clafton, F.R. 1971. 'Large weight gain by a migrant Nightingale.' BB 64:320.

4 Figures given by Emile Witschi, quoted by Spencer, R. 1963. *Instructions to Young Ornithologists* (p. 29). The Brompton Library. Museum Press. London.

5 https://youtu.be/U3Fy2_8I8Q0

Chapter 4: Triggers of migratory behaviour

1 https://en.wikipedia.org/wiki/Galileo

2 Rowan, W. 1931. *The Riddle of Migration*. Williams and Wilkins. Baltimore.

3 Hooper, M. 1975. *Nature through the Seasons* (p. 15). Penguin Books. Harmondsworth, Middlesex, England.

4 Holberton, R.L. & Dufty, A.M. 2005. 'Hormones and variation in Life History Strategies of Migratory and Nonmigratory Birds.' In *Birds of Two Worlds*, Greenberg, R. & Marra, P.P (eds), 2005. Johns Hopkins University Press. Baltimore, USA and London.

5 Hau, M., Wikelski, M. & Wingfield, J.C. 2000. 'Visual and nutritional food cues fine-tune timing of reproduction in a Neotropical rainforest bird.' *Journal of Experimental Zoology* 286:494–504.

6 Putzig, P. 1938. 'Beobachtungen uber Zugunruhe beim Rotkehlchen (*Erithacus rubecula*).' *Vogelzug* 9:10–14.

Chapter 5: The physiology of migration

1 Piersma, T. & Gill, R.E.J. 1998. 'Guts don't fly: small digestive organs in obese Bar-tailed Godwits.' *Auk* 115:196–203.

2 Karasov, W.H. & Pinshow, B. 1998. 'Changes in lean mass and in organs of nutrient assimilation in a long-distance migrant at a springtime stopover site.' *Physiological Zoology* 71:435–448.

3 Cooke, W.W. 1904. 'Some new facts about the migration of birds.' In *Yearbook of Department of Agriculture for 1903*. Washington DC: GPO. pp. 371–386.

4 Gauthreaux, S.A. Jr. 1971. 'A radar and direct visual study of passerine spring migration in southern Louisiana.' *Auk* 88:343–365.

5 Moreau, R.E. 1961. 'Problems of Mediterranean–Saharan migration.' *Ibis* 103:373–472, 580–623.

6 Sayed Ahmed, A.A. 1948. 'Khamsin and khamsin conditions.' *Meteorological Department of Cairo, Paper 1*. (Quoted by Moreau in reference 22, p. 386.)

7 Odum, E.P. 1960. 'Lipid deposition in nocturnal migrant birds.' *Proceedings of the 12th International Ornithological Congress*. 1958:563–575.

8 Kollmansperger, F. 1959. 'Ornithologische Beobachtungen in Ennedigebirge.' *Bonner zoologische Beiträge*. 10:21–67.

9 Bairlein, F. 2008. 'The mysteries of bird migration – still much to be learnt.' *BB* 101: 68–81.

10 Holberton, R.L. & Dufty, A.M. 2005. 'Hormones and variation in Life History Strategies of Migratory and Nonmigratory Birds.' In *Birds of Two Worlds*, Greenberg, R. & Marra, P.P (eds), 2005. Johns Hopkins University Press, Baltimore, USA and London. 11 Gladwin, T.G. 1963. '*Acrocephalus* weight increases.' *Bird Migration* 2 (no. 5): 319–323.

12 McGeehan, A. & Wyllie, J. 2014. *Birds of the Homeplace*, pp. 115–118. The Collins Press. Cork.

13 Jenni, L., Jenni-Eiermann, S., Spina, F. & Schwabl, H. 2000. 'Regulation of protein breakdown and adrenocortical response to stress in birds during migratory flight.' *American Journal of Physiology (Regulatory, Integrative and Comparative Physiology)*. 278:R1182–R1189.

14 Klassen, M. & Biebach, H. 2000. 'Flight altitude of trans-Saharan migrants in autumn: A comparison of radar observations with predictions from meteorological conditions and water and energy balance models.' *Journal of Avian Biology* 31:47–55.

15 Pennycuick, C.J. 1975. 'Mechanics of flight.' Pp. 1–75 in *Avian Biology*. Vol. 5 (Farner, D.S. & King, J.R., eds) Academic Press. New York.

16 Minton, C., Gosbell, K., Johns, P., Christie, P., Fox, J.W. & Afanasyev, V. 'Initial results from light level geo-locator trials on Ruddy Turnstone reveal unexpected migration route.' *Wader Study Group Bulletin* 117:9–14.

17 Gill, R.E. Jr., Tibbitts, T.L. & Douglas, D.C., *et al.* 2009. 'Extreme endurance flights by landbirds crossing the Pacific Ocean: ecological corridor rather than barrier?' *Proceedings of the Royal Society B: Biological Sciences* 267:447–457.

Chapter 6: Assessing the weather

1 Liechti, F & Bruderer, B. 1998. 'The relevance of wind for optimal migration theory.' *Journal of Avian Biology* 29:561–568.

2 Baumgartner, M. 1997. 'Wetterabhangigkeit des nachtlichen Vogelzuges im Herbst uber Suddeutschland.' PhD Diss. Universitat Basel, Sempach.

3 Hansson, L-A. & Akesson, S. 2014. *Animal Movement Across Scales*, p. 77. Oxford University Press.

4 Delingat, J., Schmaljohann, H., Mendel, B. & Bairlein, F. 2006. 'Daily stopovers as optimal migration strategy in a long-distance migrating passerine: the Northern Wheatear *Oenanthe oenanthe*.' *Ardea* 94:593–605.

5 Dierschke, V. & Delingat, J. 2003. 'Stopover of Northern Wheatears *Oenanthe oenanthe* at Helgoland: where do the migratory routes of Scandinavian and Nearctic birds join and split?' *Ornis Svecica* 13:53–61.

6 Schaub, M., Liechti, F. & Jenni, L. 2004. 'Departure of migrating European Robins, *Erithacus rubecula*, from a stopover site in relation to wind and rain.' *Animal Behaviour* 67:229–237. doi:10.1016/j.anbehav.2003.03.011

7 Bruderer, B. 1971. 'Radarbeobachtungen uber den Fruhlingszugs im Schweizerischen Mittelland.' *Ornithologische Beobachter* 68:89–158.

8 Kreithen, M.L. & Keeton, W.T. 1974. 'Detection of changes in atmospheric pressure by homing pigeon *Columba livia*.' *Journal of Comparative Physiology B* 89:73–82. doi:10.1007/BF00696164

9 Weimerskirch, H., Bishop, C., Jeanniard-du-Dot, T., Prudor, A. & Sachs, G. 2016. 'Frigatebirds track atmospheric conditions over months-long transoceanic flights.' *Science* 353:74–78. doi:10.1126/science.aaf4374

Chapter 7: Atmospheric motion – its influence on migration

1 McWilliams, B. 2008. *The Book of Weather Eye* p. 111. Gill & Macmillan. Dublin.

2 Philbrick, N. 2003. *Sea of Glory* (p. 66). Harper Perennial, London

Chapter 8: Giant-leap travellers

1 Egevang, C., Stenhouse, I.J., Phillips, R.A., Petersen, A., Fox, J.W. & Silk, J.R.D. 2010. 'Tracking of Arctic Terns reveals longest animal migration.' *Proceedings of the National Academy of Sciences* 107 (no. 5): 2078–2081; Fijn, R. *et al.* 2013. 'Arctic Terns from the Netherlands migrate record distances across three oceans to Wilkes Land, East Antarctica.' *Ardea* 101:3–12.

2 Summers, R.W. *et al.* 2014. 'Contrasting trans-Atlantic migratory routes of Nearctic Purple Sandpipers *Calidris maritima* associated with low pressure systems in spring and summer.' *Ardea* 102:139–152. doi:10.5253/arde.v102i2.a4

3 McLean, I. & Williamson, K. 1961.' Migrants at ocean weather-ships, Autumn 1960.' *Bird Migration* 1 (no. 5): 245–249.

4 McLean, I. & Williamson, K. 1957. 'Migrants at North Atlantic weather ships in 1956.' *Marine Observer* 27:152–156.

5 Barrington, R.M. 1900. *The Migration of Birds as observed at Irish Lighthouses and Lightships*. R.H. Porter and Edward Ponsonby. London and Dublin.

Chapter 9: Tracking through hurricanes

1 Dennis, R.H., Etheridge, B., Foster, S., Heaton, J. & Swann, R.L. 2011. 'Satellite-tracking of a Curlew migrating between Scotland and Finland.' *Scottish Birds* 31:3–7; British Trust for Ornithology ringing recovery FC50768. Ringed 9 August 1993, Marston, Lincolnshire; recovered Onezhskiy, Arkhangel, Russia (2,541km ENE) 10 June 1995.

2 Wader Study Group. 2016. 'Migration and non-breeding distribution of Icelandic Whimbrels as revealed by ringing recoveries.' *IWSG*:123 (no. 1), 44–48. doi:10.18194/ws.00031

3 Alves, J.A., Dias, M.P., Méndez, V., Katrínardóttir, B. & Gunnarsson T.G. 2016. 'Very rapid long-distance sea crossing by a migratory bird.' *Science Reports* 6: 38154. doi:10.1038/srep38154

4 www.birdguides.com Webzine article published online in 2011: 'Whimbrel tracked by scientists killed by hunters on Guadeloupe'.

5 Alex Lees pers. comm. December 2017.

6 www.ccbbirds.org/2015/08/28/whimbrel-tracked-into-tropical-storm-erika

Chapter 10: A hurricane called Daisy

1 Chapman, J.W., Nesbit, R.L., Burgin, L.E., Reynolds, D.R., Smith, A.D., Middleton, D.R. & Hill, J.K. 2010. 'Flight orientation behaviours promote optimal migration trajectories in high-flying insects.' *Science* 327: 682–685.

2 Williams, T.C., Williams, J.M., Ireland, L.C. & Teal, J.M. 1977. 'Autumnal bird migration over the western North Atlantic.' *American Birds* 31 (no. 3, May 1977): 251–267.

3 Elkins, N. 1983. *Weather and Bird Behaviour*. T. & A. D. Poyser. Calton.

4 Elkins, N. 1979. 'Nearctic landbirds in Britain and Ireland – a meteorological analysis.' *BB* 72:417–433.

5 Durand, A. L. 1972. 'Landbirds over the North Atlantic: unpublished records 1961–65 and thoughts a decade later.' *BB* 65:428–442.

6 Durand, A. L. 1963. 'A remarkable fall of American land-birds on the *Mauretania*, New York to Southampton, October 1962.' *BB* 56:157–164.

7 The Cornell Lab of Ornithology. 'Red-eyed Vireo, Life History.' www.allaboutbirds.org/guide/Red-eyed_Vireo/lifehistory

8 Thorbush, E.H. 1929. *Birds of Massachusetts and other New England States* p. 181. Norwood Press.

9 'Red-eyed Vireo, Life History', www.allaboutbirds.

10 Slack, R. 2009. *Rare Birds Where and When. An Analysis of Status & Distribution in Britain and Ireland* p. 349. Russell Slack. Rare Bird Books, MPG Books Group, Bodmin and King's Lynn, England.

Chapter 11: The role of instinct

1 Magee, M.J. 'Notes on the returns of the Eastern Purple Finch and their sex ratio.' *Bird Banding* 11:110–111.

2 https://app. bto.org/ring/countryrec/results2015/longevity.htm

3 Nisbet, I.C.T., Winchell, J.M., & Heise, A.E. 1984. 'Influence of age on the breeding of Common Terns.' *Colonial Waterbirds* 7:117–126.

4 Drost, R. 1938. 'Uber den Einfluss von Verfrachtungen zur Herbstzugzeit auf den Sperber, *Accipiter nisus.' IXe Congr. Orn. Int.*, (pp. 503–521).

5 van Dobben, W.H. 1939. *Stichting Vogeltrekstation 'Texel'*. Jaarverslagen 1937 en 1938 (pp. 12–14).

6 Perdeck, A.C. 1958. 'Two types of orientation in migrating Starlings and Chaffinches, as revealed by displacement experiments.' *Ardea* 46:1–37.

7 https://phys.org/news/2015-11-cuckoo-scientific-mystery-bird-migration.html#jCp

8 Vega, M.L., Willemoes, M., Thomson, R.L., Tolvanen, J., Rutila, J., & Samas, P. 2016. 'First-time migration in juvenile Common Cuckoos documented by satellite tracking.' *PLoS ONE* 11(12): e0168940.doi:10.1371/journal.pone.0168940

Chapter 12: Inborn ability

1 Mathews, G.V.T. 1968. *Bird Navigation* (second ed.), pp 26–27. Cambridge University Press, London.

2 Mathews, G.V.T. 1954. 'Some aspects of incubation in the Manx Shearwater, with particular reference to chilling resistance in the embryo.' *Ibis* 96:432–440.

3 Southern, W. 1959. 'Homing of Purple Martins.' *Wilson Bulletin* 71:254–261.

4 Kenyon, K.W. & Rice, D.W. 1958. 'Homing of Laysan Albatrosses.' *Condor* 60:3–6.

5 Gätke, H. 1895. *Heligoland as an Ornithological Observatory. The Result of Fifty Years' Experience*. David Douglas. Edinburgh.

6 von Middendorf, A.T. 1848–1875. *Reise in den aussersten Norden und Osten Sibiriens* 4 (part ii): 1168.

7 Wallace, D.I.M. 2004 *Beguiled by Birds* (p. 46). Christopher Helm. London.

Chapter 13: Nature's magnetic signpost

1 Pumfrey, S. 2002 *Latitude & the Magnetic Earth*. Icon Books. Cambridge.

2 Wulf, A. 2015. *The Invention of Nature* (p. 90). John Murray, London.

3 Philbrick, N. 2003. *Sea of Glory* (p. 156). Harper Perennial, London.

4 Merrill, R.T. 2010. *Our Magnetic Earth: the Science of Geomagnetism*. University of Chicago Press.

5 www.scientificamerican.com/article/dolphins-may-use-magnetic-sense-as-gps

Chapter 14: Earth's magnetic field

1 Wilcox, C. 2012. 'Evolution: Out of the Sea.' https://blogs.scientificamerican.com/science-sushi/evolution-out-of-the-sea/

2 Merill, R.T. 2010. *Our Magnetic Earth: the Science of Geomagnetism* (p. 151). University of Chicago Press.

3 Blakemore, R. 1975. 'Magnetotactic Bacteria.' *Science* 190:377–379.

4 Gould, Stephen Jay. 1980. *The Panda's Thumb*. Penguin Science, New York and London. In chapter 30, Gould discusses crucial discoveries in magnetotactic bacteria made by Richard B. Frankel.

5 Wegner, R.E., Begal, S. & Burda, H. 2006. 'Light perception in "blind" subterranean Zambian Mole-rats *Fukomys* species.' *Animal Behaviour* 72:1021–1024. doi:10.1016/j.anbehav.2006.02.018

6 Kimchi, T. & Terkel, J. 2001. 'Magnetic compass orientation in the Blind Mole Rat *Spalax ehrenbergi*.' *Journal of Experimental Biology* (hereafter *JEB*). 204:751–758.

7 Wegner, R.E., Begal, S. & Burda. 2006. 'Magnetic compass in the cornea: local anaesthesia impairs orientation in a mammal.' *JEB*. 209:4747–4750. doi:10.1242/jeb.02573

8 Viney, M. & Viney, E. 2008. *Ireland's Ocean* p. 167. The Collins Press. Cork.

9 Doyle *et al.* 2008. 'Leatherback Turtles satellite-tagged in European waters.' *Endangered Species Research* vol. 4:23–31. doi:10.3354/esr00076

10 Light, P., Lohmann, K.J. & Salmon, M. 1993. 'Geomagnetic orientation of Loggerhead Sea Turtles: evidence for an inclination compass.' *JEB*. 182:1–10.

11 Durif, C.M.F., Browman, H.I., Phillips. J.B., Skiftesvik, A.B., Vollestad, L.A. & Stockhausen, H.H. 2013. 'Magnetic compass direction in the European Eel.' *PLoS One* 8 (3):e59212 doi:10.1371/journal.pone.0059212

12 *The Empirical Observations of the Spawning Migration of European Eels: the long and dangerous road to the Sargasso Sea*. 2016. Research by 16 European marine biologists, published online by *Science*. https://iti.ms/2eNLgRa

Chapter 15: Evidence of magnetic perception in birds

1 Schmidt-Koenig, K. & Keeton, W.T. (eds). 1978. *Animal Migration, Navigation and Homing* (p. 127). Springer-Verlag. Berlin.

2 Walcott, C. 1992. 'Pigeons at magnetic anomalies: the effects of loft location.' *JEB*. 170:127–141.

3 Walcott, C. & Green, R.P. 1972. 'Orientation of homing pigeons altered by a change in the direction of an applied magnetic field.' *Science* 184:180–182.

4 Wiltschko, W. 1978. 'Further analysis of the magnetic compass of migratory birds' (p. 302). In: Schmidt-Koenig, K. & Keeton, W.T. (eds). 1978. *Animal Migration, Navigation and Homing* (p. 127). Springer-Verlag. Berlin.

5 Eikenaar, C., Klinner, T., Szostek, K.L. & Bairlein, F. 2014. 'Migratory restlessness in captive individuals predicts actual departure in the wild.' *Biology Letters*. 2014 10, 20140154.

6 Wiltschko, W. 1968. 'Uber den Einfluss statischer magnetfelder auf die Zugorienticrung der Rotkehlchen (*Erithacus rubecula*).' *Zeitschrift fur Tierpsychologie* 25:537–558.

7 Wiltschko, W. 1978. 'Further analysis of the magnetic compass of migratory birds' (p. 305). In: Schmidt-Koenig, K. & Keeton, W.T. (eds). 1978. *Animal Migration, Navigation and Homing* (p. 127). Springer-Verlag. Berlin.

8 Wiltschko, W. & Wiltschko, R. 1992. 'Migratory orientation: magnetic compass orientation of Garden Warblers after a simulated crossing of the magnetic equator.' *Ethology* 91:70–79.

9 Gudmundsson, G.A. & Sandberg, R. 2000. 'Sanderlings have a magnetic compass: orientation experiments during spring migration in Iceland.' *JEB*. 203:3137–3144.

Chapter 16: Light, magnetism and the avian eye

1 Schulten, K. 2014. *Quantum Effects in Biology*, chapter 10, pp. 218–236. Cambridge University Press, London.

2 Berthold, P. 201. *Bird Migration. A General Survey. Second ed*. p. 33. Oxford University Press.

3 Welty, J.C. & Baptista, L. 1988. *The Life of Birds. Fourth ed.* Thomson. Brooks/Cole, California.

4 Walls, G.L. 1942. *The Vertebrate Eye and Its Adaptive Radiation.* Cranbrook Institute of Science, Bloomfield Hills, Michigan.

5 Donner, K.O. 'The spectral sensitivity of the pigeon's retinal elements.' *Journal of Physiology* (London). 122:524–537.

6 Gegear, R.J., Cassellman, A., Waddell, S. & Reppert, S.M. 2008. 'Cryptochrome mediates light-dependent magnetosensitivity in *Drosophila*.' *Nature* August. 21; 454 (7207): 1014–17 doi:10.1038/natureD7183. Epub2008 Jul 20

7 Picot, M., Cusumano, P., Klarsfield, A., Ueda, R. & Rouyer, F. 2007. 'Light activates output from evening neurons and inhibits output from morning neurons in the *Drosophila* circadian clock.' *PLoS Biol* 5 (11):e315. doi:10.1371/journal.pbio.0030315

8 Heyers, D., Manns, M., Luksch, H., Gunturkun, O. & Mouritsen, H. 2007. 'A visual pathway links brain structures active during magnetic compass orientation in migratory birds.' *PLoS ONE* 2(9): e937. doi:10.1371/journal.pone.0000937

9 *BioScience* [online article]. 'Taking a bird's-eye view in the UV: recent studies reveal a surprising new picture of how birds see the world.' *BioScience* vol. 50, issue 10, 1 October 2000, pp. 854–859.

10 Cronin, T.W., Johnsen, S., Marshall, N.J. & Warrant, E. 2014. *Visual Ecology.* Princeton University Press.

11 Al-Khalili, J. 2017. *Quantum Mechanics* (p. 46) Ladybird Books Ltd, London.

12 Frasnelli, E. 'Brain and behavioural lateralisation in invertebrates.' *Frontiers in Psychology.* (December 2013) 4:1–10. doi:103389/fpsyg.2013.00939

13 Gunturkun, O., Diekamp, B., Manns, M. Nottelmann, F., Prior, H. Schwarz, A. & Skiba, M. 2000. 'Asymmetry pays: visual lateralisation improves discrimination success in pigeons.' *Current Biology.* 10:1079–1081. doi:10.1016/S0960-9822(00)00671-0

14 Gehring, D., Wiltschko, W., Gunturkun, O., Denzau, S. & Wiltschko. R. 2012. 'Development of lateralisation of the magnetic compass in a migratory bird.' *Proceedings of the Royal Society B.* 279:4230–4235. doi:10.1098/rspb.2012.1654

15 Golarai, G., Ghahremani, D.G., Whitfield-Gabrieli, S., Reiss, A., Eberhardt, J.L., Gabrieli, J.D. & Grill-Spector, K. 2007. 'Differential development of high-level visual cortex correlates with category-specific recognition memory.' *Nature Neuroscience.* 10:512–522. doi:10.1038/nn1865

Chapter 17: Star patterns and orientation

1 Wiltschko, W., Daum-Benz, P., Fergenbauer-Kimmel, A. & Wiltschko, R. 1987. 'The development of the star compass in Garden Warblers.' *Ethology* 74:285–292.

2 Sauer, E.G.F. & Sauer, E.M. 1960. 'Star navigation of nocturnal migrating birds. The 1958 planetarium experiment – Cold Spring Harbour Symposium.' *Quantitative Biology.* 25:463–473.

3 Fromme, H.G. 1961. 'Untersuchungen uber das Orientierungsvermogen nachtlich ziehender kleinvogel.' *Zeitschrift Fur Tierpsychologie.* 18:205–220.

4 Emlen, S.T. 1967. 'Migratory orientation in the Indigo Bunting. Part 1: Evidence for use of celestial cues.' *Auk:* 309–342.

5 Emlen, S.T. 1967. 'Migratory orientation in the Indigo Bunting. Part 2: Mechanism of celestial orientation.' *Auk:* 463–489.

Chapter 18: Skylight polarisation and navigation

1 Kramer, G. 1952. 'Experiments on bird orientation.' *Ibis* 94:265–285.

2 Kramer, G. 1959. Experiments on bird orientation and their interpretation.' *Ibis* 99:196–227.

3 Keeton, W.T. 1969. 'Orientation by pigeons: is the sun necessary?' *Science* 165:922–928.

4 von Frisch, K. 1927. *The Dancing Bees* (first published under the title *Aus dem Leben der Bienen*). Springer-Verlag OHG. Berlin

5 Able, K.P. 1993. 'Orientation cues used by migratory birds: a review of cue-conflict experiments.' *Trends in Ecology & Evolution*. 8:367–371.

6 Cronin, T.W. & Marshall, J. 2011. Patterns and properties of polarised light in air and water. *Philosophical Transactions of the Royal Society B*. 366:619–626 doi:10.1098/rstb.2010.0201

7 Pomozi, I., Horvath, G. & Wehner, R. 2001. 'How the clear-sky angle of polarisation pattern continues underneath clouds: full-sky measurements and implications for animal orientation.' *JEB*. 204:2933–2942.

8 Cochran, W.W., Mouritsen, H. & Wikelski, M. 2004. 'Migrating songbirds recalibrate their magnetic compass daily from twilight cues.' *Science* 304:405–408.

Chapter 19: Other beacons

1 Massa, B., Benvenuti, S., Ioale, P., Lovalvo, M. & Papi, F. 1991. 'Homing of Cory's Shearwaters carrying magnets.' *Bollentino di Zoologica*. 58:245–247; Bonadonna, F., Bajzak, C., Benhamou, S., Igloi, K., Jouventin, P., Lipp, H.P. & Dell'Omo, G. 2005. 'Orientation in the Wandering Albatross: interfering with magnetic perception does not affect orientation performance.' *Proceedings of the Royal Society of London B*. 272:489–495.

2 Fisher, J. 1952. *The Fulmar*. Collins New Naturalist Series. London.

3 Personal observations, based on survey work carried out by A. McGeehan on Skellig Michael in 2012.

4 Wenzel, B.M. & Meisami, E. 1987. 'Number, size, and density of mitral cells in the olfactory bulbs of the Northern Fulmar and Rock Dove.' *Annals of the New York Academy of Sciences*. 510:700–702.

5 Grubb, Thomas C. 1972. 'Smell and foraging in shearwaters and petrels.' *Nature* 237: 404–405. doi:10.1038/237404a0.

6 Nevitt, G.A. 'Sensory ecology on the high seas: the odor world of the procellariiform seabirds.' *JEB*. 211:1706–1713. doi:10.1242/jeb.015412.

7 Roper, T.J. 'Olfaction in birds.' *Advances in the Study of Behaviour*. 28:247–332.

8 Bonadonna, F., Caro, S., Jouventin, P. & Nevitt, G. A 2006. 'Evidence that Blue Petrel *Halobaena caerulea* fledglings can detect and orient to dimethyl sulphide.' *JEB*. 209:2165–2169.

9 https://advances.sciencemag.org/content/2/11/e1600395.

10 Bonadonna, F. & Nevitt, G.A. 2004. 'Partner-specific odor recognition in an Antarctic seabird.' *Science* 306:835.

11 van Bemmelen, R., Moe, B., Hanssen, S. A., Schmidt, N.M., Hansen, J., Lang, J., Sittler, B., Bolache, L., Tulp, I., Klassen, R. & Gilg, O. 'Flexibility in otherwise consistent non-breeding movements of a long-distance migratory seabird, the Long-tailed Skua.' *Marine Ecology Progress Series* (February 2017). doi:10.3354/meps12010.

12 Dias, M.A., Granadeiro, J.P., Phillips, R.A., Alonso, H. & Catry, P. 2010. 'Breaking the routine: individual Cory's Shearwaters shift winter destinations between hemispheres and across ocean basins.' *Proceedings of the Royal Society B.* doi:10.1098/rspb.2010.2114.

Chapter 20: Statistics of slaughter

1 Owen, D.F. 1953. Migration at the Kentish Knock Lightship. *BB* 10:353–364.

2 Elkins, N. 1983. *Weather and Bird Behaviour.* T. & A.D. Poyser. Calton.

3 Spencer, R. 1963. *Instructions to Young Ornithologists. III Bird Migration* (p. 84). Museum Press Limited, London.

4 www.flap.org/hierarchy-of-threats.php

5 www.terrain.org/articles/15/kousky.htm

6 www.flap.org/hierarchy-of-threats.php

7 Author's personal observations, September 2014.

8 www.audubon.org/magazine/march-april-2015/star-trek-how-birds-use-electromagnetic-cues

Chapter 21: Flights of reckoning

1 Sharrock, J.T.R. (ed.) 1976. *The Atlas of Breeding Birds in Britain and Ireland.* T. & A.D. Poyser. Calton.

2 Kennedy, Revd P.G., Ruttledge, R.F. & Scroope, C.F. 1954.*The Birds of Ireland.* Oliver & Boyd. London and Edinburgh.

3 Newton, I. 2008. *The Migration Ecology of Birds* (p. 264). Academic Press, London.

4 Prof. Karel Voous, quoted in Gooders, J. (ed.) 1970. *Birds of the World* (vol. 4) IPC magazines.

5 Massa, B., Benvenuti, S., Ioale, P., Lovalvo, M. & Papi, F. 1991. 'Homing of Cory's Shearwaters carrying magnets.' *Bollentino di Zoologica.* 58:245–247.

6 Johnson, E.D.H. 'Observations on a resident population of Stonechats in Jersey.' *BB* 64: 201–213, 267–79.

7 Farnsworth, A. 2005. 'Flight calls and their value for future ornithological studies and conservation research.' *The Auk* 122(3):733–745.

8 Schuz, E. 1950. 'Fruh-Auflassung ostpreussischer Jungstorche in West-Deutschland durch die Vogelwarte Rossiten 1933–36.' *Bonner zoologische Beiträge.* 1:239–253.

9 Ian Newton, pers. comm. November 2017.

10 J. Van Remsen Jr, Louisiana State University Museum of Natural Science, quoted in response to A. McGeehan's criticism of collecting migrants. *Birdwatch*, May 1994 (p. 20).

11 Kelsey, G. Martin. 1991. 'A well-travelled warbler's repertoire.' *Natural History* 4:6–10.

12 Durand, A.L. 1963. 'A remarkable fall of American land-birds on the *Mauretania*, New York to Southampton, October 1962.' *BB* 56:157–164.

13 Durand, A.L. 1972. Landbirds over the North Atlantic: unpublished records 1961–65 and thoughts a decade later. *BB.* 65:428–442.

14 Lees, A. & Gilroy, J. 2009. 'Vagrancy mechanisms in passerines and near-passerines.' In Slack, R., *Rare Birds Where and When: An Analysis of Status and Distribution in Britain and Ireland* (pp. 1–22). Rare Bird Books. York.

15 Thorup, K., Ortvad, T.E., Holland, R.A., Rabol, J., Kristensen, M.W. & Wikelski, M. 2012. 'Orientation of vagrant birds on the Faeroe Islands in the Atlantic Ocean.' *Journal of Ornithology*. doi:10.1007/s10336-012-0883-6.

16 Thorup, K. 1998. 'Vagrancy of Yellow-browed Warbler *Phylloscopus inornatus* and Pallas's Warbler *P. proregulus* in northwest Europe: misorientation on great circles?' *Ringing & Migration*. 19:7–12.

Chapter 22: Winning the migration lottery

1 Sharrock, J.T.R. 1973. *The Natural History of Cape Clear*. T. & A.D. Poyser. Berkhamsted.

Chapter 23: Ivory Gull

1 White, E.B. 1977. *Essays of E.B. White*. Quotation from a 1961 essay entitled 'The Years of Wonder', p. 169. Harper & Row. New York, Hagerstown, San Francisco, London.

2 Forbush, E.H. 1925–1929. *The Birds of Massachusetts and Other New England States* (three volumes). Vol. 1 (1925): 'Water Birds, Marsh Birds and Shore Birds' (p. 61). Massachusetts Department of Agriculture, Commonwealth, MA.

3 Excerpt from 'Meeting Point' by Louis MacNeice. MacNeice, L. 2002. *Collected Poems, 1925–1948*, (p. 189). Faber, London.

4 http://ivorygull.npolar.no/ivorygull/en/index.html

Chapter 24 Song Thrush traditional routes

1 Davies, P.W. & Snow, D.W. 1965. 'Territory and food of the Song Thrush.' *BB*. 58:161–175.

2 Werth. I. 1947. 'The tendency of Blackbird and Song Thrush to breed in their birthplaces.' *BB*. 40:328–330.

3 Ruttledge, R.F. 1957. 'The Birds of Inishbofin, Co. Galway.' *Bird Study* 4:71–80.

4 Wallace. D.I.M. 2004. *Beguiled by Birds*. Christopher Helm. London.

5 Barrington, R.M. 1900. *The Migration of Birds as Observed at Irish Lighthouses and Lightships*. R.H. Porter and Edward Ponsonby. London and Dublin.

6 Carson, C. 2009. *Technology and the Big House in Ireland*. Cambria Press. New York.

7 Goodacre, M.J. 1960. 'The origin of winter visitors to the British Isles. 6. Song Thrush.' *Bird Study* 7:108–110.

8 Kieran Grace, pers. comm. January 2017.

9 Constantine, M. & Hopper, N. 2012. *Catching the Bug* pp. 117–119. The Sound Approach, Dorset, UK.

Chapter 25: Wintering out

1 Stafford, J. 1956. 'The wintering of Blackcaps in the British Isles.' *Bird Study* 3:251–257.

2 Leach, I.H. 1981. 'Wintering Blackcaps in Britain and Ireland.' *Bird Study* 28:5–15.

3 Bland, R.L. 1986. 'Blackcap.' In *The Atlas of Wintering Birds in Britain and Ireland* (ed. P. Lack), pp. 332–333. T. & A.D. Poyser. Calton.

4 *Ibid*.

5 Berthold. P. & Terrill, S. 1988. 'Migratory behaviour and population growth of Blackcaps wintering in Britain and Ireland: some hypotheses.' *Ringing & Migration* 9:153–159; Berthold. P. 1995. 'Microevolution of migratory behaviour illustrated by the Blackcap *Sylvia atricapilla*: 1993 Witherby Lecture.' *Bird Study* 42:89–100.

6 Ridley, M. 1993. *Evolution.* Blackwell Scientific Publications. Boston.

7 Langslow, D.R. 1979. 'Movements of Blackcaps ringed in Britain and Ireland.' *Bird Study* 26:239–252.

8 Blackcap ringing details. Ring number GBT HN 11537. Trapped in Norfolk on 17 September 1968; found dead in Lebanon on 6 May 1969. Ring number GBT JH 90180. Trapped in Yorkshire on 3 October 1971; trapped in Lebanon on 2 May 1973.

9 Langslow, *op. cit.*

10 Blackcap ringing details. See note 8 above.

10 Zink, G. 1973. 'Der Zug europaischer Singvogel.' *Ein Atlas der Wiederfunde beringier Vogel.* Radolfzell.

Chapter 27: G is for gull

1 Hume, R.H. 1978. 'Variations in Herring Gulls at a Midland roost.' *BB.* (August 1978) 71:338–345.

2 Dietzen, C., Witt, H-H. & Wink, M. 2003. 'The phylogeographic differentiation of the European Robin *Erithacus rubecula* on the Canary Islands revealed by mitochondrial DNA sequence data and morphometrics: evidence for a new robin taxon on Gran Canaria.' *Avian Science* 3:115–131. ISSN 1424–8743.

3 Grant, P.J. 1986. *Gulls: A Guide to Identification.* T. & A.D. Poyser, London.

4 *British Birds* (February 1967) 60:75 41–44.

5 McGeehan, A. 2002. 'Total birding: Look, don't listen.' *Dutch Birding* 24 (number 1):

6 www.anythinglarus.com/2017/07/the-post-thayers-gull-era.html

7 Garner, M. & McGeehan, A. 'Identification of juvenile and first-winter Thayer's Gull.' *Birding World* vol. 11, no. 3, pp. 94–101.

8 McGeehan, A. & Millington, M. 'The adult Thayer's Gull in Donegal.' *Birding World* vol. 11, no. 3, pp. 102–108.

Chapter 28: A trip to Newfoundland

1 Baird, J. quoting a letter from Wingate, D. in 'Returning to the Tropics: the epic flight of the Blackpoll Warbler', p. 71 in Able, K.P. 1999. *Gatherings of Angels.* Comstock Books. Ithaca & London.

2 Ralph, C.J. 1981. 'Age ratios and their possible use in determining autumn routes of passerine migrants.' *Wilson Bulletin.* 93(2):164–188.

3 McNeil, R. & Cadieux, F. 1972. 'Fat content and flight range of some adult spring and fall migrant North American shorebirds in relation to migration routes on the Atlantic.' *Naturaliste Canadien* 99:589–606.

4 Alerstam, T. & Gudmundsson, G.A. 1999. 'Migration patterns of tundra birds: tracking radar observations along the Northeast Passage.' *Arctic* 52(4):346–371.

5 Heibl, I. & Braunitzer, G. 1988. 'Anpassungen der Hamoglobine von Streifengans (*Anser indicus*) Andengans (*Chloephaga melanoptera*) und Sperbergeier (*Gyps rueppellii*) an hypoxische Bedingungen.' *Journal of Ornithology.* 29:217–226.

6 Duiven, C.S. & Spaans, A.L. 1982. 'Numerical density and biomass of macrobenthic animals living in the intertidal zone of Suriname, South America.' *Netherlands J. Sea Res.* 15:406–418.

7 Harrington, B. 'The hemispheric globetrotting of the White-rumped sandpiper' pp. 119–133, in Able, K.P. 1999 *Gatherings of Angels.* Comstock Books. Ithaca & London.

8 *Ibid.*

9 Antas, P. de T.Z. 1983. 'Migration of Nearctic shorebirds shorebirds in Brasil – flyways and their different seasonal use.' *Wader Study Bull.* 39:52–56.

Chapter 29: Heritage lost

1 Herbert, Sir Thomas. 1634. 'A relation of some years travaille into Afrique and the Greater Asia.' Source: Wikipedia.

2 Gooders, J. (ed.) 1969. *Birds of the World*, vol. 2, p. 638. IPC Magazines, London.

3 Royal Irish Academy. 1913–1976. *Dictionary of the Irish Language.* Article entitled 'caileach'. Dublin; Murphy, G. 1953. *Duanaire Finn, the Book of the Lays of Fionn, pt.3: introduction, notes, appendices and glossary.* Dublin.

4 Thompson, W. 1850. *The Natural History of Ireland*, vol. 2, p. 31. Reeve, Benham & Reeve. London.

5 Harvie-Brown, John Alexander. 1879. *The Capercaillie in Scotland* pp. 1–2. D. Douglas, Edinburgh.

6 *Ibid.*

7 To decide if the departure point for imagining that a male Capercaillie sounds like a galloping horse, you can listen here: https://www.youtube.com/watch?v=JdwYna8w1Lk

8 Van Wijngaarden, Louise H. 1989. 'Faunal remains and the Irish Mesolithic' in Clive Bonsall (ed.) *The Mesolithic in Europe: Papers Presented at the Third International Symposium, Edinburgh, 198.*, pp. 125–133. Edinburgh University Press, Edinburgh.

9 Horgan, J. 2010. *The Song at Your Backdoor.* The Collins Press. Cork.

10 Rutty, J. 1772. 'Urugallus major, Gesneri: *Tetras urugallus*, Linnaei – 'The Cock of the Wood'. *Natural History of the County of Dublin*, vol. i. p. 302, footnote.

11 Comber, Thomas. 1788. *Memoirs of the Life and Death of the Lord Deputy Wandesforde*, p. 104. Cambridge.

12 Hall, J.J. 1981. 'The Cock of the Wood.' *Irish Birds* vol. 2, no. 1 38–47.

13 Harvie-Brown, J. A. *op. cit.*, pp. 1–2.

14 A recording of the same bird can be heard at: https://soundcloud.com/ryouell/capercaillie-lek-black-river-valley-sweden

INDEX

Note: figures in *italics* refer to illustrations or captions.